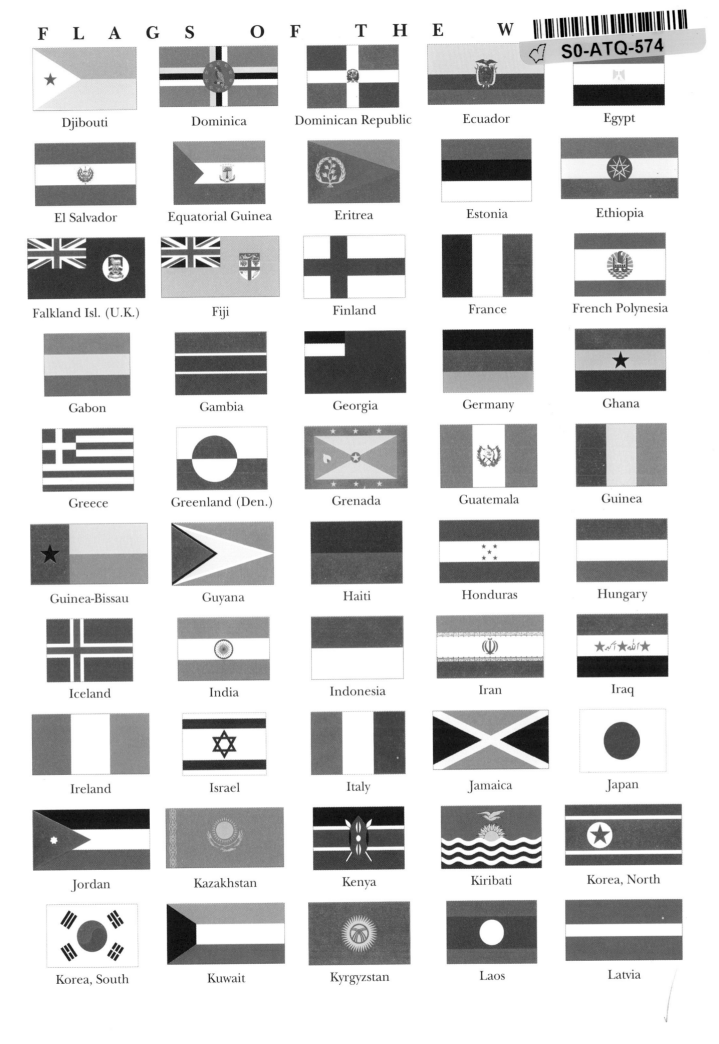

Djibouti

Dominica

Dominican Republic

Ecuador

Egypt

El Salvador

Equatorial Guinea

Eritrea

Estonia

Ethiopia

Falkland Isl. (U.K.)

Fiji

Finland

France

French Polynesia

Gabon

Gambia

Georgia

Germany

Ghana

Greece

Greenland (Den.)

Grenada

Guatemala

Guinea

Guinea-Bissau

Guyana

Haiti

Honduras

Hungary

Iceland

India

Indonesia

Iran

Iraq

Ireland

Israel

Italy

Jamaica

Japan

Jordan

Kazakhstan

Kenya

Kiribati

Korea, North

Korea, South

Kuwait

Kyrgyzstan

Laos

Latvia

WORLD GEOGRAPHY

WORLD GEOGRAPHY

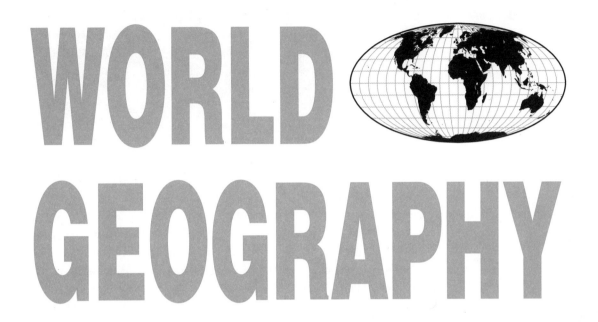

Volume 3

South and Central America

Editor

Ray Sumner

Long Beach City College

Managing Editor

R. Kent Rasmussen

SALEM PRESS, INC.

Pasadena, California   Hackensack, New Jersey

Editor in Chief: Dawn P. Dawson

Managing Editor: R. Kent Rasmussen   *Research Supervisor:* Jeffry Jensen
Manuscript Editor: Irene Struthers Rush   *Acquisitions Editor:* Mark Rehn
Production Editor: Cynthia Beres   *Page Design and Layout:* James Hutson
Photograph Editor: Philip Bader   *Additional Layout:* William Zimmerman
Assistant Editors: Andrea Miller, Heather Stratton   *Graphics:* Electronic Illustrators Group
Cover Design: Moritz Design, Los Angeles, Calif.

Frontispiece: South America from space. *(Corbis)*

∞ The paper used in these volumes conforms to the American National Standard for Permanence of Paper for Printed Library Materials, Z39.48-1992 (R1997).

Library of Congress Cataloging-in-Publication Data

World geography / editor, Ray Sumner ; managing editor, R. Kent Rasmussen.
    p. cm.
    Contents: v. 1. The World. — v. 2. North America and the Caribbean. — v. 3. Central and South America. — v. 4. Africa. — v. 5. Asia. — v. 6. Europe. — v. 7. Antarctica, Australia, and the Pacific. — v. 8. Glossary and Appendices.
    Includes bibliographical references (p.   ).
    ISBN 0-89356-024-3 (set : alk. paper) — ISBN 0-89356-276-9 (v. 1 : alk. paper) —
ISBN 0-89356-277-7 (v. 2 : alk. paper) — ISBN 0-89356-335-8 (v. 3 : alk. paper) —
ISBN 0-89356-336-6 (v. 4 : alk. paper) — ISBN 0-89356-399-4 (v. 5 : alk. paper) —
ISBN 0-89356-650-0 (v. 6 : alk. paper) — ISBN 0-89356-699-3 (v. 7 : alk. paper) —
ISBN 0-89356-723-X (v. 8 : alk. paper)
    1. Geography—Encyclopedias. I. Sumner, Ray.

G133.W88 2001
910′.3—dc21

                                                                                                2001020281

First Printing

CONTENTS

SOUTH AND CENTRAL AMERICA

ECONOMIC GEOGRAPHY

GAZETTEER 863

WORLD GEOGRAPHY

REGIONS

SOUTH AMERICA

*Map
Page 679*

South America is a region of great diversity, contrast, and change. Students in the United States often mistakenly perceive South America in stereotypes, depicting it as a tropical land inhabited by poor peasant farmers, bound to Roman Catholic traditionalism, and shaken by revolution, military dictators, and drug lords. The physical and human diversity of South America make it possibly the most heterogeneous of all the world regions; the least understood; and because of the historical and cultural links to Europe and North America, one of the most interesting places to study and visit.

PHYSICAL DIMENSIONS. South America covers an area of 6.9 million square miles (17.8 million sq. km.), which is about three-quarters the size of North America. The continent's northernmost point is Punta de Gallinas, on the Caribbean Sea at 12 degrees north latitude. South America extends southward 4,500 miles (7,200 km.) to the frigid Antarctic waters off Cape Horn, located at 56 degrees south latitude. Apart from Antarctica, South America extends farther south than any other continent. The widest east-west distance is 3,300 miles (5,300 km.) between João Pessoa in Brazil and Punta Pariñas in Peru. The tropic of Capricorn bisects South America, placing about 55 percent of the continent within the Tropics, but leaving a significant portion in the middle latitudes. The equator passes through Ecuador, Colombia, and Brazil.

PHYSICAL GEOGRAPHY. South America has virtually every physiographic, climatic, and vegetation type found on earth. Among its notable landforms are the Andes Mountains, which span the entire western edge of the continent, and three of the world's top five river systems in terms of volume of water. The mighty Amazon River flows through Brazil but has tributaries originating in eight other countries. The Orinoco River drains northern South America. The Paraná River system drains southern Brazil, Paraguay, and Argentina, and includes the Gran Pantanal, which is the largest wetland area in the world, five times the size of the Florida Everglades. South America's great plains include the Llanos of Venezuela and Colombia, the Gran Chaco of Paraguay, and the fertile Pampas region of Argentina.

Given the continent's vast size, variety in landforms, and large latitudinal span, the variation in climate and vegetation is truly remarkable. A large portion of the continent lies within the Tropics. The humid areas receive up to 160 inches (400 centimeters) of rainfall a year and are blanketed in a thick rain forest canopy. However, 45 percent of the continent lies outside the Tropics.

Central Chile has a Mediterranean type of climate similar to that of Southern California. Southern Chile has a marine west coast climate similar to the coasts of Oregon and Washington. Southern Brazil and the Buenos Aires area of Argentina have a humid subtropical climate similar to the mid-Atlantic states in the United States.

Arid regions include the steppes of the Argentine Patagonia and the bone-dry Atacama Desert of southern Peru and northern Chile, which can go for decades without measurable rainfall. In the Andes Mountains, elevation greatly influences temperature, precipitation, and vegetation. On the equator, areas at sea level are

641

Aerial view of the vast Amazon rain forest. (PhotoDisc)

*Guyana
rain forest
Page 880*

tropical, the mountain valleys have pleasant springlike weather, and the high peaks are covered in tundra and frozen snow caps.

AMAZON BASIN. The Amazon Basin contains the world's largest rain forest and about a fifth of the world's freshwater. The Amazon River carries the greatest volume of water of any river on Earth, emptying 46 million gallons per second at its mouth. At 4,000 miles (6,400 km.) in length, the Amazon River is the world's second-longest river—after Africa's Nile—stretching from the slopes of the Andes Mountains eastward to the Atlantic Ocean.

The rain forests of the Amazon contain more species of plants and animals than any other place on earth. A single patch of rain forest about the size of a typical American shopping mall might contain 500 varieties of birds, 250 varieties of trees, 100 varieties of other animals, and 12 million varieties of insects. By contrast, all of

North America has only 400 species of trees. This vast forested area also plays a vital role as one of the earth's lungs, absorbing carbon dioxide and releasing oxygen into the air. To many people in South America, the basin is perceived as a frontier with untapped potential. Although more than 80 percent of the Amazon remains forested, development pressures from logging, agriculture, cattle ranching, mining, road building, and poorly planned settlement schemes result in the loss of 2 percent of the remaining forest each year.

POPULATION AND CULTURE. South America is divided among thirteen countries: Argentina, Bolivia, Brazil, Chile, Colombia, Ecuador, French Guiana, Guyana, Paraguay, Peru, Suriname, Uruguay, and Venezuela. The size of each territory varies widely. Brazil is the largest country, with a land area of 3.3 million square miles (8.5 million sq. km.), which is slightly smaller than the United States, and the fifth largest country in the world. French Guiana is the smallest territory at 34,747 square miles (89,647 sq. km.), about the size of Maine. The total population of South America is 339 million. Brazil has the largest population with 168 million, while the Guianas (French Guiana, Guyana, and Suriname) have fewer than 1 million people combined.

The image of a typical South American is a person of mixed Amerindian and European ancestry, or mestizo. While mestizos are the majority in the region as a whole, a detailed analysis reveals a complex mosaic of peoples. The European conquest in the sixteenth century led to a dramatic decline of the native population. Nevertheless, Amerindians still make up 40 to 60 percent of the populations of Bolivia, Peru, and Ecuador, and other countries have notable Amerindian minorities.

Perhaps ten million African slaves were brought to work on the plantations of Latin America. Every country in South America has a significant population of African descent, especially in the coastal zones, the Guianas, and the northeast of Brazil. In Argentina, Uruguay, Chile, and southern Brazil, descendents of European immigrants, especially from Spain, Portugal, Italy, and Germany, make up the majority.

Immigrants have come to South America from many other countries, including England, France, Holland, India, China, Indonesia, and Lebanon. Brazil has the largest Japanese population outside of Japan. Extensive intermarriage has created practically every possible racial combination imaginable. However, this mixing has not created an egalitarian society free of prejudice.

GOVERNMENT. At the beginning of the twenty-first century, South America was still dominated by elite rule. People of European ancestry, or those who had adopted a European lifestyle, still controlled the economies and governments of the region, and large numbers of people remained poor and marginalized. Between 1990 and 2000 every country in South America democratically elected its government. Although democracy is on the rise, democratic institutions remain weak in many countries, and corruption and inequitable access to political power need to be addressed.

Patterns of language and religion also reveal much complexity. Spanish is the predominant language on the continent, but Portuguese is the official language of Brazil. Many native languages remain in use. Quechua, the language of the Inca Empire, is spoken by as many as twenty million people in the Andean countries, and the Amazon Basin still has many native groups with their own languages. English, Dutch, and French are spoken in the Guianas.

The Roman Catholic Church has been the dominant religious faith in South America since the conquest by the Spanish and Portuguese, but Evangelical Protestantism is the fastest-growing religious movement in the region. More than 10 percent of the people in South America are Protestants, dominated by sects such as the Assembly of God, Mormons, and Seventh-day Adventists. Thirty percent of Chileans and twenty percent of Brazilians are Protestants. Even the Roman Catholic Church has undergone division and reform efforts. Beginning in the 1970's, a grassroots movement within the church, known as liberation theology, has sought to connect with the poor and address issues of social inequity, justice, and political alienation.

ECONOMIC PATTERNS. The economies of South America are characterized by great contrasts, change, and potential.

Rio carnival Page 680

The region has some of the most richly endowed countries on earth. At the end of the twentieth century, average annual income per person in South America was $4,430 (compared to $29,080 in the United States); but when compared to many places in Africa and Asia where people earn less than $1,000 per year, South Americans fare better. However, there are significant differences among countries within the region. With an annual per-capita income of $8,950, Argentina is the richest South American country. Uruguay is next with $6,130, followed by Chile with $4,820. The poorest countries are Guyana with an average income of just $800, followed by Bolivia with $970.

Agricultural patterns vary from rain forest dwellers who practice slash-and-burn cultivation and subsistence farmers in the Andes who raise potatoes, to modern commercial plantations producing bananas and coffee for export, to massive cattle ranches, or *estancias*, on the Pampas of Argentina. Brazil and Colombia are the world's largest exporters of coffee. Ecuador is the world's largest producer of bananas, and Chile exports large quantities of high-value fruits. Peru and Bolivia are the largest producers of coca for cocaine production, while Colombia leads in the production and export of refined cocaine. Despite media images, however, illegal drugs make up a small part of the total economy of South America.

Mining is important to many South American countries. Brazil is the world's largest producer of iron ore. Chile leads the world in copper production, and tin and aluminum are also important exports from the region. During the last fifty years, manufacturing and service industries

One of South America's biggest and most cosmopolitan cities, Caracas, is only minutes away from the natural splendors of El Avila National Park. (AP/Wide World Photos)

have grown to dominate the economies of every South American country.

Trends toward globalization and regional trade agreements are reflected in efforts such as the Andean Common Market, Mercosur (a trading block with Brazil, Argentina, Uruguay, and Paraguay), and the potential inclusion of Chile in the North American Free Trade Agreement (NAFTA). Nevertheless, development patterns remain uneven. Brazil and Argentina have sophisticated manufacturing sectors that produce aircraft, automobiles, and high-technology equipment, while Bolivia and Guyana still depend on the export of lower-value minerals and agricultural products.

URBANIZATION. Seventy-eight percent of the people of South America reside in cities—a slightly higher percentage than in the United States. South America has seven cities with populations of over five million, topped by the megacities of Mexico City (twenty-seven million); São Paulo, Brazil (twenty-five million); Rio de Janeiro, Brazil (fourteen million); and Buenos Aires, Argentina (thirteen million).

Over the last four decades of the twentieth century, South American cities saw a flood of migrants from rural areas in search of jobs and a better life. This trend has been driven by industrialization policies, agricultural modernization emphasizing large farms and mechanization, and high birth rates in rural areas. All of South America's major cities are surrounded by shantytowns, where the poor struggle to erect makeshift housing and find basic urban services. These slums stand in stark contrast to historic city centers and elite residential neighborhoods and shopping districts.

Urbanization rates vary widely among the individual countries. Uruguay is the most urban country, with 91 percent of the people living in cities. Other highly urban countries are Argentina (89 percent), Venezuela (86 percent), and Chile (85 percent). The least urban countries are Guyana (36 percent), Paraguay (52 percent), and Bolivia (61 percent).

James R. Keese

FOR FURTHER STUDY

Blouet, Brian W., and Olwyn M. Blouet. *Latin America and the Caribbean: A Systematic and Regional Survey.* 3d ed. New York: John Wiley & Sons, 1997.

Box, Ben. *South American Handbook.* Bath, England: Footprint Handbooks, 1999.

Clawson, David L. *Latin America and the Caribbean: Lands and Peoples.* New York: McGraw-Hill, 1999.

James, Preston E., and C. W. Minkel. *Latin America.* 5th ed. New York: John Wiley & Sons, 1986.

Kane, Joe. *Running the Amazon.* New York: Knopf, 1989.

Levine, Robert M. *Historical Dictionary of Brazil.* Landham, Md.: Scarecrow Press, 1979.

South America, Central America, and the Caribbean. London: Europa Publications, 1999.

CENTRAL AMERICA

*Map
Page 682*

*Bananas
Page 816*

North America and South America are connected by a long isthmus made up of seven small and mostly Hispanic countries: Belize, Costa Rica, El Salvador, Guatemala, Honduras, Nicaragua, and Panama. Together, these countries have a population of roughly thirty-five million people living on a land mass about a quarter the size of nearby Mexico. It is in the land that the wealth of Central America lies. With only 20 percent of the region's gross domestic product coming from industry, the bulk of the nations' economies, as well as their people, depend on the area's small private farms, large plantations, and stock ranches.

PHYSICAL GEOGRAPHY. Most of Central America is dominated by three physical zones that are, at times, spatially disconnected: the interior highlands, the Pacific coastal region, and the Caribbean coastal lowlands.

The highland interior of countries such as Guatemala and Nicaragua was first occupied by Amerindians—the native peoples of the Americas—who farmed small subsistence plots. Hispanic culture has spread into the area, displacing the Amerindians and introducing larger-scale agriculture and cattle-based industries. All the Central American nations, except Belize, share this physiographic zone. The interior highlands in many ways serve as the core of the region.

Five capital cities are located in the highland interior zone—San Salvador, El Salvador; Tegucigalpa, Honduras; Guatemala City, Guatemala; San José, Costa Rica; and Managua, Nicaragua—and the highlands are the most densely settled physical zone within Central America.

This temperate zone is the area of most intense coffee production.

To the west of the highlands lies the Pacific region, with large-scale plantations focusing on such crops as bananas, and cattle ranching in the drier portions. On the east side of the isthmus, the Caribbean coastal region has seen an upsurge of agriculture by people displaced through resettlement programs from the interior's heavily populated cities. The area has also become popular as a tourist destination, especially for vacations focusing on ecological themes.

The region as a whole experiences similar weather patterns. From the northern tip of Belize to the southern portion of Panama, only nine degrees of latitude are included in the isthmian landmass. Therefore, the area is well within a temperate climate range that is affected only by altitude, which causes the climate to vary from tropical to subtropical.

A cordillera, or chain of mountains, runs the length of the isthmus, connecting with the Sierra Madre del Sur in Mexico in the north and the northern portions of the Andes in Colombia. Mountains in Central America rise to almost 14,000 feet (more than 4,000 meters) at Tajumulco, a volcano in western Guatemala.

With such a range in altitudes, Central America sustains a wide variety of plants and animals that inhabit rain and cloud forest in the higher elevations and mangrove swamps in the coastal lowlands. Such variation in elevation in a small geographic area also diminishes the amount of arable land, which ranges from a low of 2 percent in Belize to a high of 27 percent in El Salvador. Much of the farmable land

*Guatemala
City
Page 879*

produces bananas. The heavy reliance on this tropical fruit and the political power of fruit companies gave rise to the term "banana republic" for the region.

HISTORY. Amerindian civilizations rose and fell in various parts of Central America before the arrival of the Spanish. Most notable of these were the Maya, who constructed temples and cities, such as Tikal and Xunantunich, in Guatemala, Honduras, El Salvador, and Belize.

Christopher Columbus first visited Central America in 1502, and the explorer Vasco Nuñez de Balboa crossed the isthmus in 1513. In the 1520's, the Spanish began colonization in earnest. Guatemala, known as the Captaincy General of Guate-

mala, was the Spanish colonial capital for Central America. Soon after the independence of Mexico from Spain in 1821, the Central America region declared its independence. In 1823 the newly independent region formed the United Provinces of Central America. Isolation, poor communication, and personal and regional rivalries soon led to the demise of this federation, and by the late 1830's, the United Provinces of Central America no longer existed. All the countries of Central America declared their independence except Belize, formerly known as British Honduras, which did not gain independence from Great Britain until 1981.

The nineteenth century was domi-

Mayans
Page 754

BALBOA SETTING UP THE CROSS ON THE SHORE OF THE PACIFIC OCEAN, SEPTEMBER 25, 1513.

Romantic nineteenth century engraving depicting the arrival of Vasco Nuñez de Balboa on the shore of the Pacific Ocean in 1513. (Library of Congress)

nated by internal conflicts among the region's liberal and conservative factions and by United States and British efforts to expand their political influence. During this time, coffee was introduced into the region and quickly became important to the area's economy. By the end of the nineteenth century, the production of coffee had created a class of elite landowners, furthering the gap between the wealthy and peasant classes. Military regimes provided some stability for areas in the region from the late nineteenth century into the twentieth century, but often at the cost of human rights. By the beginning of the twentieth century, the United States was the dominant foreign power within the region.

Coffee plants Page 815

During the early twentieth century, the United States took a more visible role in Central America's development, especially by way of the Panama Canal. The United States dug the canal, which was opened in 1914. The United States remained in control of the Canal Zone until January 1, 2000, when Panama assumed control. Since this time, the role of the United States within the region has diminished somewhat.

Panama Canal Page 821

ECONOMIES. Central American economies traditionally have had a limited base, which has resulted in slower economic growth and human development. By the 1990's, the major existing difference in the region's economies exists between the population centers of the interior highlands and the plantation agricultural zones of the lowlands. Most Central Americans live in the highlands. The coastal areas, especially those of the eastern portions of the region and the Isthmus of Panama, have the least population density.

DEMOGRAPHY. The population of Central America grew greatly during the 1960's and 1970's, primarily because of the region's high fertility rates. Although the growth rates began dropping in the late 1990's, fertility rates hovered at three or four children per woman, still high compared to the more developed nations of North America and Europe. This demographic trend may not drop significantly in the near future, since the bulk of the region's population remains young and in their prime childbearing years.

The overall population of Central America is projected to grow by as much as 60 percent over the first three decades of the twenty-first century, increasing from about thirty-five million in the year 2000 to sixty million in 2030. Such growth would place continuing demands on the economic, social, and environmental systems of the countries of Central America.

SOCIAL DIVISIONS. Ethnic and racial differences have been the basis of Central America's social class distinctions. For example, Amerindians, who still make up a large portion of the population, particularly in Guatemala, have been relegated to the lower rungs of the socioeconomic ladder. They have maintained a pattern of subsistence farming tied to local market towns, often outside the dynamic realm of a greater world economic system.

In contrast, people of European descent and mestizos (persons of mixed Amerindian and European background) often hold social, political, and economic power—a residual of the past, when power meant owning large tracts of land, raising either crops or livestock. This power base is seen not only in land ownership but in control of manufacturing and agribusinesses.

Between the upper class of European and mestizo heritage and the peasants of Amerindian ancestry, there are smaller ethnic groups. These include persons of African heritage brought to the area as slave labor or freedmen to work in agriculture or construction. Asians who migrated

---

INFORMATION ON THE WORLD WIDE WEB

The World Factbook 2000 Web site, maintained by the U.S. Central Intelligence Agency (CIA), features profiles of individual Central American countries. (www.odci.gov/cia/publications/factbook/es.html#geo)

The Lonely Planet Web site features general information on Central America both as a single region and as a collection of individual countries. (www.lonelyplanet.com)

---

to the region to fill a host of middle-level jobs, most in the service sector, are another dynamic piece of the Central American cultural quilt.

Central America is a region both physically and culturally. This isthmus belt comprises some of the poorest nations in Latin America, Costa Rica and Panama being the exceptions. The region's agricultural products are subject to world economic fluctuations and volatile markets. This, along with periods of political and military turmoil, has slowed socioeconomic development for the region as a whole. Many Central American countries are looking to tourism, especially ecotourism, to diversify and more adequately compete in the global economic theater.

Douglas Heffington
Judith Mimbs

FOR FURTHER STUDY

Arbingast, Stanley A., et al., eds. *Atlas of Central America.* Austin: University of Texas Press, 1979.

Burkholder, Mark A., and Lynn L. Johnson. *Colonial Latin America.* Oxford, England: Oxford University Press, 1997.

Clawson, David L. *Latin America and the Caribbean: Lands and Peoples.* New York: McGraw-Hill, 1999.

Dickenson, J. P., et al. *A Geography of the Third World.* London: Routledge Press, 1991.

Herlihy, Peter H. "Central American Indian Peoples and Lands Today." In *Central America: A National Cultural History,* edited by Anthony G. Coates. New Haven, Conn.: Yale University Press, 1997.

West, Robert C., and John P. Augelli. *Middle America: Its Lands and Peoples.* Englewood Cliffs, N.J.: Prentice-Hall, 1989.

PHYSICAL GEOGRAPHY

PHYSIOGRAPHY AND HYDROLOGY

PHYSIOGRAPHY OF SOUTH AMERICA

Map Page 683

South America has a spectacular physical environment. Its Andes range is the second highest mountain chain in the world. Its Amazon River carries more water than any other river in the world. Its Amazon Basin is the world's largest drainage basin, comparable in size to the whole United States. Angel Falls in Venezuela is the world's highest waterfall—ten times higher than North America's Niagara Falls. Lake Titicaca in Bolivia is the world's highest navigable lake; Mount Guallatiri in Chile is the world's tallest active volcano. Quito, Ecuador, is the world's largest city on the equator. The Amazon rain forest is the world's largest. When British naturalist Charles Darwin visited the continent during the 1830's, he was amazed at the diversity and grandeur of South America's natural environment.

THE ANDES MOUNTAINS. South America's great mountain chain extends down the length of the west coast of South America, stretching 4,500 miles (7,200 km.), from Venezuela to Tierra del Fuego. Although their crests are only an average of about 110 miles (150 km.) from the continent's Pacific coastline, the Andes are the continental divide for South America. Rivers that rise on the western slopes of the mountains are generally short, swift streams that enter the Pacific Ocean without creating large fertile valleys or navigable waterways. Rivers that rise on the eastern slopes are long, sometimes mighty rivers that carry sediments from the mountains into the Atlantic Ocean.

The mountains are high and continuous. Many peaks exceed 17,000 feet (5,800 meters); some exceed 20,000 feet (6,100 meters). The Western Hemisphere's highest mountain, Mount Aconcagua, rises 22,834 feet (6,960 meters) between Chile and Argentina. Most of the passes through the Andes are at an elevation of 10,000 feet (3,050 meters). The Andes have been a barrier to east-west travel from Amerindian times to the present.

Lake Titicaca Pages 689, 886

Geologists estimate that the Andes were built by a series of crustal uplifts and volcanic activity from sixty-five to seventy million years ago. The region that is now the Andes was then a long, narrow trough that gradually filled with sediments washed from surrounding highlands. Continuous pressure from movement of the great crustal plates of the Pacific region in an east-northeast direction folded, bent, warped, and broke the rocks that eventually became the Andes. All this was accompanied by vulcanism, the movement of molten rock both under the crust,

MAJOR ACTIVE ANDEAN VOLCANOES

Volcano	Country	Height Meters	Feet	World Rank	Last Eruption
Guallatiri	Chile	6,071	19,913	1	1985
Cotopaxi	Ecuador	5,911	19,388	2	1904
El Misti	Peru	5,823	19,101	4	1870
Tupungatito	Chile	5,640	18,499	5	1980
Lascar	Chile	5,592	18,342	7	1974
Ruiz	Colombia	5,321	17,458	9	1985
Sangay	Ecuador	5,320	17,454	10	1976
Tolima	Colombia	5,215	17,105	11	1943
Tungurahua	Ecuador	5,023	16,475	12	1944
Purace	Colombia	4,800	15,744	13	1977
Guagua	Ecuador	4,784	15,692	14	1981
Lautaro	Chile	3,380	11,151	58	1960
Llaima	Chile	3,125	10,250	69	1979
Villarica	Chile	2,847	9,341	83	1980
Osorno	Chile	2,660	8,727	90	1973

*Volcanoes
Pages 682,
694*

*La Paz
Page 881*

*Altiplano
Page 875*

and through volcanoes and cracks in the crust, onto the earth's surface. This mountain-building process proceeded sporadically over a long time, creating a complex system of mountain ridges, highland and lowland basins, plateaus, and fault scarps. Today, many earthquakes and an occasional volcanic eruption are proof that the mountain building is still going on.

Earth scientists do not agree on any systematic way to divide the Andes into logical regions, so they should be examined according to their general physical characteristics.

NORTHERN ANDES. Starting near the border between Ecuador and Colombia, the Andes separate into three distinct parallel mountain chains separated by deep valleys. The sierras (mountains) are named Sierra Occidental (west), Central, and Oriental (east). The western range has the highest average elevation—12,800 feet (3,100 meters)—but the central

range has several peaks exceeding 18,000 feet (5,500 meters). Bogotá, Colombia's capital city, is located at 8,660 feet (2,680 meters) in a high basin of the Sierra Oriental. The western and central Sierras end in the swampy Caribbean coastal plains, while the eastern branch forms two arms around Lake Maracaibo, extending eastward beyond Caracas, Venezuela.

CENTRAL ANDES. From the northern border of Ecuador to the northern parts of Chile and Argentina, the Andes are a complex mixture of high ridges, transverse valleys, and high platforms topped by scattered volcanoes. The mountain mass is narrowest in Ecuador and widest in southern Peru and Bolivia, where it is made up of two high ridges separated by high basins called *altiplanos*. Quito, Ecuador's capital, sits in one at 9,350 feet (2,850 meters), and La Paz, Bolivia's capital, is located at 11,900 feet (3,625 meters).

The Peruvian/Bolivian *altiplano* is one

of the world's largest interior basins at such a high altitude. With a surface elevation from 11,900 to 12,800 feet (3,600 to 3,900 meters), the basin measures 500 by 80 miles (800 by 130 km.). Several mountain peaks around the basin exceed 6,000 meters (19,700 feet). Lake Titicaca, the world's highest navigable lake, at 12,500 feet (3,810 meters) altitude, is more than 110 miles (180 km.) long and extremely deep. The lake contains freshwater, even though it has no outlet to

Altiplano valley in Peru. (Clyde L. Rasmussen)

The plume of Ecuador's Pichincha volcano rises over Ecuador during its December, 1999, eruption. (AP/Wide World Photos)

the sea, because a short river empties its waters into a salt lake farther south. Near-freezing temperatures occur almost nightly, and no trees grow under these conditions. Potatoes, which survive by growing underground, were first domesticated here, and were the Amerindians' staple food.

SOUTHERN ANDES. From the borders of Argentina, Bolivia, and Chile to Tierra del Fuego, the Andes form a single chain of massive mountains. Opposite Chile's Atacama Desert, the mountains are high, steep, and quite dry. The runoff of winter snows sends small rivers eastward into Argentina, but many of these never have enough water to reach the sea. Most passes through the mountains require a

Andes Page 684

655

climb of more than 10,000 feet (3,000 meters).

Between Mendoza, Argentina, and Santiago, Chile, the Andes reach their highest point in Mount Aconcagua. This extinct volcano has perpetual ice and snow at its summit and is the tallest mountain in the Western Hemisphere. From here to Tierra del Fuego, the Andes show more distorted peaks and valleys as a result of glaciers eroding the mountain masses. Ice and snow also produced the lakes and ski slopes of Chile and Argentina. Both countries have created national parks in this region to preserve the area's natural beauty.

While the Andes decline to about 6,000 feet (1,800 meters) at South America's southern tip, the action of ice in sculpting the terrain has carved the land into rugged and picturesque formations. South-

ern Chile is a land of volcanoes, fjords, lakes, hanging valleys, remnant glaciers, innumerable islands, and glacial deposits; only Alaska has similar features on so grand a scale. In middle Chile, the line of permanent ice and snow is about 12,000 feet (3,650 meters); but progressing toward Antarctica, it falls to 5,000 feet (1,500 meters) on Mount Osorno, and to 2,300 feet (700 meters) at Tierra del Fuego. Puerto Montt (41 degrees south latitude, longitude 73 degrees west) is the start of the Chilean fjord region.

During the Ice Age, mountain glaciers covered this area and most of Argentine Patagonia. Glaciers ground mountains into barren rocky surfaces with weird shapes, gouged out deep, rounded valleys, left perpendicular valleys hanging up to several hundred feet above their main

Sugar Loaf Mountain. (Clyde L. Rasmussen)

Glaciers Page 685

Christ the Redeemer statue, which overlooks Rio de Janeiro's harbor. (PhotoDisc)

river, and built up large deposits of loose rock and sand.

THE EASTERN HIGHLANDS. Comprising two separate areas—the Guiana Highlands and the Brazilian Plateau—the Eastern Highlands are quite different from the Andes Mountains. Their maximum elevation is only 9,075 feet (2,770 meters) in Venezuela's Mount Roraima; a mountain northeast of Rio de Janeiro, Brazil, reaches a similar altitude. The average elevation of both highlands is less than 2,000 feet (610 meters). The Eastern Highlands are mostly made up of highly eroded plateaus of sedimentary rocks over ancient crystalline rock and lava flows. These crustal features are much older than the Andes. Lack of earthquakes and volcanic activity in the area today show that the landforms are no longer in the mountain-building phase. After eroding for so many millennia, the highlands have many flat surfaces and chains of low hills.

Resistant granite rocks stand above the general plateau and form such features as Sugar Loaf Mountain in Rio de Janerio's harbor and Corcovado Peak, on which the famous statue of Christ the Redeemer stands, overlooking Rio de Janeiro.

GUIANA HIGHLANDS. This area covers most of southern Venezuela, Suriname, French Guiana, and a small part of southern Brazil. Most of the mountainous parts of this plateau are on its western and southern fringes. Sloping generally toward the Caribbean and Atlantic coastlines, it has major rivers rising in the south, crossing the high tablelands, and dropping over waterfalls before entering the coastal plains. A tributary of Venezuela's Caroní River bursts from an aquifer near the top of a high tableland and drops 3,212 feet (980 meters) in Angel Falls, the world's highest waterfall. Forests and grasslands form a complex pattern on the highlands, the type and density of tropical vegetation depending on rainfall and soil types. Rough terrain, infertile soils, and thick forests make the Guiana Highlands a remote and underdeveloped region.

Mineral deposits have been worked for many years in the highlands, and the existence of more deposits is likely. Gold and diamonds have attracted prospectors since the nineteenth century. Iron ore and bauxite have been mined extensively; their presence indicates that soils are poor for agriculture. Near Venezuela's Orinoco River is Cerro Bolívar, a mountain of high-grade iron ore that has been mined since the 1940's.

THE BRAZILIAN HIGHLANDS. This region is located on the southern side of the Amazon Basin, extending all the way to Brazil's eastern seaboard, from Fortaleza to Pôrto Alegre—an area almost the size of Alaska. Averaging about 2,000 feet (610 meters), the surface of the highlands is broken by rounded crystalline mountains in the south and scattered masses trending parallel to the east coast. The São Francisco River rises in southern Brazil and runs in a deep canyon for 2,000 miles (3,200 km.) northeast and parallel to the coast before it descends in a series of waterfalls to the Atlantic Ocean just south of Recife.

Many tributaries of the Amazon have cut deep canyons into the highlands, adding to the roughness of the general terrain. The southern end of the highlands, the Paraná Plateau, is made up of thick layers of diabase lava. Reaching about 6,000 feet (1,800 meters), this lava plateau is one of the world's largest. Rich soils for coffee and other crops form from the lava. The mild climate of the midlatitudes and the rich soils make this one of Brazil's most productive farm regions.

The Brazilian Highlands end in steep cliffs along the eastern seaboard, but their northern side grades gently into the Amazon plain. The sharp edge of the highlands, called an escarpment, lies within sight of the coast. Rising 2,000 feet (610 meters) or higher in a series of steps, the escarpment has made transportation from the coast to the interior difficult and costly. The new Brazilian capital, Brasília, was built on the highlands to encourage people to move into the nation's interior.

THE AMAZON BASIN. There is great concern about destruction of the Amazon rain forest, the world's largest rain forest. More than 117 species of plants have been counted in half a square mile, and the number of other life forms in the same area is unknown. Many plants are used to make medicines, and loss of the rain forest could mean loss of potential new medicines and much of the world's biological diversity. The Amazon Basin is one of the least populated places on earth, and continued population growth will increase pressure to develop more of the region. New mineral discoveries in the basin also encourage development. Geologists believe the basin may contain large petroleum and natural gas fields.

The Amazon Basin covers most of Brazil and parts of Venezuela, Colombia, Ecuador, Peru, and Bolivia, an area about the same size as the United States. This is the largest area of lowland in South America. A vast inland sea five million years ago, the structural basin that became the Amazon was filled with sediments from the Andes and Eastern Highlands. More than one thousand rivers flow into the basin and form branches of the mighty Amazon. These rivers deposit sediments in some places and cut valleys into the surface at others.

Although the basin is only about 300 feet (91 meters) above sea level at the Peruvian border, the plain has numerous hills and rolling terrain. Low spots create vast swamps; the huge floodplains along the rivers become lakes during the rainy season from November through June; but the hilly land remains permanently above water. Widest in the west, the plain narrows to about 250 miles (400 km.) in the east where the Guiana Highlands and Brazilian Highlands almost meet. The Amazon has not built an impressive delta at its mouth, because the huge amount of silt brought across the continent by the rivers is carried north by ocean currents. Hourly, 170 trillion gallons of freshwater are flushed into the sea, pushing sea water about 100 miles (160 km.) back from the Amazon's mouth.

The equator passes through South America just north of the Amazon River. Rain comes to the basin in all seasons, but November through June bring floods when most of the rivers overflow. Average annual rainfall in the basin is 100 inches (1,500 millimeters). Flooding brings new soil to the river lowlands, but also covers good farmland with water. Warm temperatures of 80 degrees Fahrenheit (27 degrees Celsius) and plentiful rain are the right combination for a tropical rain forest.

In many places, there is a complete covering of interlaced leaves high up in the giant trees. The forest floor is dark, and little vegetation grows on the ground; where sunlight reaches the floor, masses of vegetation grow in dense tangles, making it difficult to walk among the trees. Patches of grassland and scrub forest occupy especially well-drained land, or land where trees have been cut and burned. Soils away from the rivers are not fertile for crops, and disturbance of the forest-soil-water ecology can create a sterile wasteland until nature has time to restore the environmental balance. Rubber, Brazil nuts, and hardwood lumber are valuable Amazonian products.

ORINOCO LOWLANDS. Located in Colombia and Venezuela, the Orinoco Lowlands have some of the same characteristics of the Amazon Basin. Relatively flat land slopes from the Andes Mountains and Guiana Highlands. The Orinoco River and its tributaries drain the *llanos* (plains) and form a large swampy delta opposite Trinidad. The major difference between the Amazon and Orinoco Lowlands is that the Orinoco has a six-month-long dry season and a six-month wet season. Another difference is that the natural vegetation of the *llanos* is grass, not trees; this is a land of tropical savanna. Soils are poor for crops on both plains.

From June through October, so much rain falls that large areas of the *llanos* are flooded. Dry winters make many rivers disappear and make grass hard, brittle, and parched. Cattle roaming on open pastures have been the traditional use of this almost unpopulated land. Even for cattle, both rainy and dry seasons make life difficult.

THE PARANÁ–PLATA PLAINS. This region starts at the edge of the Andes foothills and Brazilian Plateau at about 16 degrees south latitude, longitude 60 degrees west. Patagonia borders the southern part of this lowland, which runs into the sea at Buenos Aires Province, Argentina. These lowlands are made up of a huge basin that was filled by sediments washed down from the Andes and the Brazilian Highlands over thousands of years. The northern and western parts of the plains have sediments that are 10,000 feet (3,050 meters) deep before bedrock is reached.

At Buenos Aires, the sediments are 965 feet (300 meters) deep. Few stone fragments or pebbles can be found on the plains, and tall buildings cannot be constructed on this loose subsoil. In the south, the plains have many characteristics similar to the U.S. plains from Denver to Chicago. The Paraná-Plata Plains comprise the Pantanal, Chaco, and Pampas.

THE PANTANAL. This tropical swamp, located in southwest Brazil, is made up of the drainage basin of the upper Paraguay River. About the size of South Dakota, it is one of the world's largest wetlands. The Paraguay River and its tributaries overflow in the rainy season (February) and the region becomes a maze of swamps, bays, canals, lakes, and marshes. Even in the dry season, the water table is never far below the surface. Waterbirds, fish, reptiles, and many species of mammals thrive in this environment. World environmentalists have made this a prime target for conservation efforts.

THE CHACO. This vast alluvial plain stretches from tropical latitudes just south of the Pantanal to the middle latitudes of northern Argentina. Larger than Texas, it extends 700 miles (1,125 km.) in a north-south direction. Receiving much less rain than the Pantanal, it is a dry tropical/semi-tropical region crossed by rivers that dry up in the winter dry season and flood into swamps during the wet summers. As a result of salt deposits building up, many low basins have cactus and other dry-land plants. The region is poor for agriculture. *Chaco* means hunting land in the local Amerindian language, and the area teems with wildlife of all types. Some *quebracho* forests in wetter areas support lumbering and tannin industries; livestock graze and cotton grows in favored places.

THE PAMPAS. One of the world's greatest food-producing regions, the Pampas are Argentina and Uruguay's midlatitude plains, similar to the U.S. Midwest. Mendoza is in the dry foothills of the Andes, as Denver is in the Rockies; Buenos Aires is at the end of the humid prairies, as Chicago is. Mendoza's elevation is 2,500 feet (760 meters), and the Pampas grade gently to Buenos Aires at sea level. Tall grass is the natural vegetation of the humid east; short grass and scrub plants cover the arid west. Rivers from the mountains water the oases at the Pampa's west-

Negro River
Page 686

ern margins, making them garden spots for fruits and vegetables. Only in the far southeast corner of Buenos Aires Province do low mountains break the flat surface of the Pampas.

Rich soils develop under midlatitude grasslands that receive adequate rain, allowing such excellent animal feed as alfalfa, corn, and soybeans to grow. Beef is a major source of income for farms in this part of the Pampas, just as it is in Iowa and Illinois. In the drier west, wheat and sheep find ideal conditions, like their counterparts in eastern Colorado and western Nebraska.

PATAGONIA. The high, cold, windswept tablelands of southern Argentina are called Patagonia. Rocks that form the tablelands are either flat-lying sedimentary rocks or old lava flows. Seaside cliffs range from only a few feet to 300 feet (90 meters) in the north. The tablelands rise in step-like fashion toward the Andes, where they reach 5,000 feet (1,500 meters) in some places. Low mountains of resistant crystalline rocks stick up above the general surface in a few places.

At the Andean foothills, there are many lakes and shallow depressions where glacial troughs and cirques are partly filled with meltwater from the mountains' snow cover. This is good sheep country. The Colorado, Chubut, and Negro are among the few rivers with enough water to have cut steep-sided and flat-bottomed valleys into the tablelands all the way to the sea. Farmers have settled in some of these valleys, taking advantage of irrigation waters, good soils, and protection from the strong, cold southwest winds.

Most of Patagonia is classified as a cold desert. Permanent settlements have succeeded only in the sheltered valleys and seaports, and near mineral deposits. Off the coast of Patagonia is a broad continental shelf, and marine life is plentiful in this part of the south Atlantic. Petroleum around Comodoro Rivadavia and coal in the Río Gallegos district support small centers of urban development. Patagonia's huge empty spaces, about the size of Texas, are likely to remain empty.

Robert J. Tata

FOR FURTHER STUDY

Bonini, William E., Robert B. Hargraves, and Reginald Shagam, eds. *The Caribbean-South American Plate Boundary and Regional Tectonics.* Boulder, Colo.: Geological Society of America, 1984.

Brawer, Moshe. *Atlas of South America.* New York: Simon & Schuster, 1991.

Butland, Gilbert J. *Latin America: A Regional Geography.* 3d ed. London: Longman, 1972.

Caviedes, César, and Gregory Knapp. *South America.* Englewood Cliffs, N.J.: Prentice Hall, 1995.

Clawson, David L. *Latin America and the Caribbean: Lands and Peoples.* New York: McGraw-Hill, 1999.

Espenshade, Edward B., Jr., ed. *Goode's World Atlas, Nineteenth Edition.* Chicago: Rand McNally, 1995.

HYDROLOGY OF SOUTH AMERICA

Watershed Page 687

Most areas of South America are well supplied with water. The only region of the continent classified as a desert is the Atacama of northern Chile, where some locations have registered no significant precipitation for more than one hundred years. Other areas, such as the interior of northeast Brazil, coastal Peru, the highlands of southeast Peru and western Bolivia, and the eastern slope of the Andes mountains in Argentina, receive only slight and intermittent precipitation.

Snowfall in South America is restricted to the higher mountains and extreme south, but heavy rainfall occurs in many regions. In the southwest portion of the continent, the continuous westerly winds off of the Pacific Ocean are forced to rise along the western side of the Andes. The uplift causes water vapor to condense on the windward side of the mountains (the orographic effect), causing rainfall.

Southern Chile, therefore, is one of the wettest areas of the continent.

Similar areas of heavy rainfall exist along the southeast coast of Brazil and the Pacific shores of Ecuador and Colombia in northwest South America. The greatest amount of precipitation occurs in the middle of the continent, in the equatorial regions of northwest Brazil and the eastern provinces of Bolivia, Peru, Ecuador, and Colombia. Throughout the year, sunlight beats down on the surface, causing the moist air to rise and condense into massive, electrically charged clouds that produce torrential downpours in the late afternoon.

The highest mountains in South America are the Andes, which extend from the Caribbean Sea in the north to Tierra del Fuego in the far south. Formed along the western edge of the continent where the South American and Pacific plates grind

*Urubamba
River
Page 688*

together and force crustal rock high into the air, the mountains divert most of the rainfall runoff toward the east. Only a few short streams, such as the Esmeraldas and Guayas Rivers of Ecuador, Santa River of Peru, and the Bio-bio River in Chile, flow down the mountains into the Pacific Ocean. Most of the rain in South America falls on the large, relatively flat interior surface, where the runoff merges with streams flowing toward the east from the Andes. The water collects into ever-broader rivers, eventually making its way to the Atlantic Ocean after a journey that can exceed several thousand miles.

The heavy precipitation and warm temperatures in the north central region of the continent help produce the tropical rain forest, the most diverse, yet one of the most fragile, ecological systems in the world. The climate is also partially responsible for the low agricultural productivity in the region, because the heavy rainfall causes important plant nutrients to be dissolved and washed out of the upper layers of the soil in a process called leaching. The characteristics of the climate, vegetation, and soil have an important impact on the population and life-style along the rivers in central South America.

*Belém
Page 876*

*Manaus
Pages 681,
883*

*Negro
River
Page 686*

The water moving from the west and central regions toward the east collects in two dominant river basins: the Amazon system in the north, and the Paraná/Paraguay/Uruguay system in the south. Although not as large, the Orinoco in Venezuela and São Francisco in Brazil are also major rivers that help drain water toward the east, while the Essequibo in Guyana and the Colorado in Argentina are locally significant. A few streams flow directly north from the Andes into the Caribbean Sea, the most important being the Magdalena and Cauca Rivers of Colombia.

AMAZON RIVER SYSTEM. The largest rivers in South America are located in the heart of the continent. With a total length of nearly 4,000 miles (more than 6,400 km.), more than one thousand tributaries, a capture basin of approximately 2,007,200 square miles (5.2 million sq. km.), and a discharge of more than 6 million cubic feet (170,000 cubic meters) per second at the mouth, the Amazon, in many ways, is the largest river in the world. Named after a mythological Greek tribe of warrior women, the stream begins high in the Andes of southwestern Peru. Water collects in the Ucayali and Maranon, which flow north along the eastern side of the mountains and eventually come together south of the port of Iquitos. As the merged flow moves downstream from the city, it takes on the name Solimões in Peru, and when it reaches Brazil, Amazon.

Along its journey to the mouth (the place where a river empties into the sea), the volume of water is increased from several large tributaries that join along the southern flank. The largest of these are the Madeira, Tapajós, and Xingú. Sometimes the Tocantíns and its large tributary, the Araguáia, are considered to be part of the Amazon system, for they empty into the Atlantic within the complex Amazon delta region near the city of Belém and just south of the large island of Marajó. From the north, the only major tributary is the Negro, which passes through the large and historically important city of Manaus. The Negro is named for the dark color of its water, which is caused by the tannic acid that it transports.

Most tributaries feed the Amazon from the south, and they drain a large interior area of the continent that is dominated by the tropical savanna climate. The most important feature of the weather in these areas is the seasonality of the rainfall. During the summer months, which in this region and other areas south of the equator is in December, January, and February, the savanna climate produces heavy rainfall. This occurs because during this period, the Sun's position directly overhead causes intense convectional uplift and afternoon thunderstorms. Six months later, the Sun will have moved north across the equator, so the areas experience descending and drying air, high surface barometric pressure, and little precipitation.

The amount of water transported by the south-joining Amazon tributaries reflects this climate variability, and because most of the water in the Amazon comes from these rivers, the volume in the Amazon itself varies greatly during the year. The Amazon experiences low water levels during June, July, and August; six months later, high water marks are reached. This also has a major effect on the tropical forest wildlife and the inhabitants along the rivers.

Beyond the natural levees at the water's edge exist large lowland areas, known in Brazil as *várzeas*, that are subject to regular flooding caused by the variability in the flow. The swampy nature of these areas causes difficulties for people attempting to farm the land and build roads and bridges. The *várzeas* are also favorite homes for many species of tropical birds, insects, and reptiles, including the huge Anaconda snakes.

Because of the depth and large volume of water that flows down the Amazon River, it can be used by ocean-going ships for much of its course. These vessels travel from the mouth to the interior ports of Santarém, Manaus, and Iquitos with little difficulty. For some types of bulky cargo, transportation between Lima, on the western side of the mountains of Peru, and Iquitos, in the Peruvian eastern lowlands, is less expensive by ship than over land. Despite the greater distance of passage through the Panama Canal, around northern South America, and up the entire length of the lower Amazon, ship transport is less costly than overland travel in the Andes mountains.

The Amazon and its tributaries also are used by a wide variety of smaller boats, ranging from the dugout canoes of the native peoples to the large riverboats that provide supplies to the residents along the water's edge. Because the population in the interior of South America is sparse and building roads is difficult, the rivers provide the only connection to the outside world for many people.

Settlements tend to cluster along the streams because that is where people can purchase or trade for items such as pots and pans, textile fabric, fuel, and other common necessities of life. The river edge is also where people are able to sell some of the things that are produced in the area, such as agricultural products, rubber extract, and the fish caught in the river or game hunted in the forest. The river trading boats, many of which are operated by families who live aboard, are important to the people of the Amazon region.

PARANÁ RIVER SYSTEM. In many ways the Paraná system, which also includes the Paraguay and Uruguay Rivers, is the most important in South America. The Paraná River originates in central Brazil; flows through the southeast region of that country, along the international borders between Brazil and Paraguay, and between Argentina and Paraguay; goes through northern Argentina; and finally enters the Atlantic Ocean at the wide estuary known as the Rio de La Plata.

The approximate total length of the Paraná is 2,485 miles (4,000 km.). Along its course, it is joined by the Paraguay River, which also originates in Brazil, bounds the territories of Brazil and Bolivia, and then bisects the landlocked country of Paraguay. After their beginning in Brazil, the waters of the Uruguay River

SOUTH AMERICA'S LONGEST RIVERS

River	Flows Into	Length Kilometers	Length Miles	World Rank
Amazon	Atlantic Ocean	6,436	4,000	2
Paraná	Rio de la Plata	3,998	2,485	11
Purús	Amazon River	3,379	2,100	15
Madeira	Amazon River	3,239	2,013	16
Sâo Francisco	Atlantic Ocean	3,199	1,988	17
Japurá	Amazon River	2,816	1,750	22
Tocantins	Amazon River	2,698	1,677	25
Orinoco	Atlantic Ocean	2,574	1,600	26
Paraguay	Paraná River	2,549	1,584	27
Negro	Amazon River	2,253	1,400	33
Xingu	Amazon River	2,091	1,300	37

Source: The World Almanac 2000. Mahwah, N.J.: World Almanac Books, 2000.

form the border between Uruguay and Argentina before merging into the Paraná/Paraguay at the estuary. The combined rivers discharge about 2.8 million cubic feet (80,000 cubic meters) of water per second into the Atlantic Ocean and drain a capture basin of almost 1.7 million square miles (4.4 million sq. km.).

In comparison to the Amazon system in the north, the Paraná system is not as long, discharges less water, and drains a smaller area. The greater importance of the rivers in the south is the result of their location. They form boundaries among South America's most important countries and flow through the industrial and urban areas of the continent. Waterborne trade on the Paraná has always been important, even though the riverbeds, unlike those of the Amazon, need to be constantly dredged, levied, and otherwise maintained to prevent ships from running aground.

Since the colonial period, the waters of these rivers have been fought over frequently. They played a significant role in the Paraguayan War (sometimes called the War of the Triple Alliance) of the 1860's, which pitted Argentina, Brazil, and Uruguay against the small nation of Paraguay. The gunboat battles and land conflicts destroyed most of the population of Paraguay, although it left its territory more or less intact. More recently, the rivers have caused international disputes over water rights. The nations along the lower course of the Paraná have claimed that the vital water necessary to support farms, cities, and boat traffic has been diverted for other uses upstream in Brazil. Some disputes have arisen because of the construction of large hydroelectric projects in the region.

In some areas of Brazil, the Paraná and its tributaries flow from areas that are underlain by hard volcanic rocks (basalt) onto regions of softer sedimentary formations. When this happens, waterfalls develop because the harder rocks upstream are more resistant to weathering and erosion than the softer surfaces of the lower course.

WATERFALLS. The most famous of the waterfalls are located on the Iguaçu, attracting many tourists to the area where that river joins the Paraná near the borders among Brazil, Argentina, and Paraguay. Other waterfalls have disappeared, however, because dams have been constructed across the major rivers and flooded the valleys. This has been done to supply the electricity needed by the factories and homes of this area of South America, especially in Brazil's industrial southeast.

One of the largest hydroelectric projects in the world was completed near the still-existent Iguaçu Falls. A similar series

Iguaçu Falls Page 879

of falls on the Paraná, once known as the Guaíra Falls, was destroyed by the construction of the Itaipú dam. Most of the generated electricity is sent by high-tension lines back to the factories near the city of São Paulo, Brazil.

Two major projects on rivers of the Paraná system caused much debate at the end of the twentieth century. One involves planned modifications to the river bed along the Paraguay River, in the region north of the city of Corumbá on the Bolivia-Brazil border, which are hoped to increase the navigability of the river. In this region, the Paraguay passes through the Pantanal, a wide area where a substantial percentage of the land remains submerged through the rainy season.

The large expanses of water and wetlands attract thousands of species of birds and animals, and the Pantanal is considered to be one of the richest wildlife repositories in the world. Many fear that modification of the drainage caused by disturbances to the Paraguay River will destroy the complex ecology of this region. Environmentalists in Brazil and from around the world have appealed to the government to halt the proposed effort.

The other project, somewhat less controversial, involves ongoing construction that will turn the Paraná and its major Brazilian tributary, the Tietê, into a navigable artery from its mouth near Buenos Aires and Montevideo to an area near the city of São Paulo in Brazil. The many dams are being fitted with locks with the capacity to lift large vessels around the barriers. This will benefit industry by decreasing the cost of transporting raw materials to the industrial heart of Brazil, but it will also increase the environmental stress to the rivers and neighboring lands in the region.

Many major cities are located along the Paraná and its tributaries. In Brazil, these include São Paulo, Campinas, Piracicaba,

Sorocaba, Ribeirão Preto, and São Jose do Rio Preto. Corumbá in western Brazil and Paraguay's capital city of Asunción are located on the Paraguay, as well as Uruguay's and Argentina's largest cities and capitals, Montevideo and Buenos Aires. Other important centers on the lower course of the Paraná and Rio de la Plata include Santa Fe, Paraná, Rosario, and La Plata.

OTHER RIVERS. Several other rivers in South America are important to the countries through which they flow. In Venezuela, the Orinoco has played a major role in the country's history. Approximately 1,340 miles (2,150 km.) long and draining an area of 364,900 square miles (945,000 sq. km.), it flows toward the east through a grassy plains region known as the *llanos*. The cowboylike animal herders from this region were an important element of Simon Bolivar's army when he fought for the independence of South America from Spain in the early nineteenth century.

In modern times, the Orinoco transports raw materials such as iron ore to the east coast, from where they are exported to the industrial centers of Western Europe and the United States. Important cities on the Orinoco are Ciudad Bolivar and Ciudad Guayana. The latter was established in the late twentieth century as a manufacturing center to take advantage of locally available raw materials and capital generated from revenue derived from Venezuela's petroleum exports.

In Colombia, the Magdalena and Cauca Rivers were important to the settlement of the country. Both provided links between the interior Andean highlands and the communities of the northern coast. Over the colonial period, the Magdalena was used to transport people into the interior and bring gold and emeralds down to the ports of Baranquilla and Cartagena. The Cauca flows through Colombia's most productive areas, and near

Cartagena
Page 877

665

its banks can be found the large cities of Medellin, Cali, and Manizales.

Brazil's São Francisco River flows more than 1,800 miles (2,900 km.) through the dry interior regions of the eastern states of Minas Gerais, Bahia, Pernambuco, Sergipe, and Alagoas. The region is used primarily for raising cattle, so the river has provided a means for moving animals to markets near the coast. As with the rivers of the Paraná system further south, the hydroelectric potential of the São Francisco has also been tapped, most notably at the Paulo Afonso Falls on the northern border of the state of Bahia.

LAKES. South America includes relatively few significant lakes. There are no massive systems of lakes such as the Great Lakes of North America or the large inland seas of central Asia. Most lakes in South America are produced by the dams along the rivers, and the largest human-made lake in the world is the Dr. W. J. van Blommestein Meer reservoir in Suriname.

In the north, Lake Maracaibo near Venezuela's coast is the most important body of freshwater. Technically it is not a lake, for there is an outlet to the sea, but the passage is shallow and its waters are fresh. The rocks under the lake include extensive petroleum deposits, and although reserves are no longer as extensive as they were at one time, the area remains a major oil producer. Refineries, pipelines, and population growth in places like Maracaibo City provide evidence of this resource.

In the highland border between Peru and Bolivia, Lake Titicaca has nurtured human settlement for several thousand years. Indigenous cultures have made the lake shore their home, and the population is dominated by the Aymara and Quechua-speaking descendants of the Incas and previous cultures. The lake is deep, and the large volume of water has a moderating effect on the harsh, cold climate of the

highlands. The people live off of the fish and other wildlife in the water and grow meager crops in the hard soil. They travel across the waters of the lake on boats made from the fiber of reeds that grow along its shore.

Melting snows on the surrounding mountains flow into Lake Titicaca, and excess water in the lake flows out to the southeast in the Desaguadero River. The landscape is quite dry, but small communities exist along the river. Eventually the river, by this time a trickle, empties into Lake Poopo—an extensive area on a map but of little significance because of its high saline content and shallow depth.

Among the other lakes in South America, few have any great significance. Along the coast of extreme south Brazil, the Patos and da Mangueira Lakes are large but not very important. The southern Brazilian city of Porto Alegre fronts onto the Lagoa dos Patos, and ocean-going shipping passes to the Atlantic where the lake links to the Atlantic at Rio Grande. Glacially formed lakes in the Andes of Chile and Argentina have great natural beauty and draw tourists from the urban centers of the east to the nearby ski slopes.

In summary, the hydrology of South America reflects the climate and terrain. Although impressive, the Amazon system has had limited economic impact because it drains regions that are sparsely populated and not very productive. The Paraná system in the south, however, has been economically and politically important. This area of South America is developing rapidly, so the southern rivers will continue to play a vital role in the history of Brazil, Argentina, Uruguay, and Paraguay.

Cyrus B. Dawsey

FOR FURTHER STUDY

Blouet, Brian W., and Olwyn M. Blouet. *Latin America and the Caribbean: A System-

Venezuela tanker Page 820

Lake Titicaca Pages 689, 886

atic and Regional Survey. 3d ed. New York: John Wiley & Sons, 1997.

Clawson, David L. *Latin America and the Caribbean: Lands and Peoples.* New York: McGraw-Hill, 1999.

James, Preston, and C. W. Minkle. *Latin America.* 5th ed. New York: John Wiley & Sons, 1986.

Preston, David. *Latin American Development.* Essex, England: Longman, 1996.

PHYSIOGRAPHY AND HYDROLOGY OF CENTRAL AMERICA

Map Page 690

Seven countries between Colombia and Mexico—Guatemala, Belize, Honduras, El Salvador, Nicaragua, Costa Rica, and Panama—make up Central America. El Salvador is the smallest at 8,100 square miles (20,900 sq. km.), close to the size of Massachusetts. Nicaragua is the largest, with 50,900 square miles (131,800 sq. km.), about the size of New York State. The combined area of all seven countries is 203,100 square miles (526,000 sq. km.).

The region is narrowest in Panama, about 35 miles wide (56 km.), and widest, at 350 miles (560 km.), across Honduras. North to south, Central America measures 1,200 miles (1,930 km.). If Central America were to be placed over the eastern United States, it would reach from the tip of Florida to Washington, D.C.

SEISMIC ACTIVITY. When Pangaea, the supercontinent first described by Alfred Wegener in 1912 as a single continental landmass, broke apart about two hundred million years ago, North America and South America were not connected. As tectonic activ-

ity intensified, a series of islands were formed that ultimately joined. This created the isthmus link, about fifty million years ago.

Seismic activity is induced by the convergence of the Cocos, Caribbean, North American, South American, and Nazca Plates. These plate movements cause the Cocos Plate to dive under the Caribbean Plate. Along the western edge of Nicara-

Looking west along the Motagua fault after an earthquake in Guatemala in 1976. (U.S. Geological Survey)

667

gua, a rift has occurred. A fault between the North American Plate and the Caribbean Plate, similar to the San Andreas Fault in California, exists across southern Guatemala. These tectonic movements generate the earthquakes and volcanoes that persist in the region.

*Volcano
Page 689*

Seismic activity is a major concern to inhabitants of the area. Active volcanoes extend in the west from Panama to Guatemala and beyond. Only Belize is without an active volcano. In the 1990's there were eight eruptions, three each in Guatemala and Costa Rica and two in Nicaragua. Small-magnitude earthquakes occur frequently and are widespread across the western portion of the region. Most earthquakes cause little or no damage, but violent quakes do occur. The last major earthquake of the twentieth century there, a magnitude 7.0 on the Richter scale, struck southwestern Nicaragua in 1992. It caused the deaths of 116 people.

PHYSIOGRAPHIC REGIONS. Central America has four physiographic regions. Most of the region is underlain by granitic rock, except in the Petén where limestone persists.

The Caribbean Lowlands, with elevations below 1,000 feet (300 meters) are irregular; their width varies from a few miles in places to as much as 75 miles (120 km.) in others. These lowlands are relatively flat and crossed by many rivers. It is a region of deltas, shallow lagoons, and salt marshes. Soils range from those that are heavily leached and have low fertility to the fertile, alluvial soils. Most of the native vegetation has been removed. The eastern peninsula shared by Nicaragua and Honduras is by far the largest of these lowlands.

The Central Highlands above 1,000 feet (300 meters) were formed by tectonic uplift with a volcanic band along the western edge. High, rugged relief and interior valleys are typical. Elevation ranges from

*Gatun Lake
Page 821*

about 1,000 feet to 6,500 feet (2,000 meters), but there are several peaks over 6,500 feet. The highest peak is Volcan Tajumulco in Guatemala, at 13,767 feet (4,196 meters). These highlands extend from Panama to Guatemala.

The Pacific Lowlands are the least extensive of the four regions. The largest of these lowlands is the combined Guanacaste region of Costa Rica and lake region of Nicaragua. A unique feature off the coast of Panama is the great tidal range. On the Caribbean side, the tidal range is about 28 inches (70 centimeters); on the Pacific side, the range is nearly 275 inches (700 centimeters)—almost 23 feet.

The Petén, in northern Guatemala, has different characteristics from the rest of Central America. Flat to moderately rolling topography dominates the area. Elevation ranges from about 490 feet (150 meters) to about 740 feet (225 meters). Geologically, the Petén is an extension of Mexico's Yucatán peninsula and was not formed by the tectonic activity that created most of Central America. Soils are of low fertility and very porous.

HYDROLOGY. In the south, from Panama to Honduras and El Salvador, there are hundreds of watercourses. Those rivers flowing west from the continental divide into the Pacific Ocean are generally short but swift, and some are intermittent. Those draining east are longer and slower moving. Because these rivers originate in the Central Highlands, many have been harnessed by dams for inexpensive hydroelectric power. In the north of Guatemala, most rivers flow north to Mexico or east through Belize. Since the soil in this area is porous, some rivers drain underground.

Gatun Lake, created by damming the Chagres River, supplies the water to operate the locks of the Panama Canal. Lake Nicaragua is the largest lake in the region. This lake, together with Lake Managua, was once a bay connected to the Pacific Ocean. When Lake Nicaragua became isolated from the ocean, many marine species became trapped. Over time, the lake became fresh and salt-water species such as sharks and tarpon adapted to the new conditions. Lake Atitlán in Guatemala is more than 985 feet (300 meters) deep in spots.

Donald Andrew Wiley

FOR FURTHER STUDY

Arbingast, Stanley A., et al., eds. *Atlas of Central America.* Austin: University of Texas Press, 1979.

Bonini, William E., Robert B. Hargraves, and Reginald Shagam, eds. *The Caribbean-South American Plate Boundary and Regional Tectonics.* Boulder, Colo.: Geological Society of America, 1984.

Butland, Gilbert J. *Latin America: A Regional Geography.* 3d ed. London: Longman, 1972.

Clawson, David L. *Latin America and the Caribbean: Lands and Peoples.* New York: McGraw-Hill, 1999.

Janzen, Daniel H., ed. *Costa Rican Natural History.* Chicago: University of Chicago Press, 1983.

McCullough, David. *The Path Between the Seas: The Creation of the Panama Canal.* New York: Simon and Schuster, 1977.

Lake Atitlán Pages 691, 876

CLIMATOLOGY

SOUTH AMERICA

*Map
Page 693*

*South
America
from space
Page 692*

Covering 13 percent of Earth's total land mass—about 7 million square miles (18 million sq. km.)—South America extends over 67 degrees of latitude and has a diversity of climates. This diversity is a product of six factors: latitude, the equator, the varying width of the continent, high mountains, prevailing winds, and ocean currents.

LATITUDE. South America's position straddling the equator makes it primarily a tropical continent. Tropical climates in South America extend over 62 percent of its landmass. The continent's landmass is widest between the tropic of Cancer and the tropic of Capricorn. Only Uruguay and the southern parts of Brazil, Argentina, and Chile extend south of the tropic of Capricorn. The rest of the continent is entirely within the Tropics.

THE EQUATOR. South America is divided into unequal portions by the equator, which runs through the northern part of the continent at the mouth of the Amazon River. Only twelve degrees of latitude out of the sixty-seven spanned by South America are in the Northern Hemisphere. The climatic belts of South America are not symmetrical in relation to the equator as they are in Africa.

CONTINENTAL WIDTH. The greater east-to-west extent of the northern portion of the continent, along the equator, does not create a continentality effect as it

does in Africa because insolation varies little during the year. The southern part of the continent, which is much narrower, allows the maritime influence to extend further inland.

HIGH MOUNTAINS. The presence of high mountain ranges acts as a climatic barrier. The Andes of South America deeply modify the climate of South America. These mountains prevent winds from the South Pacific anticyclone (high-pressure area) from reaching the continent's interior. South America's high mountains and plateau modify the low-elevation climates by lowering temperature, increasing precipitation on the windward side of the mountains, and creating a rain shadow effect on the lee side.

PREVAILING WINDS. South America is divided into two wind belts: the trade winds and the westerlies. The trade winds or tropical easterlies blow toward the equator out of the subtropical anticyclones centered near 30 degrees north and south latitude. Because of the rotation of the earth, winds flowing from these high-pressure areas are deflected to their right in the Southern Hemisphere and to their left in the Northern Hemisphere. Therefore, the air moving toward the equator flows from east to west (the tropical easterlies or trade winds), while the air moving toward the poles flows from west to east (the westerlies).

The subtropical highs are located over the Pacific and Atlantic Oceans. The strongest high-pressure region is located off the east coast of South America, so that strong westerly winds blow toward the continent. Two low-pressure centers affect wind patterns inland: one located at about 60 degrees south latitude, north of the South Polar region, and the other extending from northeastern Brazil to the Gran Chaco region of Argentina. The trade winds flow toward the low pressure that is centered just below the equator in January and on the equator in July. The low pressure is associated with uplift, producing intense convective rains and attracting moisture-laden winds from the Atlantic.

The circulation of air over South America is influenced by winds related to these anticyclones. The trade winds coming from the subtropical high located over the south Atlantic Ocean do not blow over the Andes, which also prevent winds from the South Pacific anticyclone from reaching the interior of the continent.

The North Pacific anticyclone has little influence on the climate of northwestern South America; its effects are felt only as far south as Costa Rica. It seldom affects Colombia and Venezuela. The thermal continental and equatorial low-pressure belts are of seasonal importance. The thermal low-pressure center is maintained by the warming of the continent during the high-sun season (December to February) when air pressure is lowest in the center of the continent, near 20 degrees south latitude and longitude 60 degrees west.

OCEAN CURRENTS. Three ocean currents have a strong influence on South American climates. The Peru (or Humboldt) Current in the southwest and the Falkland Current in the southeast both carry cold water from the temperate zone into the Tropics. The Brazil Current brings warm water from the equatorial region of the Atlantic Ocean toward the east coast of South America, south of the equator, along the coast of Brazil. Cold currents chill the winds that blow over them and reduce the amount of moisture that reaches the neighboring shores; warm currents increase rainfall.

On occasion, during an El Niño event, the South Equatorial Current flows eastward instead of westward and brings warm water to the west coast of South America. The name "El Niño" (the boy child) was coined in Peru because this phenomenon occurs around Christmas (a reference to the Christ Child).

El Niño
Page 694

Higher pressure than normal on the western Pacific Ocean weakens the trade winds that normally flow westward. The South Equatorial Current flows eastward across the Pacific Ocean. The warm surface water slows the normal upwelling of the Peru Current. Surface water, depleted in nutrients, replaces the nutrient-rich water of the Peru Current. The whole food chain—phytoplankton, fish, marine mammals, and birds—suffers from the lack of nourishment, and massive fish kills occur, leaving local fishing-based economies in turmoil. Coastal Ecuador and northern Peru receive abundant rains and experience devastating floods. El Niño events happen every two to seven years. The two strongest El Niño events of the twentieth century occurred in 1982-1983 and 1997-1999.

On the west coast of South America, trade winds blowing parallel to, and slightly away from, the coast skim off warm surface water and contribute to the upwelling of cooler subsurface water; this cool water chills the air and further inhibits convection in the desert climate of coastal Peru and northern Chile. The Peru Current carries cold water to the coast of southern Ecuador, where the flow turns westward. Cold currents chill the winds that blow over them and reduce the amount of moisture that reaches the neighboring shores.

The east coast of South America is bathed by the cold Falkland Current in the south. Rio Gallegos, Argentina, has a maximum monthly temperature during the summer of 57 degrees Fahrenheit (13.1 degrees Celsius), which is much colder than would be expected at this latitude.

The coastal area of Brazil, south of the equator, is washed by the warm Brazil Current. Warm ocean currents heat the adjacent air, providing abundant water vapor and energy for convective storms. In the absence of an El Niño event, only the far northwestern coast of South America lies within reach of a warm current, the Equatorial Countercurrent.

MOUNTAINS. Elevation helps to explain the division of South America into climatic belts. The highest mountain, the Aconcagua, reaches about 22,800 feet (6,960 meters) above sea level. Many peaks are higher than 19,000 feet (5,800 meters). All climates are modified by elevation. The temperature range remains identical to the sea-level climate type, but each monthly temperature is decreased by about 11.7 degrees Fahrenheit (6.5 degrees Celsius) for every 3,280 feet (1,000 meters) rise of elevation.

CLIMATE REGIONS. South America can be divided into several well-marked climatic regions, resulting from the interplay of the six major factors. These climates are tropical rain forest (tropical wet); tropical savanna (tropical wet and dry); monsoon; semiarid or steppe (called Sahel in Africa); subtropical dry (desert); humid subtropical (identical to the climate on the east coast of North America from New York to the northern part of Florida); Mediterranean; and mountain.

TROPICAL RAIN FOREST. The tropical rain forest (tropical wet) climate extends over 1.5 million square miles (4 million sq. km.) across the equator. In the east, it covers the Amazon Basin and part of the coast of Brazil. It extends farther to the north along the coast of the Guyanas to the Orinoco River delta. On the west coast, it covers the coastal region of Colombia from about 3 to 11 degrees north latitude. Heavy rainfall, evenly distributed all year, averages about 98 inches (2.5 meters) in Para, Brazil; about 112 inches (2.8 meters) in Iquitos, Peru; and 89 inches (2.3 meters) in Manaus, Brazil. In Buenaventura, the main harbor of Colombia and one of the wettest areas in the world, it rains more than three hundred days a year, producing more than 354 inches (9 meters) of rain per year, the highest precipitation of the continent.

The average temperature for a tropical wet climate at sea level is around 86 degrees Fahrenheit (30 degrees Celsius). The temperature range is low, usually less than 5 degrees Fahrenheit (3 degrees Celsius), because there are no great variations of solar radiation at noon and minimal changes in length of day throughout the year.

In the Amazon region, marked rainy seasons occur; the southern part receives the heaviest rain during the southern summer, while the northern part has its rainy season during the northern summer. There is no dry season and humidity is always high. The natural vegetation is the tropical rain forest called *selva* in South America.

TROPICAL SAVANNA. The second type of tropical climate is the savanna, grassland with scattered trees, also known as tropical wet and dry. It is characterized by high temperatures, with monthly minimum temperatures above 64 degrees Fahrenheit (18 degrees Celsius), but receives less precipitation than the tropical rain forest climate and has a definite dry season. This climate covers 2.6 million square miles (6.8 million sq. km.), with 73 percent of this climate in Brazil only. It is found around the rain forest belt in the Orinoco Basin, on the Brazilian highlands, and in part of western Ecuador between Guyaquil and Quito. There is a prolonged dry season centered on the local winter. Natural vegetation has adapted to the two seasons of precipitation: the savanna of Rio Branco and the *llanos* in Venezuela, the Orinoco River delta, and Colombia.

MONSOON. Monsoon is a seasonal wind that blows from the ocean during the summer and affects the coast of Colombia and south of the Amazon River mouth on a very narrow area. Laden with moisture, these winds generate intense rainfall. Monsoon climates are limited in South America. The equatorial lows over the oceans act like a magnet for the trade winds, giving rise to the intertropical convergence zone (ITCZ).

Within the ITCZ, the converging trade winds are forced upward by equatorial warming, creating active cloud bands and precipitation. In satellite images, the ITCZ can appear as two parallel cloud bands separated by a clear sky. Usually the ITCZ is located over the oceans north of the equator. In the summer, it reaches as far south as the mouth of the Amazon River on the Atlantic coast; on the Pacific coast, it is kept north by the cold waters of the Peru Current and the strong southeasterly trade winds. The migration of the ITCZ across the equator creates a localized monsoon phenomenon.

HUMID SUBTROPICAL. Humid subtropical climates characterized by lower winter temperatures are found south of the tropic of Capricorn (in Paraguay, Uruguay, parts of Bolivia, Brazil, Argentina, and Chile) and in the Andes, where, in their rainfall pattern, they resemble tropical climates. On the Atlantic side, temperatures in the warmest month average 77 degrees Fahrenheit (25 degrees Celsius), but cold month averages vary from 63 degrees Fahrenheit (17 degrees Celsius) in the north (Asunción, Paraguay) to 50 degrees Fahrenheit (10 degrees Celsius) in Buenos Aires. Rainfall is greater than 1.5 inches (35 millimeters) each month in the east, decreasing to the west. Rainfall reaches its maximum during the local summer. Some of these frontal systems are strong enough to cross the Andes and induce winter rain and snow on the Argentine plains, when the encounter of subtropical and subpolar air masses causes depressions (midlatitude cyclones) with associated severe storms.

In southern Chile, south of 40 degrees south latitude, the climate is dominated by the westerlies blowing across the Pacific Ocean. Humidity picked up from the ocean is released as the winds rise over the west flank of the Andes, making this one of the wettest spots on the continent. Rainfall averages 102 inches (2.6 meters) at Valdivia, Chile, and probably twice that amount on the western slopes of the mountains. On the leeward side of the southern Andes, the westerlies are still strong, but having deposited their moisture on the western slopes of the mountains, they only exacerbate the dryness of Argentine Patagonia. The continuous flow of maritime air keeps the temperature at lower annual levels than in the corresponding North American and European latitudes, discouraging settlement and farming. In winter, cold fronts from the south can penetrate north as far as the southern Brazilian Highlands and seriously damage the coffee and cocoa plantations.

MEDITERRANEAN CLIMATES. A Mediterranean climate is present in South America only in central Chile, between 32 and 38 degrees south latitude. This cli-

Brazilian farm Page 691

673

mate is characterized by a mild, rainy winter and dry summer. Temperatures in South America are cooler than those at the same latitude in the region of the Mediterranean Sea.

MOUNTAIN CLIMATES. The Andes, about 5,000 miles (8,000 kilometers) long, with many summits at elevations above 22,000 feet (6,700 meters) have a formidable impact on rainfall distribution. As humid air masses are forced up and over the windward side of the Andes, cooling causes condensation, often creating persistent rains associated with cloud forests. The opposite occurs on the leeward side of the mountains; as the descending air warms up, it absorbs water vapor and fosters arid conditions. This is called the rain shadow effect.

At the latitude of Peru, the Andes form two parallel cordilleras surrounding high plateaus called the *altiplano*. Near Lake Titicaca, the average annual temperature is only 34 to 36 degrees Fahrenheit (1 to 2 degrees Celsius). At altitudes above 3,000 to 4,000 feet (2,000 to 2,500 meters) the Andes experience frost, even near the equator.

More important than latitudinal differences in temperatures are temperature variations with elevation, since these influence vegetation adaptation in the tropical Andes. In general, there is an increase in rainfall with elevation, which peaks around 5,000 feet (1,500 meters). Different names have been given to the levels of elevation in the tropical Andes: *tierra caliente, tierra templada, tierra fria, tierra helada,* and *tierra Nevada.*

The *tierra caliente* is located between the foothills and the 71 to 75 degrees Fahrenheit (22 to 24 degrees Celsius) annual isotherm around 2,500 to 3,200 feet (800-1,000 meters). The *tierra caliente* exhibits year-round, fairly high temperatures that are characteristic of tropical lowlands.

Plant growth is limited only by lack of moisture. The *tierra templada*, stretching up to 61 to 64 degrees Fahrenheit (16 to 18 degrees Celsius) isotherm at about 6,500 feet (2,000 meters), has tropical crops such as coffee and cocoa.

The upper limit for coffee plantations is near 6,000 feet (1,800 meters). However, sometimes the *tierra templada* penetrates farther upward in narrow valleys, along which warm, humid air from the lowlands rises almost to the *tierra fria* boundary. In Ecuador, coffee and cotton are cultivated up to 6,900 feet (2,100 meters) of elevation in the Mira Valley, and in the eastern Andes of Bolivia similar valleys are practical corridors for subtropical vegetation and crops from the lowland, up to approximately 8,200 feet (2,500 meters).

The *tierra fria* (also called the montane zone), between 6,500 and 13,000 feet (2,000-4,000 meters) with a minimum annual temperature between 43 and 64 degrees Fahrenheit (6 to 18 degrees Celsius), is marked by the occurrence of frost. The natural vegetation seems barely changed; height and diversity decrease with elevation. Together, *tierra templada* and *tierra fria* cover about 309,000 square miles (800,000 sq. km.).

The *tierra helada* is between the lowest boundary of the snow line and the frost line, which usually coincides with the 36 to 39 degrees Fahrenheit (2 to 4 degrees Celsius) isotherm between 15,000 and 20,000 feet (5,000-6,200 meters), depending on the humidity. An Alpine meadow covers the ground. The *tierra Nevada* is the area of permanent snow and ice.

ARID CLIMATES. Arid climates cover more than 400,000 square miles (1 million sq. km.) in four areas of South America. Patagonia east of the Andes is in the rain shadow zone, and rainfall is low (about 4 inches/100 millimeters in San Juan, Argentina). The annual range in temperature is more than 36 degrees Fahrenheit (20 degrees Celsius), the highest in South America. Another arid zone is found in a narrow coastal strip along the Pacific coast between 5 and 30 degrees south latitude. This strip covers 150,000 square miles (400,000 sq. km.) and is 1,875 miles (3,000 kilometers) long.

The cold seas characterizing the Peru (Humboldt) Current and the proximity of the high Andes produce an inversion of normal atmospheric temperature, because air in contact with the water cools more rapidly than the upper strata of air. The result is a cloud layer about 1,200 feet (365 meters) thick, lying at altitudes between 1,000 and 3,000 feet (300-1,000 meters), that prevents the warming of the air near the ground. Temperatures are consequently low: Lima has an average temperature of 64 degrees Fahrenheit (18 degrees Celsius). The coast of Peru is the cloudiest desert in the world, with no sunshine for at least six months of the year. It almost never rains, but fog condensation provides some humidity. The yearly precipitation is low: only 1 millimeter (0.04 inch) in Arica and Iquique and 4 millimeters in Antofagasta (all in Chile).

Another desert extends from northeastern Colombia to Venezuela, covering a zone where rains are scarce and droughts prolonged. A final arid zone occurs in northeastern Brazil, between the Parnaiba and São Francisco Rivers. The interior highlands act as a wedge separating the sea winds from the northeast, all of which carry their moisture beyond the region. Average annual rainfall is less than 4 inches (100 millimeters) and the dry season can last seven months. Rainfall is irregular, resulting in the severe droughts that plague the region.

The seasonal movements of the ITCZ have great impact in tropical South America. When the ITCZ moves south along the coast of the Guianas toward northern Brazil during the summer, abundant rains can be expected. In years when the South Atlantic trades are quite strong, the ITCZ is prevented from moving southward along the coast of the Guianas. Summer rainfall will be scarce or fail altogether. Northeast Brazil then experiences serious droughts. These droughts, resulting in loss of life and mass migration, occur frequently. Notable drought years include 1970, 1983, 1991 through 1992, and 1997.

The air masses of temperate South America are determined by fronts, westerly winds, and air mass invasions from subantarctic latitudes. South of 40 degrees south latitude, particularly on the Pacific side of the continent, the climate is dominated by the westerlies blowing across the Pacific Ocean. Humidity gathered over the ocean is released over the west flank of the Andes, making this one of the wettest spots on the continent.

Denys Lemaire

FOR FURTHER STUDY

Blouet, Brian W., and Olwyn M. Blouet. *Latin America and the Caribbean: A Systematic and Regional Survey.* 3d ed. New York: John Wiley & Sons, 1997.

Brawer, Moshe. *Atlas of South America.* New York: Simon & Schuster, 1991.

Butland, Gilbert J. *Latin America: A Regional Geography.* 3d ed. London: Longman, 1972.

Caviedes, César, and Gregory Knapp. *South America.* Englewood Cliffs, N.J.: Prentice Hall, 1995.

South America, Central America, and the Caribbean. London: Europa Publications, 1999.

CENTRAL AMERICA

Map Page 743

The complex physical geography of Central America produces a variety of climates, including virtually every type of tropical and subtropical climate as well as a few midlatitude types. This diversity relates to several climatic controls, including latitude, altitude, maritime and continental influences, and the dominant wind systems. Some of these characteristics are shared by Central America's northern neighbor, Mexico, which is an extension of Central America.

CLIMATE CONTROLS. All seven of Central America's nations lie entirely within the Tropics, and variations in their climates are functions primarily of altitude. By contrast, the chief control of the climate of their northern, subtropical neighbor, Mexico, is latitude. The greatest impact of latitude is in temperature seasonality. Because Central America is within the Tropics, temperatures lack seasonality, with annual temperature ranges of only 15 degrees Fahrenheit (8 degrees Celsius) or less. Daily temperature ranges are usually higher than annual ranges. By contrast, northern Mexico experiences hot summers and cool winters.

Central America is a mountainous region, and altitude exerts a control on climates. Average temperatures drop 6 degrees Celsius per 1,000 meters (3.5 degrees Fahrenheit per 1,000 feet), so that highlands lack tropical heat. The Spanish colonial settlers named the various altitude zones they found in Central America and Mexico after their temperature characteristics: *tierra caliente* (hot land), *tierra templada* (temperate land), *tierra fria* (cold land), and *tierra helada* (frozen land).

The *tierra caliente*, lying between sea level and about 3,000 feet (900 meters), is the true tropical lowlands, typical of the half of tropical Central America near sea level. It was an uncomfortable and unhealthy climate for Europeans, whose activities there were confined primarily to tropical plantation agriculture. Spaniards preferred the cooler *tierra templada*, between altitudes of 3,000 and 6,000 feet (900-1,800 meters), where they built numerous cities and grew coffee or raised livestock. Most of the indigenous population also occupied that zone.

The *tierra fria*, between 6,000 and 12,000 feet (1,800 and 3,600 meters) experiences frost and cool temperatures, which limited European activity, especially in the upper reaches of this zone, although many indigenous people lived there. The highest zone, the *tierra helada*, is found only in Mexico.

Maritime and continental influences relate mostly to the warm ocean currents that bring warm air and moisture to most coastal locales of Central America. The east coasts are bathed by the Caribbean and Gulf of Mexico currents, having waters ranging between 73 and 84 degrees Fahrenheit (23 to 29 degrees Celsius). The Equatorial Countercurrent along the southern half of Central America's Pacific coast brings in waters of about 81 degrees Fahrenheit (27 degrees Celsius) all year.

These currents produce warm, moist air masses that dominate the climate of coastal locales, and some interior locales as well. In contrast to the relatively narrow Central American isthmus, continentality influences the climate of Mexico, where the landmass widens. Areas distant from the ocean experience considerably hotter summers and cooler winters, and have drier climates.

Northeasterly trade winds are the main wind systems influencing Central America. These blow across warm seas, bringing warmth and moisture to the windward (eastern) coasts and upland slopes. Such locales experience average annual precipitation of 80 to 120 inches (2,000 to 3,000 millimeters). Mexico's Yucatán Peninsula is an exception, lying to windward but lacking sufficient relief for mountains to have an effect. Lee locations, including interior rain-shadow basins, have less precipitation, typically ranging between 20 and 40 inches (500 to 1,000 millimeters).

From December to April, North American cold fronts and the northerly winds behind them often intrude into Central America, triggering showers, even snow in higher elevations. Once the fronts pass, cold air arrives in what are called *nortes*, strong north winds. This influence is strongest in northern Mexico, decreasing southward, as it enters Central America proper.

CLIMATE TYPES. At least four climate types can be identified in Central America: tropical wet, tropical wet and dry, tropical dry, and highland. Because of the variety of climatic influences, there are variations within each of these four types.

The tropical wet climate is the climate of most of the *tierra caliente* in tropical windward locales. It stretches in a narrow band from the eastern escarpment of central Mexico into Central America as far south as Panama. A band of tropical wet climates also occurs along the southern extremes of the Pacific coast from Nicaragua to Panama, resulting from warm offshore currents. Temperature seasonality is lacking—it is always hot.

Annual precipitation usually exceeds 80 inches (2,000 millimeters), and there is no significant dry season. This climate is associated with native rain forests of broadleaf evergreen trees in great variety. However, humans living there have caused a serious decrease in the extent of this veg-

CENTRAL AMERICAN CLIMATIC HAZARDS

Central America and Mexico experience an unusually large variety of climatic hazards because of their tropical location and proximity to the North American continent. Much of the region north of the tropic of Cancer suffers periodic or permanent drought, which limits population densities. Torrential rains and flooding, with accompanying landslides, can occur in any part of Central America, even in the driest regions, because of cold fronts, easterly waves, and hurricanes.

Northern Mexico and the tropical highlands are threatened by winter frost, which can damage or destroy crops. The highlands of Mexico and Guatemala receive severe summer thunderstorms and crop-damaging hailstorms. Cool northerly winds from North America occur up to twenty times per winter in northern Mexico, sometimes extending into Nicaragua, and even occasionally to northern South America. These winds can bring frost or snow in the north and, at higher elevations, dust storms in the Mexican plateau. Hurricanes, named after the Mayan god of rain and thunder, Huracan, are intense tropical cyclones that can strike both coasts. Between June and October, up to twelve hurricanes may hit the east coast annually, often seriously damaging human structures. The west coast of northern Mexico sometimes experiences *chubascos*, weaker versions of the Atlantic hurricanes.

etation. Plantation and subsistence crops typical of this climate include temperature-sensitive sugarcane, banana, coconut, mango, papaya, citrus, pineapple, cacao, manioc, and yam. In this climate zone there are various health hazards, such as malaria, yellow fever and dengue fever.

The tropical wet and dry climate occurs primarily in the lee of the trade winds, also within the *tierra caliente*. It is found in most of the Pacific coastal lowlands, interior lowlands, and the neighboring Yucatán Peninsula. Temperatures are tropical, always hot and lacking seasons. Precipitation is strongly seasonal, with less than 80 inches (2,000 millimeters) of rain falling between May and October. The four- to six-month dry season centers on December through March. Native vegetation consists of low, dry-season deciduous forests or scrub and cactus. Heavy alteration of this vegetation results from higher population densities than are found in the wet Tropics.

The highland climates are cooler and wetter than the lowland climates around them. They coincide with the *tierra templada, tierra fria,* and *tierra helada* zones from northern Mexico through Panama. Despite little temperature seasonality in the tropical highlands, at least one month averages below 64 degrees Fahrenheit (18 degrees Celsius). (North of the tropic of Cancer, the Mexican highlands experience temperature seasonality, with frequent winter freezes and snowfalls.) Precipitation in the highland climates is mostly seasonal, coming chiefly as summer thunderstorms. Annual precipitation varies from 30 inches (760 millimeters) upward, reaching extremes in windward locales, where seasonality disappears. Within the *tierra helada*, snowfalls are com-

mon all year, even well into the Tropics, and the highest volcanoes support glaciers. Native vegetation is typically an oak-coniferous forest. Midlatitude commercial crops raised here to take advantage of cooler temperatures include maize, wheat, apple, pear, potato, cabbage, onion, and carrot. Much of the forest has been cleared for cattle pastures.

The dry climates, in which annual water losses through evaporation and transpiration exceed precipitation, occur in Central America, mostly in the interior plateau and in small lowland rain shadows. Dry climates include desert (arid) and steppe (semiarid) climates, whose annual precipitation is usually under 20 inches (500 millimeters). Temperatures are subtropical, since these regions lie mostly outside the Tropics. Summers are even hotter than in the lowland Tropics, and winters are cool. Native vegetation ranges from cactus and shrub in the deserts to oak-juniper woodlands in the wetter steppes. Commercial crop agriculture is limited to irrigated areas, where productivity is high.

P. Gary White

FOR FURTHER STUDY

Clawson, David L. *Latin America and the Caribbean: Lands and Peoples.* New York: McGraw-Hill, 1999.

Escoto, Jorge A. V. "Weather and Climate of Mexico and Central America." In *Handbook of Middle American Indians.* Vol. 1. Austin: University of Texas Press, 1964.

James, Preston E., and C. W. Minkel. *Latin America.* 5th ed. New York: John Wiley, 1986.

West, Robert C., and John P. Augelli. *Middle America: Its Lands and Peoples.* Englewood Cliffs, N.J.: Prentice Hall, 1989.

SOUTH AMERICA

Brazil's former capital city, Rio de Janeiro, is the site of one of the world's great festivals—the annual pre-Lenten carnival. During the four days leading up to Ash Wednesday, the entire city shuts down for the revelry.

Riverfront houses in Manaus, in the Amazon Basin. (Clyde L. Rasmussen)

CENTRAL AMERICA

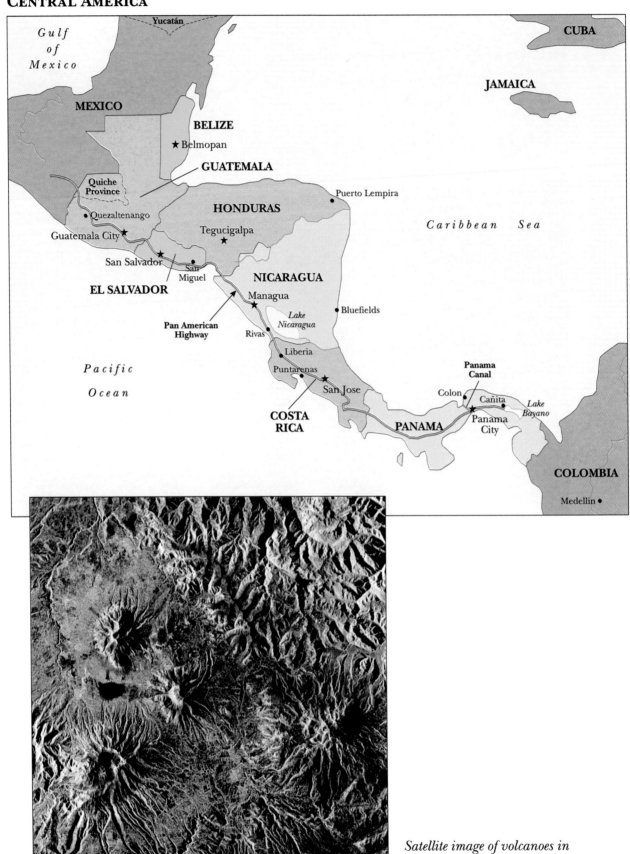

Satellite image of volcanoes in northern Ecuador. (PhotoDisc)

PHYSICAL GEOGRAPHY OF SOUTH AMERICA

North
Atlantic
Ocean

Maracaibo •
Caracas ★
Orinoco Lowlands
Lake Maracaibo
Bogotá ★
Caroni
Angel Falls
Guiana Highlands

Galápagos
Islands

★ Quito
Negro R.
Amazon Basin
Equator
• Fortaleza

Amazon River
Amazon Basin
• Recife

Lima ★
Sierra Occidental
Sierra Oriental
A N D E S
B r a z i l i a n

Lake Titicaca
★ La Paz
Altiplano
Sierra Central
Sierra Oriental
Brasilia ★
H i g h l a n d s

Tropic of Capricorn
Atacama Desert
M O U N T A I N S
Paraguay R.
Chaco
• Belo Horizonte

South
Pacific
Ocean

Asunción ★
Rio de Janeiro •
São Paulo •

• Porto Alegre

Mount Aconcagua •
Santiago ★
• Mendoza
Pampas
Buenos Aires ★
★ Montevideo

Río Colorado
Río Negro

South
Atlantic
Ocean

Patagonia
Río Chubut

Río Gallegos

Falkland Islands

Tierra del Fuego

Waved mountain rocks at Tres Cruces, along the Andean border of Chile and Argentina. (American Stock Photography)

Moreno Glacier in the Argentine Andes. (PhotoDisc)

Argentina's Fitzroy National Park. (PhotoDisc)

Cable car in Venezuela's Sierra Nevada National Park that provides a view of the northern Andes. The cable car system was the longest and highest in the world in the late 1990's. (AP/Wide World Photos)

One of the major tributaries of the Amazon River, the Negro River (Río Negro) originates in the Andes Mountains in Colombia and joins the Amazon below Manaus in Brazil. The Negro is named for the dark color of its water, which is caused by the tannic acid that it transports. This photograph, taken from the space shuttle Co-lumbia in January, 1986, shows a section of the river passing through virgin rain forest. (Corbis)

Major Watersheds of South America

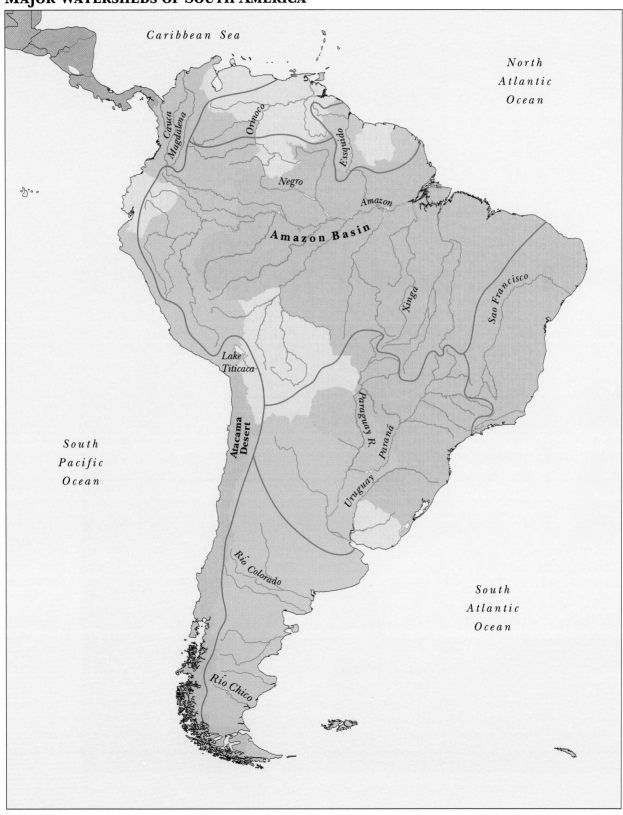

Caribbean Sea

North
Atlantic
Ocean

Cauca
Magdalena

Orinoco

Essquido

Negro

Amazon

Amazon Basin

Xinga

Sao Francisco

Lake
Titicaca

**Atacama
Desert**

South
Pacific
Ocean

Paraguay R.

Paraná

Uruguay

South
Atlantic
Ocean

Río Colorado

Río Chico

The Urubamba River Valley, which is overlooked by Peru's famous Machu Picchu Inca ruins. (Clyde L. Rasmussen)

Andean pink flamingos take flight over Lake Titicaca, the world's highest-altitude navigable lake. A drought in the Bolivian highlands attracted the rare birds to the lake in early 1999. (AP/Wide World Photos)

Eruption of Costa Rica's Rincon de la Vieja volcano in November, 1995. (AP/Wide World Photos)

PHYSICAL GEOGRAPHY OF CENTRAL AMERICA

Gulf
of
Mexico

Caribbean Sea

Pacific
Ocean

Petén

★ Belmopan

Volcán
Tajumulco

CENTRAL

• Puerto Lempira

CARIBBEAN LOWLANDS

Guatemala City
★

Lake Atitlán

Tegucigalpa
★

Río Coco o Segovia

San Salvador ★
San Miguel
•

Lake
Managua

HIGHLANDS

Managua
★

PACIFIC LOWLANDS

Lake
Nicaragua

• Bluefields

• San Juan

★San
José

**Panama
Canal**

Colon •

★

Gatún
Lake

Panama City

Lake
Bayano

Guatemala's Lake Atitlán fills a 985-foot-deep crater and is surrounded by other volcanoes. (Isaac Hernández/ mercurypress.com)

A southern Brazilian farmer surveys his broccoli crop, ruined by unusually cold temperatures in January, 2000. It was feared that the cold weather would threaten Brazil's vital coffee crop. (AP/Wide World Photos)

Virtually all of South America can be seen in this photo of the earth taken from the Apollo 15 Moon flight in 1971.
(Corbis)

CLIMATE REGIONS OF SOUTH AMERICA

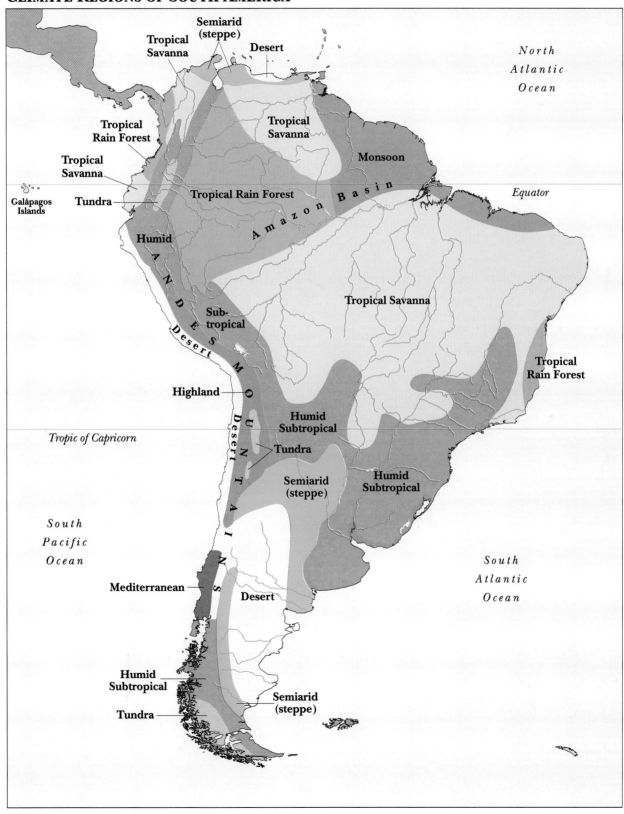

Semiarid (steppe)

Tropical Savanna

Desert

Tropical Rain Forest

Tropical Savanna

Galápagos Islands

Tundra

Tropical Savanna

Monsoon

Tropical Rain Forest

Amazon Basin

Humid

ANDES MOUNTAINS

Subtropical

Desert

Highland

Tropical Savanna

Humid Subtropical

Tropical Rain Forest

Tundra

Semiarid (steppe)

Humid Subtropical

Mediterranean

Desert

Humid Subtropical

Tundra

Semiarid (steppe)

North Atlantic Ocean

Equator

Tropic of Capricorn

South Pacific Ocean

South Atlantic Ocean

693

Residents of Guayaquil, Ecuador, attempt to conduct business as usual in the midst of early 1998's El Niño event. The weather phenomenon known as an El Niño event occurs every two to seven years when the South Equatorial Current flows eastward instead of westward and brings warm water to the west coast of South America. Coastal Ecuador and northern Peru then receive abundant rains and experience devastating floods. (AP/Wide World Photos)

A worker at Quito's Mariscal Sucre Airport tries to sweep volcanic ash from a runway after the eruption of Ecuador's Pichincha volcano in November, 1999. The showers of ash that rained on the capital city prompted officials to close the city's schools and shut down the airport. (AP/Wide World Photos)

BIOGEOGRAPHY AND NATURAL RESOURCES

NATURAL RESOURCES

SOUTH AMERICA

*Map
Page 744*

The world's fourth largest continent, South America has a diversity of climates, terrains, altitudes, and latitudes. Shaped somewhat like a large ice cream cone, about 75 percent of the continent is within tropical latitudes, while the southern cone of middle latitudes covers most of the rest. Tierra del Fuego extends to about 56 degrees south latitude, only 700 miles (1,126 km.) from the Antarctic Circle. Because South America tapers to its pointed cone, sea-level temperatures at the far south never get as cold as similar latitudes in Canada or Russia.

South America has an abundance of natural resources, both renewable—fisheries, soils, forests, climate, and water—and nonrenewable—minerals and energy. Many of these resources are far from where they are needed and are costly to develop, which limits their ability to satisfy human needs and wants. Location and land quality can also be considered nonrenewable resources. For example, the amount of land available for growing populations to use is an important resource. The quality of land, including location, surface roughness, climate, soil fertility, and attractive landscapes, is part of the resource base. As population grows in a place, pressure to use more resources grows; conservation programs attempt to ensure that resources will be available when needed.

RENEWABLE RESOURCES: FISHERIES. Chile and Peru were two of the first nations in the world to claim control of the oceans up to 200 miles (320 km.) from their coasts. The Peru (Humboldt) Current flows from the Antarctic and then along the coasts of Chile and Peru. This cold water contains great amounts of plankton, and countless numbers of fish live in the current to catch this food. Peru and Chile usually rank second and third in the world in total fish catch. Most of the fish are ground up to make fishmeal, a source of protein for animal food and fertilizers. Most South American nations catch at least some fresh and saltwater fish for food. Most do this in an unorganized way. To keep fisheries a renewable resource, people have to avoid overfishing, which does not allow fish enough time to reproduce. Overfished fisheries soon lose such large quantities of fish that fishing becomes unproductive.

SOILS. Three-fourths of South America is tropical, and tropical soils are not fertile for crops. They lack humus, potash, phosphates, and nitrogen, and they are acidic. High iron and aluminum content, drought, and too much water in some places are all problems for farmers that require expensive solutions to fix. Faced with these handicaps, South American farmers work hard but do not produce as much food as they would if soils and other environmental factors were better.

Brazil is a major exporter of corn (maize) and a major producer of rice but must import wheat and rice to feed its people. Most countries produce enough basic foods, but there are still food deficits in many highland Amerindian communities and in urban slums. Many tropical South American countries produce large quantities of luxury foods: coffee from Brazil, Colombia, and Venezuela; cacao (chocolate) from Ecuador, Colombia, and Brazil; sugar from Brazil, Venezuela, and Colombia; and bananas from Brazil, Ecuador, Colombia, and Venezuela. Illegal drugs are grown in Bolivia, Peru, and Colombia.

The southern cone middle-latitude countries of Chile, Argentina, and Uruguay produce surplus foods. The Pampas of Argentina and Uruguay are one of the world's great breadbaskets, producing wheat, corn, and soybeans, and beef, pork, and lamb. Argentina is the world's fourth-largest producer of wine, and Chile produces high-quality wine at low prices. Soils are excellent in these countries, and farmers are highly productive.

Conservation programs to keep soils a renewable resource have started in South America. Land destruction is a big threat in mountainous terrain where erosion can wash away the topsoil, and in tropical environments where a disturbance of the natural ecology can ruin land. The United Nations and regional agencies operate demonstration projects for conservation in all countries. Brazil, Chile, Argentina, and Venezuela have started national park systems to preserve fragile and unique physical environments.

National parks Pages 685, 686

FORESTS. Fully half of South America is forested. The largest forest areas are the tropical hardwood forests of Brazil, Colombia, Peru, and Venezuela, and the softwood pine forests in the Andes Mountain regions of Chile and Argentina. Forest products are used throughout the world. Wood for construction and furniture come from South America's tropical and middle-latitude forests. Rosewood, Amazon cedar, mahogany, and balsa are harvested from the rain forests of Brazil, Peru, Colombia, and Venezuela. Rubber trees are native to Amazonia, and Brazil had a monopoly on this valuable industrial product until trees were transplanted to Southeast Asia and Africa.

There are so many species of trees in the Amazon that rubber trees and nut trees are scattered among many miles of rain forest. This makes gathering rubber and nuts an expensive job. In Brazil's drier tropical forests, one palm tree gives carnauba wax, another forest product in demand throughout the world. Another palm growing on the semiarid Brazilian Plateau yields vegetable cooking oil.

Yet another dry tropical forest product is tannin from Paraguay's quebracho trees, used for tanning animal hides. Cinchona trees give quinine for the treatment of malaria, and chicle from the sapodilla tree is the base for chewing gum. Pine wood is used in construction and for making pulp, paper, plastics, plywood, tar, pitch, and turpentine. The great distances from consuming centers and the rough terrain make these forest products expensive to gather. Some South Americans have mistakenly believed that conservation is only a concern for rich people. Leaders are now educating people that conservation is in everyone's best interests.

CLIMATE. Climate and water resources are closely related, because a region's climate is determined by the amount of heat provided by the Sun and the amount of precipitation. Because three-fourths of South America is within the Tropics, it receives a surplus of the Sun's energy. Varied tropical climates can be found in the mountains. For every 1,000 feet (305 meters) that one travels up the side of a mountain, the temperature decreases about 3.3 degrees Fahrenheit (1.8 degrees Celsius). On a 15,000-foot (4,572-meter) mountain in the Tropics, there would be five bands of climate types based on average temperature: warm land, temperate land, cold land, cold grassland (too cold for trees), and permanent ice and snow.

Different crops are found in each climate band, because plants have different temperature requirements. For example, rice grows in the warm land; coffee grows in the temperate land; wheat grows in the cold land; pasture grasses grow in the cold grassland; and nothing grows in permanent ice and snow. All these climates and crops are affected by differences in rainfall. Some tropical places get 100 inches (2,510 millimeters) of rain, while others get only 20 inches (510 millimeters). Rain forest would grow in the first region, but only cactuslike plants would grow in the second.

This great ecological diversity means that many types of food and other plants can grow in a small area. However, in the warm and wet areas especially, many plant, animal, and human disease vectors also grow. Much food is lost to disease, and expensive chemicals are needed to control diseases. Medicines can control most human and animal diseases, but they too are expensive. For many South American countries, it is cheaper to import food from other countries than to invest large sums of money in their own land.

Excess energy from the Sun can have good and bad effects. If the technology were widely developed, people probably could get most of their electricity directly from the Sun. Tropical regions would benefit most when this happens. Tropical warmth means that cold-weather clothing is not necessary, and buildings do not need to be heated. Although electrical-

powered air conditioning is often desirable, it is not as essential as heating systems are in cold climates. Plant biomass produced under wet tropical heat is tremendous; however, it will take new technology to make maximum use of this potential resource.

WATER. Great water environments exist in Amazonia, the high Andes, the Pantanal, and the other major river valleys. Fish, birds, reptiles, and water plants grow in large quantities in those places. The usefulness of these resources for human and animal food and for industrial materials has yet to be determined. One possible use is fish farming. Tropical ponds can produce large amounts of protein for human and animal food. Many sites for hydroelectric power lie in South America's mountains and plateaus. Brazil, Venezuela, Paraguay, Argentina, and Chile have begun to develop river basins for power, irrigation, recreation, and navigation. More sites are available, but the cost to develop them is high. Once developed, given normal climate conditions, water resources are largely self-sustaining. A serious problem in every country is the need to develop more sources of clean drinking water.

NONRENEWABLE RESOURCES: MINERALS. Spanish conquerors frantically searched for gold and silver from the beginning of European colonization of South America. They found some gold in the Caribbean, a great deal of gold and silver in Central America, and large quantities of silver and gold in Colombia, Peru, Bolivia. The Portuguese found gold later in Brazil. The fabulous silver reserves found in 1545 at Potosí, Bolivia, produced half the world's silver for the next fifty years. Trade monopolies were established between Spain and Portugal and the colonies, preventing use of some South American minerals such as mercury, because the

Coffee plants Page 815

Charcoal worker Page 820

Venezuela tanker Page 820

Nuclear power plant Page 745

mother countries produced those minerals. After independence, especially in the late nineteenth and twentieth centuries, mineral exploitation accelerated. Some of this was done with the help of foreign capital and technology.

South America produces about 20 percent of the world's iron ore. Venezuela, Brazil, and Bolivia have especially large deposits; Brazil is the world's leading producer. These deposits are found in remote places where few people live: the Guiana Highlands, the Amazon Basin, and southeastern Bolivia. Cheap strip-mining is carried out without the restraint of protests by local environmentalists.

About half the world's copper is produced in Chile and Peru. Mines in the northern desert of Chile are especially rich, with 2.5 percent copper in the ore. Bauxite (ore for aluminum) is another world-class resource, coming mostly from Guyana, Suriname, Venezuela, and Brazil. Around the year 1900, nitrates from northern Chile were the only source in the world for making gunpowder and fertilizers. Now nitrogen can be collected directly from the air, and Chile's nitrates are used for iodine, a much less valuable product.

Brazil and Bolivia are world leaders in tin exports. Bolivia's tin is located in solid rock ores on the *altiplano* at elevations of up to 15,000 feet (4,570 meters) and is costly to extract. Brazil's tin is found in recently discovered gravel deposits in the northern Amazon Basin, where production costs are low.

Peru is a world leader in lead and zinc production. Industrial diamonds used in cutting tools are another recently discovered resource in Brazil's Amazon. Venezuela's small production of gem diamonds has been worked for many years. Gold, platinum, and emeralds are all mined in Colombia, and gold is another major product from Peru and Brazil.

ENERGY RESOURCES. South America lacks large, high-quality coal resources. Coal is a valuable fuel for the smelting of metals, and shortages of this fuel hurt such important industries as iron and steel production. Brazil, Colombia, Chile, Peru, and Argentina have important coal deposits, but they are located in rough terrain and far from consuming centers.

Argentina, Bolivia, Brazil, Chile, Colombia, Ecuador, Peru, and Venezuela produce petroleum and natural gas, but only Venezuela is a world-class producer. Venezuela's oil is located in the Maracaibo Basin and near the Orinoco Delta. The Orinoco fields produce a heavy crude with much tar and sulphur content. These deposits are not as valuable as the lighter crudes. Uranium is mined in Uruguay, Bolivia, Brazil, and Argentina.

Nuclear power plants operate only in Argentina (two plants were producing and one was under construction in 1999) and Brazil (one producing and one under construction). Geothermal energy resources should be plentiful in the Andes, but at the end of the twentieth century, there was no program to exploit them. The wind and sun are other potential sources of energy that will have to wait for demand, capital, and technology to push their development. There is a strong tidal bore (incoming wave) from the Atlantic into the mouth of the Amazon that has energy-generating possibilities, but as long as cheaper energy resources exist, this will not be developed. The great biomass of South America's forests is another potential energy resource.

LOCATION AND LAND QUALITY. Many people do not understand how location and land quality can be natural resources. The location of a person, place, or resource on the earth's surface determines how easy or difficult it is to reach other people, places, or resources on the earth.

Movement of anything from one place to another takes time, costs money, and requires energy. If one place is close to people and resources, it is cheaper, faster, and requires less energy to bring all factors together to satisfy peoples' needs and wants. The Ukraine has iron ore, coal, limestone, water, many people, and many industries located close together, on flat terrain, and it is cheap, fast, and requires a minimum of energy to make steel and deliver it to markets that need it. In Argentina, by contrast, the factors of steel production are located in Buenos Aires, Tucumán, and Río Gallegos, places separated by 2,000 miles (3,218 km.) of fairly rough terrain. Steel production and distribution are much more efficient in the Ukraine than in Argentina.

In Colombia, the distances among resources is not great, but the mountainous terrain is so rough that the time, costs, and energy needed to combine resources are excessive. Similar handicaps exist in many resource situations for most South American countries.

GLOBAL LOCATION. South America is located in the Southern Hemisphere, far from the world's great population centers in Asia, Europe, and North America. Despite jet airplanes and fast ocean liners, the distances remain great: It is 8,000 miles (13,000 km.) from Colombia to Japan; 4,800 miles (7,750 km.) from Chile to the United States; and 7,335 miles (11,800 km.) from Uruguay to Spain. Improved transportation and communications systems have lowered the time, costs, and energy spent to send people, goods, or messages from South America to the rest of the world. However, relative to locations in Europe, North America, or Asia, South America is still at a disadvantage. This results in less production, less human contact, and less sales to world markets. Competition with other world resource centers brings less profits to South American producers.

REGIONAL VARIATION IN RESOURCES. Brazil has the best-balanced resource base in South America. Amazon and Paraná Plateau hardwood and softwood forests, good water resources in the Amazon Basin, good farmland in the southern states, and good minerals and energy resources throughout the country mean that Brazil's people should have comfortable living conditions. The fact that many Brazilians remain poor is partly caused by the country's late start in exploiting its resources and some inefficiencies in using them.

Argentina has the next best-balanced resource base, with the great food production of the Pampas, minerals in the Andes, and oil and natural gas in Patagonia. Beautiful mountain scenery also brings in large amounts of tourist income.

The Guianas, Uruguay, and Paraguay are resource deficient, having only one or two major natural resources. Their small sizes partly account for this situation. Venezuela, Colombia, Ecuador, Peru, Bolivia, and Chile all have outstanding mineral and energy resources, but all have the handicaps of rough terrain, making it inefficient to develop their resources. If all the South American countries were united in one common market, their resource bases would be rich enough to secure a comfortable future for their people.

Robert J. Tata

FOR FURTHER STUDY

Clawson, David L. *Latin America and the Caribbean: Lands and Peoples.* New York: McGraw-Hill, 1999.

Goulding, Michael, et al. *Floods of Fortune: Ecology and Economy Along the Amazon.* New York: Columbia University Press, 1996.

Margolis, Mac. *The Last New World: The Conquest of the Amazon Frontier.* New

York: W. W. Norton, 1992.

Tenenbaum, Barbara, ed. *Encyclopedia of Latin American History and Culture.* New York: Charles Scribner's Sons, 1996.

Terborgh, John. *Diversity and the Tropical*

Rain Forest. New York: Scientific American Library, 1992.

World Bank. *World Resources 1996-1997: The Urban Environment.* New York: Oxford University Press, 1996.

*Map
Page 747*

CENTRAL AMERICA

Spain once ruled most of Central America, but the region's mineral resources and sparse Amerindian population caused it to be largely ignored. After independence came to the region's countries in the mid-nineteenth century, their natural resources remained largely underdeveloped for several reasons. First, the countries there are small and typically lack significant resources. Second, the transport infrastructure is poorly integrated, due in large part to rugged terrain. Third, as poor countries, they have little capacity to develop their resources. What development has taken place often relies on foreign investment. Only two resources have been widely exploited: forests and soils. However, in the mid-twentieth century the development of other resources began accelerating.

SOILS. All the Central American countries depend heavily on agriculture in their domestic and export economies, and are thus reliant on productive soils. However, due to steep terrain and wide expanses of humid tropical climates, good agricultural soils are limited. There are pockets of highly fertile soils, especially in the floodplains of larger stream valleys and in areas of weathered volcanic ash. These areas are largely dominated by large-scale commercial agriculture, primarily for the production of sugarcane, bananas, coconuts, coffee, citrus, cotton, and tobacco.

Most of the farmland occupies lands less suitable for agriculture for a variety of reasons. Lands of the upland interior suffer from steep slopes that are prone to rapid erosion. Lowlands along the Pacific coast occupy the lee side of the uplands and suffer from drought. Rain forests typically contain soils that are badly leached of nutrients, making farming unproductive. Farms on these less-suitable lands are usually owned by peasants. The holdings are small and fragmented and tend to be farmed using relatively primitive methods and tools, yielding lower productivity while often degrading the already marginal soils.

Peasant production is commonly at the subsistence level, largely devoted to food crops such as maize, beans, squash, plantains, manioc, and rice. Slash-and-burn agriculture, practiced by precolonial Amerindians, is still widely employed in remote upland areas. In this system, forest land is cleared by cutting and the slash is dried and burned. In the ashes are planted various crops, most important of which is maize. Such plots can be used only two or three years before they are abandoned and the cycle is started anew, at the expense of forests.

Grazing has expanded in both the natural grasslands (savannas) and within forest clearings. In some cases, African grass varieties have been introduced. Expansion of grazing pastures is in response to foreign demand for beef, especially by the United States.

MINERALS. Economic deposits of minerals are few in Central America, based on incomplete geologic surveys of the region. Northern Central America has large areas of older igneous and metamorphic rocks, containing some silver, lead, mercury, antimony, and tin. More recent volcanic rocks may contain gold, silver, lead, zinc, and manganese. Certain granites have copper and molybdenum ores.

During Spanish occupation, mining was the chief economic activity, primarily for gold and silver. A variety of minerals are still mined, but the operations are generally small and marginal. Among the metallic minerals still produced are modest quantities of gold, silver, lead, zinc, manganese, nickel, iron ore, and copper. Other minerals include limestone (for cement) and sea salt, produced along the coast in evaporation ponds. The low value of limestone and salt preclude their export, and they supply domestic markets.

Oil has been found in several areas, but no large quantities have yet been produced. Notable is the Chapyal-Petén Basin of Guatemala. Costa Rica's Limón Basin shows potential. Exploration for oil is underway in various other areas, but results have been disappointing.

FORESTS. Every country in Central America once had abundant forests, most notably evergreen rain forests, but also coniferous softwoods in the uplands and deciduous forests in drier areas. The rain forests are extraordinarily rich in species diversity. One biological station of only 3,250 acres (1,300 hectares) in Costa Rica contains more species of plants than California, and Costa Rica alone has more than 12,000 species of plants and 2,000 species of broadleaf trees.

In colonial times forest destruction was extensive, and only a fraction of native forests remain. Wood was used primarily to shore underground mines, for fuel, for building construction, and for commercial purposes. Logwood production is an interesting case in early commercial production. Deforestation is occurring as a result of continued commercial wood harvesting, firewood gathering, and burning as a method of clearing for pasture and farmland.

Of the remaining forests, the rain forests are economically the most important. Among the many valuable tree species they contain are mahogany, lignum vitae, Spanish cedar, balsa, rosewood, ceiba, iron wood, sapodilla and chicosapote (for chewing gum), and rubber. The complexity of

LOGWOOD CUTTING OFF THE CARIBBEAN COAST

As piracy in the Caribbean declined, many British seamen, called "baymen," turned to the cutting of logwood along the Caribbean coast of contemporary Belize, Honduras, and Nicaragua. Logwood contains a core from which red and brown dyes were produced for use in English woolen mills.

Once logwood was depleted, the baymen began cutting mahogany. Despite attempts by the Spanish to remove them, the baymen became well established, leading to the creation of the colony of British Honduras, renamed Belize at independence in 1981.

species of trees in the rain forests, plus the lack of road access, has hampered production. There have been attempts to establish plantations of certain commercial species. Mahogany trees require up to one hundred years to reach economic size.

Most Central American countries have instituted reforestation and conservation programs in order to save their remaining rain forests. The leaders in this effort are Panama, with 8.6 percent of its territory in preserve, and Costa Rica, with 8.1 percent. These programs have had limited success because of illegal logging and the expansion of peasant agriculture.

Shrimp boats Page 746

MARINE RESOURCES. Every Central American country has at least one coastline, providing access to marine resources. Fisheries are vast and varied, due to the variety of environments, which include mangrove swamps, shallow mudflats, coral reefs and islands, and the deep sea. Various marine animals have economic value, including crustaceans, scale fish, and sea turtles. The people of Central America generally do not consume these in significant quantities. In fact, Guatemala has the lowest per capita fish consumption of any coastal country in the world. Most of the catch is exported to the United States.

The most important crustaceans harvested here are shrimp and lobster. Shrimp favor muddy, shallow waters, whereas lobster are more common in coral beds. El Salvador and Honduras lead in crustacean harvesting. Scale fish include anchovies, herring, grouper, snappers, and sharks. Sea turtles are also harvested, but a recent trend is to raise them on farms because their numbers have dwindled due to destruction of nesting grounds. Overall production of marine resources has declined in recent years due to overexploitation.

INLAND WATER RESOURCES. All countries in Central America have numerous rivers. Rivers of the Caribbean watersheds are longer and have relatively even flow year around due to humid climates. Those of the Pacific watersheds tend to be more seasonal and are prone to flash flooding. Most streams have steep gradients and frequent rapids and waterfalls, making them useless for commercial boat navigation. Because of deforestation and erosion, water quality is typically low.

The chief use of streams, other than for domestic water and irrigation, is for hydroelectric power generation. The potential power production is large, but development to date has been modest. Leading power-generating dams include El Cajón (Honduras), La Fortuna (Panama), and Arenal (Costa Rica). El Salvador and Honduras have the greatest development, Belize and Honduras the least. Most countries have plans to expand their hydroelectric power production, in the absence of significant fossil fuels. A threat to reservoirs in this region is high rates of sedimentation due to erosion from the uplands. Sedimentation reduces the life span of reservoirs, also reducing the economic return of hydroelectric plants. Planning for new hydroelectric dams continues, despite this problem.

GEOTHERMAL POWER. Much of Central America lies within an active volcanic region; thus, geothermal energy is abundant. Several countries have begun to develop this energy resource, including El Salvador, Guatemala (in the Amatitlan area), Costa Rica (Miravalles), and Honduras (six sites). This form of energy is perhaps most valuable because it is abundant, nearly infinite, and clean and cheap. A serious impediment to development is lack of local capital.

OTHER RESOURCES. Central America has an abundance of beautiful locales that attract foreign tourists, especially ecotourists, including spectacular volcanoes, unspoiled tropical beaches, streams, rich rain forests, and a variety of fauna, along with rich cultural resources. Ecotourists come chiefly to enjoy the natural environment. Ecotourism is growing rapidly in this region, with the potential for even greater development. In addition to the foreign exchange gained, ecotourism carries with it the incentive to protect what remains of natural areas. Perhaps the greatest threat to ecotourism, indeed to all tourism in Central America, is political and social instability. In fact, resource development was hampered in various areas of Central America in the late twentieth century due to disturbances and terrorism. With the arrival of the twenty-first century, relative calm has come to the region, and with it hopes for the future.

P. Gary White

INFORMATION ON THE WORLD WIDE WEB

The Library of Congress Country Studies Web site presents economic, historical, social, and political information about countries throughout the world, including most Central American countries. (lcweb2.loc.gov/frd/cs/cshome.html)

FOR FURTHER STUDY

Arbingast, Stanley A., et al. *Atlas of Central America.* Austin: University of Texas, 1979.

Denevan, W. M. *Causes of Deforestation and Forest and Woodland Degradation in Tropical Latin America.* Washington, D.C.: U.S. Congress, Office of Technology Assessment, 1982.

Kennedy, Denis, ed. *The Atlas of Central America and the Caribbean.* New York: Macmillan, 1985.

Leonard, H. Jeffrey. *Natural Resources and Economic Development in Central America: A Regional Environmental Profile.* New Brunswick, N.J.: Transaction Books, 1987.

Weeks, John. *The Economies of Central America.* New York: Holms and Meier, 1985.

West, Robert C. and John P. Augelli. *Middle America: Its Lands and Peoples.* Englewood Cliffs, N.J.: Prentice Hall, 1989.

Weyl, Richard. *Geology of Central America.* Berlin: Gebruder Borntroeger, 1980.

FLORA AND FAUNA

FLORA OF SOUTH AMERICA

South America is the most diverse continent in terms of flora, primarily because of its unique location and geography. South America is relatively narrow, especially in the southern part, and long, extending from a little more than 10 degrees north of the equator to a little below 50 degrees south. An additional factor that increases floristic diversity is the high mountains, especially the Andes Mountains, which extend from north to south along the western part of the continent for much of its length. As a result, South America has such diverse biomes as tropical rain forests, tropical savannas, extremely dry deserts, temperate forests, and alpine tundra. The largest of these biomes are deserts, savanna, and tropical forest. The flora of South America are less well studied than those of any continent, and with the rapid rate of deforestation in places like the Amazon Basin, some plants may become extinct before being catalogued, let alone studied.

Amazon deforestation. (PhotoDisc)

The subtropical desert biome is the driest biome in South America and is considered the driest desert in the world, with an average annual precipitation of less than 0.25 inch (4 millimeters). The desert biome is restricted primarily to the west coast of South America from less than 10 degrees south of the equator to approximately 30 degrees south. Dry conditions prevail from the coast to relatively high elevations in the Andes. The Atacama Desert, in northern Chile, and the Patagonian desert, in central Chile, are the most notable South American deserts. Smaller desert regions also occur in the rain shadow portions of the Andes.

Next on the moisture scale are the savanna biomes. Annual rainfall averages from just under 27.6 inches (700 millimeters) to more than 55 inches (1,400 millimeters). Savanna occurs in two distinctly different areas of South America. The largest savanna region includes three distinctive regions: the cerrado, a region of gently rolling plateaus in east-central Brazil; the Pantanal, a lower-elevation region with extensive wetlands; and farther south, in southern Brazil, Uruguay, and northern Argentina, the famous grassland called the Pampas. The other savanna region, the *llanos*, is found in lower-elevation areas of Venezuela and Colombia. Portions of the *llanos* can be quite wet part of the year and extremely dry the rest of the year.

Although a few of the forests in South America are dry, most are rain forests, receiving annual precipitation from more than 79 inches (2,000 millimeters) to almost 118 inches (3,000 millimeters). The Amazon rain forest, the world's largest, accounts for more than three-fourths of the rain forest area in South America. During the rainy season, the Amazon region receives so much rain that the entire river system floods extensively. The Amazon rain forest is one of the most species-rich areas of the world, but it is being rapidly destroyed by logging, ranching, and other human activities. Smaller rain forests are located along the southeastern cost of Brazil and in the northern part of Venezuela.

Covering much smaller areas are Mediterranean and temperate forest biomes. A small Mediterranean region in central Chile is characterized by cool, wet winters and warm, dry summers with annual precipitation of 28 inches (700 millimeters). In the far south of Chile and Argentina is a small area of temperate forest, becoming alpine tundra in the far south. Temperatures are relatively cool and mild year-round (except in the far south, where it can be extremely cold in the winter), and annual precipitation is approximately 18 inches (450 millimeters). This area includes Tierra del Fuego, near the infamous Cape Horn where many ships have been lost.

PLANTS OF SUBTROPICAL DESERT. In the Atacama desert, one of the world's driest, some moisture is available, but it is limited to certain zones. Coastal regions below 3,280 feet (1,000 meters) receive regular fog (called *camanchacas*) and most plants in this zone use it as their primary source of water. At midelevation areas there is no regular fog and rainfall is almost nonexistent; thus, there is almost no plant cover. At higher elevations, the rising air has cooled sufficiently to produce moderate amounts of rainfall, although the vegetation is still desertlike.

As in most deserts, the plants have adapted by either growing near water, storing water, or germinating and growing only when rains have soaked the ground adequately. Shrubs fall into the first category and typically grow near streambeds where their roots can reach a permanent source of water. Rainfall is so low in the Atacama Desert that even cacti (which normally store water) can hardly acquire enough water from rainfall alone, so many plants receive a portion of their water from fog. In addition to the cacti, bromeliads (a member of the pineapple family) also survive on fog. Some bromeliads are popular house plants. They commonly are called air plants because their moisture needs are met solely by what they absorb through special hairlike structures on their leaves.

Although the Atacama Desert often appears barren, when a good dose of moisture becomes available ephemerals change that view, seemingly overnight. Ephemerals are typically annuals that remain dormant in the dry soil as seeds. When moisture increases, they quickly germinate, grow, flower, and set seed before dry conditions prevail again. In the days and weeks following a good rain, many grasses appear and provide a backdrop for endless varieties of showy flowers. Some of the species will appear familiar to persons acquainted with desert flowers from the Sonora or Mojave deserts, but many are endemic to the Atacama Desert. Among the more showy flowers are species of *Alstroemeria* (commonly called irises, although they are actually in the lily family), *Nolana* (called pansies, although they are members of a family found only in Chile and Peru), *Leucocoryne* (spring onions), and *Calandrinia.*

A few familiar plants from North American deserts also occur here. *Ephedra* (called Mormon tea in North America), an unusual shrub somewhat related to pines, is abundant in places. In deserts like this, evaporation rates are high, which increases the salt content of some soils. Pigweed and saltbush often occur in these areas.

Conditions in the Patagonian desert are less harsh. The vegetation ranges from tussock grasslands near the Andes to more of a shrub-steppe community farther east. Needlegrass is especially abundant throughout the Patagonian region, and cacti are a common sight. In the shrub-steppe community in the eastern Patagonian desert, the shrubs quilembai and the cushionlike colapiche are common. Where the soil is salty, saltbush and other salt-tolerant shrubs grow.

PLANTS OF THE TROPICAL SAVANNA BIOME. The cerrado region of east central Brazil and southward is not only the largest savanna biome of South America, it is also one of the most romanticized of the world's savannas. Like the Old West of North America, the grasslands of Brazil have cowboys who traditionally have used the cerrado for farming and cattle ranching. With ever-increasing pressure from agriculture, the cerrado is now under attack in various ways. Extensive fertilization, associated with modern agriculture, planting of trees for timber production, and introduction of foreign species, especially African grasses, have all begun to change the cerrado. Frequent fires also have taken their toll. The cerrado contains more than ten thousand species of plants with 44 percent of them being endemic (found only in the cerrado). As much as 75 percent of the cerrado has been lost since 1965 and what remains is fragmented. A number of conservation groups are trying to save as much as possible of what is left.

The terms "savanna" and "cerrado" give the misleading impression that this area is one vast grassland. Some areas truly are grassland, such as the *campo limpo,* but other plant assemblages include *campo cerrado* (grassland with sparse shrubs), cerrado "proper" (grassland with scattered shrubs and trees), and cerradão (a more continuous cover of trees and shrubs). The last of these assemblages is closer to a forest than a savanna and is a transition type of habitat. Scattered randomly across the cerrado are forest gaps called *veradas,* which are spring-fed and have a high density of buruti or mauritia palms, a species of palm endemic to Brazil.

Two other savanna regions farther south are the Pantanal and the Pampas. Although the Pantanal is a savanna, during the rainy season it becomes a wetland and is a haven for aquatic plants, including giant water lilies, so large and sturdy that a grown human can lie on one of the floating leaves without breaking through, and water hyacinth, which has become a serious foreign invader in places like Florida. Later, the Pantanal dries out and grasslands appear in place of the water. Near the many rivers of the Pantanal and in waterlogged areas, acuri, carandá palms, and the beautiful paratudo tree, which produces a profusion of yellow flowers at the end of the rainy season, occur. This unique area is under attack by a variety of human activities, including navigation and artificial drainage projects, mining, agriculture, and urban waste.

The Pampas, like the great prairies that once covered central North America, is composed almost solely of grass. Trees and shrubs grow near bodies of water, but everywhere else grass predominates. Cattle ranching and wheat and corn farming are the primary occupations of the area and are thus the primary threat. Instead of a wet and dry season, as on the Pantanal, rain is distributed throughout the year, and because the area is farther south, it has a more temperate climate. Pampas grass has been exported as an ornamental plant. Unfortunately, pampas grass easily reproduces asexually and produces large numbers of seeds, so it has become a fairly invasive weed in some parts of the world.

The last major savanna region is the *llanos*, located at lower elevations in the drainage area of the Orinoco River in Venezuela and Colombia. Much like the Pantanal, this area has pronounced wet and dry seasons; the wet season is from

Ecuadorian raft made with wood from the balsa tree, a tropical American tree known for its low-density and unusually lightweight wood. Balsa wood is commonly used for model airplanes. (Arkent Archive)

May to October and the dry season is from November to April. At the lowest elevations, treeless grasslands persist after the water from the rainy season subsides. On the higher plains is a scattering of smaller trees, which on steeper slopes becomes more densely wooded. The mauritia palm can also be found here in poorly drained areas.

*Water lilies
Page 750*

PLANTS OF THE TROPICAL FOREST BIOME. The Amazon rain forest is the largest contiguous rain forest in the world. It is so large and so lush with tree growth that it is actually responsible, in part, for the wet climate of the region. Plant diversity is so great here that it overwhelms even experienced botanists. Currently, no comprehensive plant guide exists for many parts of the Amazon rain forest, and this should be no surprise, considering that there are tens of thousands of plant species, with a large number having never been described.

*Rain forest
Page 880*

This one-of-a-kind botanical treasure is being destroyed at a rapid pace of between 5,000 and 10,000 square miles (13,000-26,000 sq. km.) per year. The causes for this rapid destruction are primarily logging, agriculture, and cattle ranching. A common practice for preparing an area for cattle ranching or farming has been to simply burn the forest, not even necessarily logging it first, and then letting grass and other vegetation or crops grow in its place. The soils of the rain forest are so poor, however, that this practice usually depletes the soil within a few years and the land becomes a useless wasteland fit only for weeds. Mining and oil drilling have also taken their toll.

The Amazon rain forest is an extremely complex biome. The main plant biomass is composed of trees, which form a characteristically closed canopy that prevents much of the light from reaching the forest floor. Consequently, the forest floor has little herbaceous growth, and most smaller plants tend to grow as epiphytes on the branches and trunks of trees. The trees that form the canopy are stratified into three fairly discrete levels. The lowest two levels are the most crowded and comprise smaller to medium-size trees and relatively tall trees. These two levels alone block out much of the light from above. The highest level comprises extremely tall trees, often referred to as emergent trees because they stand out above the fairly continuous lower two layers.

Emergent trees are randomly scattered about and typically do not form a closed canopy like the lower two levels. Many of the tallest trees are buttressed at the base, an adaptation that seems to give greater stability. Beneath the canopy, there are some smaller palms, shrubs and ferns, but these never occur in high density, except where there is a break in the canopy that allows in greater light.

Although many of the trees of the rain forest are unfamiliar to everyone but an experienced botanist or logger, some species are well known, primarily because of their economic value. A favorite tree for

making furniture is the mahogany. The "classic" mahogany trees are species of *Swietenia*, but many species from the *Meliaceae* (mahogany family) are also called mahogany and have fine wood as well. Because they are highly prized, many species of mahogany are becoming rare or extinct.

The South American rain forests are also the original source of rubber. Brazil had a monopoly on rubber until seeds were smuggled out and planted in Malaysia. Synthetic rubber has now replaced natural rubber for many applications. Another popular tree is the Brazil nut tree, an abundant food source that has been exploited by suppliers of mixed nuts.

The cacao tree, which is the source of chocolate, produces flowers and fruits that emerge right out of the trunk rather than from the branches, a type of fruiting called cauliflory. The fruits are football-shaped, although smaller, and produce up to about sixty cacao beans, which when removed can be processed to make chocolate.

Many of the smaller plants of the rain forest are epiphytes (or parasites, in some cases) on the trunks and branches of the canopy trees. Lianas, or vines, are a prominent component as well. The strangler fig begins as a liana and eventually grows to tree proportions by an unusual method. The fruits are eaten by monkeys, birds, or bats who then defecate the seeds onto branches high in the canopy. The seeds germinate and send down a vine-like root all the way to the ground. Once this nutrient line is established, more roots grow down. Then branches, with leaves, begin growing up the tree, eventually surrounding it completely. Sometimes the host tree dies and rots, leaving just the tubelike strangler fig holding the shape of the dead tree.

The most common epiphytes in the Amazon rain forest include orchids, bromeliads, and even some cacti. The orchid flora is particularly diverse, with some odd species. Some orchids have flowers that mimic the females of certain species of wasps. Their similarity is so striking that male wasps readily attempt to copulate with the flowers, thus transferring pollen from one orchid to another.

There is a large diversity of bromeliads, ranging from small, inconspicuous species to larger species, such as tank bromeliads, that can collect significant amounts of water in their central whorl of leaves. The water in these plants can contain a whole miniature ecosystem, complete with mosquito larvae, aquatic insects, and frogs. Ferns are another significant member of the epiphyte community. Some larger species of ferns, often called tree ferns, also grow in the understory.

Every year during the rainy season, the lowest elevation areas of the Amazon rain forest are flooded with several feet of water, which recedes after a few months. The trees are well adapted to this flooding cycle and flourish. A few even have unique adaptations, such as trees that produce fruits that are eaten by fish, thus assuring the spread of their seeds. The flooding can be so extensive in some areas that the water reaches the lower parts of the canopy.

Coastal tropical rain forests also occur in northwestern and southeastern South America. These forests have many of the same characteristics and a similar flora to that found in the Amazon rain forest. Despite their similarities, there are many endemic species in each of these forests. In fact, endemism is extremely high throughout the rain forests of South America. Some tree species are so rare that they may be found in only a few square mile area and nowhere else. Other rare species may be widespread in a particular rain forest, but be found only as single trees separated by many miles. One unique feature of the costal rain forests is coastal mangroves. Where the tropical rain forest meets the

ocean, certain species of trees have become adapted to the tidal environment. Many mangrove trees have prop-roots, which make the trees look like they are growing on stilts. They also frequently have special root structures that extend above the water at high tide and allow the roots to breathe. Mangrove trees are also extremely salt tolerant.

PLANTS OF THE MEDITERRANEAN AND TEMPERATE FOREST BIOMES. One of the world's five Mediterranean climate regions is found in central Chile. This climate is characterized by warm dry summers and cool wet winters. The vegetation, called matorral, is composed primarily of leathery-leaved, evergreen shrubs that are well adapted to the long summer drought. Overall, the vegetation is similar to the chaparral found in the Mediterranean climate areas of California, although all of the species and some of the genera are different.

The only trees found in both California and matorral are willows and mesquite. Oaks, dominant in Mediterranean California, are not found in the matorral, but rather southern beech. Some shrubs, such as creosote bush and coyote brush, are found in both places. The matorral is the only Mediterranean area that has bromeliads. At lower elevation areas, somewhat inland, many of the shrubs are drought-deciduous, that is, they drop their leaves in the summer. In more inland parts of this biome, the espino tree is common. Historically, this native species was probably confined to disturbed habitats; with the many disturbances caused by humans, it has become more common.

Because South America extends so far south, it actually has a small region containing temperate forests. These forests range from temperate rain forest to drier temperate forests, and in all cases are typically dominated by southern beeches. The undergrowth is dominated by small evergreen trees and shrubs. Fuchsias, which are valued the world over for their showy flowers, are common in the undergrowth.

The monkey puzzle tree, an unusual conifer, is also abundant in some areas and has been grown as an ornamental in other parts of the world. Although not rich in species, the temperate rain forests of southern South America can be lush. In the far south, before the extreme climate restricts the vegetation to alpine tundra, a region of elfin woodlands predominates. These woodlands can be nearly impenetrable, with the densest growth often associated with patches of tall bamboo.

Bryan Ness

FOR FURTHER STUDY

Gentry, Alwyn H., ed. *Four Neotropical Rainforests.* New Haven, Conn.: Yale University Press, 1993.

_____, and Adrian G. Foryth. *A Field Guide to the Families and Genera of Woody Plants of Northwest South America: Colombia, Ecuador, Peru.* Washington, D.C.: Conservation International, 1996.

Kircher, John. *A Neotropical Companion.* 2d ed. Princeton, N.J.: Princeton University Press, 1997.

McCarry, John, and Robert Caputo. "Suriname." *National Geographic* (June, 2000): 38-55.

Maxwell, Nicole. *Witch-Doctor's Apprentice: Hunting for Medicinal Plants in the Amazon.* New York: Citadel Press, 1990.

Peck, Robert McCracken. "The Secrets of the Cloud Forest." *Audubon* 101, no. 5 (September/October, 1999): 88-ff.

Plotkin, Mark J. *Tales of a Shaman's Apprentice: An Ethnobotanist Searches for New Medicines in the Amazon Rain Forest.* New York: Penguin Books, 1994.

Rice, Richard E., Raymond E. Gullison, and John W. Reid. "Can Sustainable Management Save Tropical Forests?" *Scientific American* 276, no. 4 (April, 1997): 44-49.

Young, Kenneth R., and Blanca Leon. "Nature on the Rebound." *Americas* 51, no. 1 (January/February, 1999): 32-34.

Zimmerer, Karl S. "The Ecogeography of Andean Potatoes." *Bioscience* 48, no. 6 (June, 1998): 445-454.

Map Page 748

FAUNA OF SOUTH AMERICA

A wide range of animals, both ordinary and exotic, inhabit the continent of South America. The types of animals found in any geographical area are determined by the climate and the terrain. In the Andes, animals such as the llama have adapted to the terrain and climate of the high, steep mountains.

In the Galapagos Islands, off the coast of Ecuador, live animals that are found in no other area of the world. Charles Darwin studied the animals of the Galapagos and developed many of his ideas related to the theory of evolution from this study. North of Antarctica, in the archipelago known as Tierra del Fuego, there are many penguins,

Chileans drive a herd of alpacas and llamas through the foothills near Santiago. (AP/Wide World Photos)

whose layers of feathers help them to survive the frigid sea waters in that area.

ANIMALS OF THE ANDES. Four members of the camel family live in the Andes Mountains of Peru, Bolivia, Ecuador, and Chile: alpacas, vicunas, guanacos, and llamas. These camelids all have commercial value in the Andes, as pack animals and for their meat and fur. Many people of the Andes also raise sheep on the mountains for both wool and meat.

More than four thousand years ago, alpacas, which are raised for meat and for their fine cashmere fur, were reserved for the exclusive use of the Incas, who prized their coats. Alpacas live from fifteen to twenty-five years. The average adult is about 3 feet (1 meter) high at the shoulder and weighs up to 180 pounds. In 1999 there were approximately three million alpacas in South America, mostly in Bolivia, Chile, and Peru.

LLAMAS. Closely related to the alpaca is the llama, domesticated as a work animal more than three thousand years ago. Llamas, used primarily in Peru and Bolivia, have historically been the beasts of burden in the Andes Mountains. A single animal can carry about 200 pounds (90 kilograms) for twelve hours a day. However, they cannot be ridden and when they tire, they often simply lie down and refuse to move. They even spit at their drivers when they no longer want to work. Reaching heights of nearly 4.5 feet (1.5 meters) llamas are generally larger than alpacas. A llama's fur is usually white with black and brown, but some are pure white and others pure black. Although llamas are used for work, they are also kept as pets in many homes of South America.

VICUNAS. Vicuna fur has historical importance in South America. It was used by Incas to make cloth, and only members of

713

Inca royalty could wear clothing made from this cloth. Anyone else found with such clothing was executed. By 1979 only four thousand vicunas were left in South America. They had been hunted for their fleeces by poachers who killed the animals. Representatives of the governments of Bolivia, Chile, Ecuador, and Peru signed a treaty for protection of the vicuna. Twenty years later, there had been a resurgence of vicunas in Peru, Chile, and Argentina: in 1999, there were 103,000 in Peru, 30,000 in Argentina, 16,000 in Chile, and a small transplanted herd in Ecuador. Even though *el chacu*, the communal hunting of vicuna, continued after 1979, laws limited these hunts to local people. Those local hunters sold the fiber from the animals as an important source of income for their families.

Vicunas weigh 90 pounds and are a little less than 3 feet (1 meter) in height at the shoulder. They have long necks, slender legs, padded cloven feet, large round eyes, and a fine, dense, tawny coat. Aside from their economic value, the vicuna is valuable for scientific study. They are highly communicative animals, signaling each other with body postures and ear and tail positions. They emit soft humming sounds as symbols of bonding and greeting.

GUANACOS. The fourth member of the camel family found in South America is the guanaco. The guanaco is more adaptable than the other three camelids. It is found throughout the Andes, in the dry Atacama Desert of Chile, and in Tierra del Fuego, where it rains year-round. This animal, from which the llama was domesticated, began life in the semiarid desert and has developed physiological mechanisms for coping with both heat and dehydration. It is similar in structure to the other camelids, but is the largest member of the camel family living in South America.

LARGE CATS. Throughout the Andes, from Argentina to Colombia, and on into Central America, pumas roam. This reddish brown feline can reach lengths of about 6.5 feet (2 meters), not including its long tail. In some areas of South America, the puma is endangered. It is a carnivore whose natural prey are elk, deer, and small wild animals; however, it also eats sheep and cattle. Thus, ranchers have retaliated by killing the predators. Another member of the cat family is the elusive Andean mountain cat. Rarely sighted by humans, it is the least-known New World cat. The Andean wild cat is considered sacred by the native people of the *altiplano* of Bolivia, the Aymara.

In the forests of the Andes lives the spectacled bear. Its range extends as far north as Ecuador. This bear, which is endangered because of overhunting and destruction of its environment, has a shaggy brown coat with yellow facial markings and a cream-colored muzzle, throat, and chest.

RODENTS. Several rodents are native to the Andes. Chinchillas were found living in crevices in the mountains when early Spanish explorers first arrived there. Living off berries and fruits in Peru, Chile, and Argentina, these rodents belonged to Inca royalty, who used their fur to make chinchilla stoles. In the latter part of the twentieth century, they were nearly extinct in the wild but existed in captivity. Related to the chinchilla is the viscacha, which is prey for such animals as the Andean mountain cat. Mountain viscachas have long rabbitlike ears, and long, squirrel-like tails. East of the mountains lives the plains viscacha, which has shorter ears and a blunter head. The cavy, the South American guinea pig, lives in the crevices of the Andes.

BIRDS. Various exotic birds also live in the Andes, many of which also are found in the Amazon Basin to the east. Among these birds are the Andean cock-of-the-rock, the scarlet macaw, the quetzal, the Andean condor, and the James flamingo. The cock-of-the-rock is a huge dancing bird found in the mountain forests. The scarlet macaw, a brilliantly plumed member of the parrot family, is an endangered species. The quetzal had religious significance to early Andeans; even at the beginning of the twentieth-first century, it is regarded as a symbol of the Andes Mountains. The Andean condor is found in the high plain area of Bolivia and Chile. With a wingspan of 12 feet (4 meters), it is the largest flying bird in the world. It can soar to a distance of 26,000 feet (7,925 meters) above sea level.

In the southern Andes lives the rhea, a flightless bird related to the ostrich, which often is called the South American ostrich. The rhea is much smaller than an ostrich and has three toes on each foot, whereas an ostrich has two toes on each. Rheas live in flocks of twenty to thirty in Brazil's southern plains and in Argentina, Paraguay, and Uruguay.

ANIMALS OF THE AMAZON BASIN. Representatives of almost one-fourth of all known varieties of animals live in South America, mostly in the Amazon Basin. The basin includes the rain forests, plateaus, rivers, and swamps southeast of the Andes Mountains.

The tapir, found in the Andes and in the forests east of the Andes, is South America's largest animal. With its short, hairy body, it resembles a pig, but is actually related to the horse and the rhinoceros. The number of tapirs in South America lessened over the twentieth century because they were hunted for their flesh and their thick hides, and also because the cutting of forest has reduced the land available for their habitat.

The tapir's natural enemy, the jaguar, also is found in the eastern Andes and in the forests east of the high mountains. This feline, which was worshipped by pre-

ENDANGERED MAMMALS OF SOUTH AMERICA

Common Name	Scientific Name	Range
Armadillo, giant	*Priodontes maximus*	Venezuela and Guyana to Argentina
Cat, Andean	*Felis jacobita*	Chile, Peru, Bolivia, Argentina
Chinchilla	*Chinchilla brevicaudata boliviana*	Bolivia
Deer, pampas	*Ozotoceros bezoarticus*	Brazil, Argentina, Uruguay, Bolivia, Paraguay
Manatee, Amazonian	*Trichechus inunguis*	South America (Amazon River basin)
Marmoset, buff-headed	*Callithrix flaviceps*	Brazil
Monkey, wooly spider	*Brachyteles arachnoides*	Brazil
Otter, giant	*Pteronura brasiliensis*	South America
Porcupine, thin-spined	*Chaetomys subspinsosus*	Brazil
Vicuna	*Vicugna*	Andes countries

Source: U.S. Fish and Wildlife Service, U.S. Department of the Interior.

Columbian civilizations as a god, lives in the area between the southern United States and northern Argentina and is especially prevalent in Brazil. Strong swimmers, jaguars like to live near rivers and other streams. At the end of the twentieth century, they were on the list of threatened animals in South America. They were threatened because farmers were farming lands that previously were their natural habitat, and also because farmers, claiming that the cats killed their cattle and sheep, were killing the jaguars.

Also living within the Amazon Basin are the giant anteater, the sloth, and the peba. The giant anteater has value to the environment and to farmers because it consumes up to thirty thousand insects per day. The peba, a nine-banded armadillo found widely throughout South America, also contributes to agriculture by consuming insects and worms. This nocturnal animal is protected from its predators by a horn and bony plates covering its body. The sloth is the world's slowest-moving large mammal.

Within the Amazon Basin lives one of the world's most interesting rodents, the huge capybara. It generally is as large as a big dog, but can reach 4 feet (1.2 meters) in length and can weigh as much as 100 pounds (45 kilograms). Humans have little to fear from the amphibious capybara, however, since it is a vegetarian.

Both the land iguana and the lava lizard live in the Amazon Basin. Land iguanas can live up to twenty-five years and weigh up to 15 pounds (6.8 kilograms). They eat low-growing plants, shrubs, fallen fruits, and cactus tree pads. The lava lizard, about 1 foot (30.5 centimeters) long, is smaller than the land iguana. Lava lizards are beneficial to agriculture because they eat beetles, spiders, and ants.

The coatimundi inhabits areas from Arizona to northern Argentina. A member

Tree boa
Page 749

of the raccoon family, it is brown or rust-colored. It eats snails, fish, berries, insects, spiders, lizards, birds, eggs, and mice, and is often kept as a pet by South Americans.

Many types of birds live in the Amazon Basin, some deep within the rain forest, others closer to the mountains. Among the birds in the basin are hummingbirds, parrots, ospreys, macaws, boat-billed herons, great egrets, white-necked herons, least bitterns, and blue and yellow macaws. Toucans, which also live at high elevations up to 10,000 feet (3,050 meters), can be found deep within the Amazon rain forest.

The rain forest is also inhabited by many bats, squirrels, and parrots, which eat the fruits and nuts of the upper and lower canopies. In the lower canopy live lemurs, flying squirrels, and marmosets, small monkeys found mostly in eastern Brazil. These animals use their sweat glands for communication. Animals of the lower canopy eat the fruits, nuts, and insects that are found there. Within the rain forests also live vampire bats; these fascinating animals have to have two tablespoons of blood per day in order to survive.

Other residents of the Amazon Basin include the yapok, a member of the opossum family that has webbed feet for swamp travel; the sapajou monkey, a small New World primate; and the octodont, an eight-toothed rodent also known as a spiny rat or a spiny hedgehog because of the sharp spines embedded in its fur.

The boa constrictor also lives in the jungles of this basin. This snake, which is usually 6-9 feet (2-3 meters) in length, but can reach 13 feet (4 meters), kills its prey by squeezing it to death, using its body coils to suffocate its victims. After killing its meal, the boa constrictor stretches its jaws wide apart and pulls the entire victim into its mouth. Using this method of killing, a boa is able to eat animals that are much larger than its head.

Another large snake native to the Amazon Basin is the anaconda. Most anacondas weigh several hundred pounds (100 kilograms) but can reach weights of 550 pounds (250 kilograms) and can reach 36 feet (11 meters) in length. The anaconda is found in the Guyanas and throughout tropical South America, east of the Andes. With eyes high on its head, the anaconda can submerge its body in water and watch for the approach of unsuspecting prey.

Several types of foxes are indigenous to the Amazon Basin and roam through lower mountain areas to the east and the west of the Amazon. Among them are the gray fox and the crab-eating zorro. The gray fox roams over the plains, the Pampas, the desert, and the low mountains, but its number is decreasing because farmers are cultivating lands that previously were its habitat. In Argentina, where it has been hunted for its skin, the gray fox has been placed on the endangered species list. In Chile it is protected by law, but enforcement of the law has been lax. The crab-eating zorro is found in Colombia, Venezuela, Suriname, eastern Peru, Bolivia, Paraguay, Uruguay, Brazil, and northern Argentina. An omnivore, it eats not only crabs but also insects, rodents, fruit, reptiles, and birds.

RIVER ANIMALS. Many animals spend all or part of their lives within the Amazon. The black caiman, an alligator that is nearly extinct, is one such animal. It can weigh as much as a ton. It will eat all vertebrates, including humans if that is the only food available.

The semi-aquatic brown water lizard also is found in the jungle area around the Amazon. Within the Amazon are manatees as well as Boto River dolphins, also known as an Amazon River dolphin. This endangered animal is the only dolphin to have a neck. Giant otters live in the waters of the Amazon as do many types of fish, including

THE ANACONDA

Another name for the anaconda is the water boa, an appropriate name for a snake that is almost always found near water. Anacondas live in the Amazon and Orinoco basins of tropical South America, and their habitat extends to Trinidad. Like the crocodile, the anaconda has nostrils high on its snout so that it can swim with its head mostly below water and still breathe. The anaconda lies near the shore, waiting for its prey. When a deer, bird, or other prey comes to the water to drink, the anaconda quickly strikes, dragging its victim underwater to drown it. The anaconda then eats the unfortunate animal whole. A good meal can last an anaconda for months, during which it will lie in the water, digesting its food.

piranhas, which, with their sharp teeth, can quickly strip the flesh from their prey.

ANIMALS OF THE EASTERN HIGHLANDS. The Eastern Highlands of South America host many unique animals, including the bush dog, woolly tree porcupine, maned wolf, peccary, bushmaster, and coypu rat, and many birds such as flamingos.

The bush dog is a wild dog, but, with its webbed feet, it resembles an otter more than a dog. Bush dogs live in packs and hunt small deer and rodents. Bush dogs can be found from the rain forests into the grasslands, in Colombia, Venezuela, the Guyanas, Brazil, Paraguay, northeastern Argentina, eastern Bolivia, and eastern Peru.

The maned wolf is one of South America's most beautiful and revered animals. Weighing on average 100 pounds (45 kilograms), it is South America's largest canid. It is found mostly in Argentina and Brazil and has no natural enemies. An omnivore, it will eat nearly anything, including fruits, insects, and small vertebrates. At the end of the twentieth century, the Smithsonian

Galápagos penguin. (Clyde L. Rasmussen)

Institution estimated that fewer than ten thousand maned wolves existed in the wild, living mostly in Argentina and Brazil. Because of its beautiful red and gold fur, the maned wolf is a tourist attraction. Many South Americans regard it as an important part of their cultural heritage. The rural people of the Sierra de Canastra of Brazil believe that the maned wolf has medicinal and supernatural powers.

The peccary and the bushmaster are also found in the Eastern Highlands. The peccary resembles the tapir, but is much smaller. It has a big head, sharp teeth, and prickly fur. It eats smaller animals and plants such as cactus flowers. The bushmaster, the largest poisonous snake in the Americas, is a type of pit viper related to the rattlesnake. Like the rattlesnake, it shakes its tail before striking, but it has no rattles. Gray and brown with a diamond pattern, it averages 8-12 feet (2.5-5.5 meters) in length.

The coypu rat is also known as a swamp beaver. This relative of the muskrat is found in southern Brazil, Bolivia, and Colombia. The agouti, a rodent nearly 2 feet (60 centimeters) long, also lives in the Eastern Highlands. Farmers detest the agouti because it eats sugar and banana plants. A cousin of the jaguar, the ocelot, also makes its home in this area. This slender cat is camouflaged in the forests and deserts of the highlands.

Birds that live in the Eastern Highlands include the James flamingo, which lives on Bolivia's frigid salt lakes, and the giant antshrike, more than a foot (30 centimeters) in length.

ANIMALS OF TIERRA DEL FUEGO. In the islands that make up Tierra del Fuego, many unusual animals are found, including penguins and many other types of birds. Penguins cannot fly; they use their wings for swimming in the icy waters near their home. Penguins are insulated from the frigid ocean waters by three layers of short feathers and an underlying layer of fat. Other birds common to Tierra del Fuego are Magellanic cormorants, imperial cormorants, albatrosses, and various petrels. Sea lions also live on these islands.

ANIMALS OF THE GALAPAGOS ISLANDS. In the Pacific Ocean, 600 miles (960 kilometers) off the coast of Ecuador, lie the Galapagos Islands. These islands, owned by Ecuador, are officially known as the Archipelago de Colón. In the 1830's, Charles Darwin visited the Galapagos aboard the HMS *Beagle*. His interest in the diversity of animal life on the Galapagos—particularly the thirteen distinct species of finches found there, each of which had adapted a distinct-shaped bill suitable for the type of seeds available on the island on which the particular species lived—eventually led to the development of his theory of evolution.

Many other birds live on the Galapagos. One is the flightless cormorant, which has lost its ability to fly because food is so abundant near shore that the bird, having no predators, has no need to fly. The flightless cormorant has powerful wings and webbed feet, but its wings are only about one-third of the wingspan that would be needed to lift its body.

On the Galapagos are found many flamingoes and Galapagos penguins, the closest penguins to the equator. The frigate bird also lives there. It has long wings and a forked tail. Incapable of taking off from a flat surface, it must run downhill in order to fly. Galapagos hawks have a variety of feather colors, from white and brown to bright yellow and black. These hawks are much tamer than many of their cousins in other parts of the world.

The Galapagos are also home to the blue-footed booby, which lays its eggs directly on the ground, and the masked booby, which lays two eggs, but raises only one chick to maturity. There is also the red-footed booby, which makes a nest of twigs and spends much of its time at sea hunting for food. The waved albatross, a rare seabird, nests on Head Island in the Galapagos. It cannot be said to live there because the only time it is not far out at sea is during the nesting period.

The Galapagos fur seal grows to about 5 feet (1.5 meters) in length and is the smallest of the fur seals. A special subspecies of the California sea lion lives in the Galapagos. It is 6 feet (1.8 meters) in length, rarely goes far from shore, and is very intelligent. The Pacific waters around the Galapagos Islands also contain hammerhead sharks, marine iguanas, and Sally Light crabs. The marine iguanas there can swim as far as 50 feet (15 meters) below sea level. The Sally Light crab, yellowish orange in color, was named after an eighteenth century English dancer.

One of the most famous inhabitants of these islands is the giant land tortoise,

Iguanas Page 749

Marine iguana. (Clyde L. Rasmussen)

which can weigh up to 500 pounds (225 kilograms) and can live to be 150 years old.

Annita Marie Ward

FOR FURTHER STUDY

Dunphy, Madeline. *Here Is the Tropical Rain Forest.* Westport, Conn.: Hyperion Press, 1997.

Kalman, Bobbie, and Barbara Bedell (illustrator). *Rainforest Birds (Birds Up Close).* New York: Crabtree Publications, 1998.

Matthews, Downs. *Beneath the Canopy: Wildlife of the Amazon Rain Forest.* San Francisco: Chronicle Books, 1999.

Savage, Steven. *Animals of the Rain Forest.* Austin, Tex.: Steck Vaughn, 1995.

*Map
Page 751*

FLORA AND FAUNA OF CENTRAL AMERICA

*Flowers
Page 752*

Because Central America is a land bridge that connects North America and South America, its plants and animals have similarities with the flora and fauna of both those continents. While northern species such as white-tailed deer, racoons, rattlesnakes, and mountain lions may be seen in the northern part and the highlands of Central America, tropical species such as monkeys, coral snakes, jaguars, and sloths abound in the coastal rain forests and southern regions of this geographic area.

PLANT LIFE. Types of vegetation are influenced by climate, soil quality, land elevation, and human activity. Lowland tropical rain forests lie on the eastern half of Central America and typically have many tall, broad-leaved evergreen trees 130 feet (40 meters) or more in height, and 4-5 feet (1.2-1.5 meters) in diameter that form a dense canopy. Shade-seeking plants, such as palms, figs, ferns, vines, philodendrons, and orchids, form the forest undergrowth beneath the trees.

Epiphytes such as orchids, ferns, bromeliads, and mosses cling to the branches of the trees in a dense mat of vegetation—these plants have no roots but grow by clinging to the trunks of trees and drawing moisture and nourishment from the air. Rain forest trees that are harvested for their commercial value include mahogany, kapok, cedarwood, tagua, ebony, and rosewood for making furniture; breadfruit, palm, and cashew for food; sapodilla, used to make latex; and the rubber tree. Many brilliantly colored flowers also grow in Central America. The most common of these are orchids (with close to a thousand species), heliconias, hibiscus, and bromeliads.

Elsewhere in the Caribbean lowlands, where the soil is porous and dry, extensive savanna grasslands with sparse forests of pines, palmettos, guanacastes, cedars, and oaks are found. Along the Caribbean coast (called the Mosquito Coast), mangroves and coconut palms flourish in swamps and lagoons.

Nineteenth century traveler's depiction of a Central American forest. (Arkent Archive)

Costa Rica forest
Page 753

On the western side of the mountains, facing away from the moist Caribbean winds and receiving rain only seasonally, vegetation is sparse and semiarid, and soils are poor and unproductive. Tropical deciduous forests dominate there, and vegetation is characterized by evergreen herbs and shrubs, frangipanis, eupatorium pines, myrtles, and sphagnum mosses.

ANIMAL LIFE. Wildlife in Central America generally has many similarities with that of South America, but species common to North America, or unique to Central America, also exist. Although the overall number of animal species is smaller than that of South America, Central America has a rich range of wildlife in relation to its small geographic area.

Competition between Central American animal species is intense; as a result, animals tend to be small and highly specialized as to where they live and what they eat. Mutualism between plant and animal species is also common, with each depending on the other for nourishment and survival. Ant acacias, for example, feed on the nectar of acacia trees, but also defend it vigorously from attacks by any other animals or invading plants. Similarly, hummingbird beaks are often shaped to allow them easy access to only one or two species of flowers—the flowers, in turn, have evolved special colors and shapes to encourage hummingbirds to drink their nectar and spread pollen from one blossom to another.

The central mountains and highlands of Central America are cooler than the coastal lowlands, and the vegetation there is mainly deciduous hardwood trees such as walnuts, pines, oaks, and balsas. The eastern slopes of the mountains have abundant rainfall. "Cloud forests" that are 5,000 feet (1,525 meters) above sea level are thickly choked with evergreen oaks, sweet gums, pines, and laurels, which grow to a height of about 65 feet (20 meters) and are festooned with ferns, bromeliads, mosses, and orchids.

The forests of Central America support an especially rich array of bird species, with nearly one thousand species represented in total. The majority of these birds live in the tropical forests, where North American species of warblers and flycatchers (part of a large family of insectivorous birds called Trogons) feed on the abundant insect life, along with more tropical species such as woodcreepers and flycatchers.

More than ninety species of hummingbirds feed upon the many colorful tropical flowers, and large-beaked birds such as toucans, parrots, and macaws feed upon the fruits and seeds of the numerous fruiting trees. Hawks, falcons, and eagles (including the world's largest eagle, the Harpy eagle) hunt smaller birds, reptiles, and rodents in the forests and grasslands of Central America. Waterbirds and wading birds—ducks, egrets, storks, herons, ibis, kingfishers, and spoonbills—live along the riverbanks and lagoons. Ocean birds, including terns, gulls, and frigate birds, live along the coastal areas. Central American birds display an extraordinary variety of shapes and brilliant colors.

Many species of animal life in Central America are also native to South America. Tapirs, capybaras, giant anteaters, peccaries, and small brocket deer live in the forest undergrowth, along with a variety of rodents, such as armadillos, agoutis, and pacas. These mammals are secretive and mainly nocturnal. Monkeys—howler, squirrel, woolly, spider, and capuchin—live in the forest canopy, along with tree sloths, tree squirrels, porcupines, tree rats, and tamarins. Many of Central America's predators are members of the cat family—jaguars, jaguarundis, margays, pumas, and ocelots. Other carnivores are coatimundis, kinkajous (racoon-like animals), tayras (a large member of the weasel family), and vampire bats.

Central America is particularly rich in the many species of reptiles that inhabit it, including such venomous snakes as the fer-de-lance, bushmaster, pit viper, green palm viper, parrot snake, and coral snake,

ENDANGERED CENTRAL AMERICAN WILDLIFE

Deforestation is a major environmental concern throughout Central America, where population growth has led to the harvesting of trees for economic profit and the need to create new farmland. About one-third of the area's original forests remain, but a high rate of deforestation continues. Typically, loggers remove the most valuable trees, and the land is then farmed or used for cattle ranching for three to seven years. As invasive weeds soon take over the newly cleared land, the land is quickly exhausted and human settlement then moves on to clear new areas of the forest. In recent years, all Central American countries have made efforts to create protected natural areas and to control illegal logging.

The wildlife of Central America is threatened not only by the loss of natural habitat through deforestation, but also by uncontrolled hunting, human population growth, and a world market for rare and exotic species. Many Central American species are endangered or nearly extinct—the many parrot species, squirrel monkeys, sea turtles, and the quetzal (with its beautiful feathers) are all becoming rare. As more and more land is deforested, only fragmented islands of forest remain, making it difficult for the remaining animals to forage and breed.

ENDANGERED SPECIES OF CENTRAL AMERICA

Common Name	Scientific Name	Range
Cat, tiger	*Leopardus tigrinus*	Costa Rica to northern Argentina
Jaguarundi, Panamanian	*Herpailurus yagouaroundi panamensis*	Nicaragua, Costa Rica, Panama
Marmoset, cotton-top	*Saguinus oedipus*	Costa Rica to Colombia
Monkey, red-backed squirrel	*Saimiri oerstedii*	Costa Rica, Panama
Monkey, spider	*Atele geoffroyi frontatus*	Costa Rica, Nicaragua
Ocelot	*Leopardus pardalis*	U.S.A. (Arizona, Texas) to Central and South America
Puma, Costa Rican	*Puma concolor costaricensis*	Nicaragua, Panama, Costa Rica
Tapir, Central American	*Tapirus bairdii*	Southern Mexico to Colombia and Ecuador

Source: U.S Fish and Wildlife Service, U.S. Department of the Interior.

and many species of iguanas.

The warm rivers and coastal reefs of Central America also support many different species of fish, including catfish, barracudas, tarpons, groupers, and damselfish. Amphibians—tree frogs, true frogs and toads—thrive in the wet environment of the rain forests, with the poison-arrow frog being perhaps the best known. Central America has five species of sea turtles—Ridley's, green, loggerhead, hawksbill and leatherback—that nest on coastal beaches. The manatee (sea-cow) is increasingly rare, but still lives in the rivers and lagoons of coastal areas.

The rain forests of Central America support an incredible variety of insects and arachnids, with many species of ants, spiders, termites, millipedes, cockroaches, cicalas, beetles, chiggers, praying mantis, and scorpions, and such flying insects as bees, butterflies, blackflies, mosquitos, and sandflies. These animals feed on plant growth and animal life at all levels of the forest and the undergrowth, as well as in the marshy coastal areas of Central America. The insects are a food source for the many and varied reptiles, bats, birds, rodents, and amphibians that contribute to the rich diversity of life in this neotropical wildlife habitat.

Helen Salmon

FOR FURTHER STUDY

Beletsky, Les. *Belize and Northern Guatemala: The Eco-Traveller's Wildlife Guide.* San Diego: Academic Press, 1998.

Kricher, John. *A Neotropical Companion: An*

INFORMATION ON THE WORLD WIDE WEB

The Lonely Planet Web site features information on the plants and animals of Central America, categorized under the Environment link within each individual country's site. (www.lonelyplanet.com.au/dest/)

Introduction to the Animals, Plants, and Ecosystems of the New World Tropics. 2d ed. Princeton, N.J.: Princeton University Press, 1997.

Moser, Don. *Central American Jungles.* New York: Time-Life Books, 1975.

Parker, Edward. *Central America.* Austin, Texas: Raintree Steck-Vaughn, 1999.

HUMAN GEOGRAPHY

PEOPLE

SOUTH AMERICA

The nature and pattern of the gradual habitation of South America by humans is similar to that of North America in some important aspects. The first South Americans were most likely the descendants of Asian hunters who dispersed throughout the Americas and physically and culturally evolved in accordance with the demands of their respective environments. There may have been other prehistoric migrants from Japan, Southeast Asia, and Europe.

Permanent migration began in 1492 with Christopher Columbus's arrival in the New World. In sharp contrast to most of North America, European settlement of the southern half of the Western Hemisphere was dominated by the Portuguese and the Spanish. In more modern times, emigrants into South America have come from central and southern Europe, the Middle East, and Japan. The ethnic complexity created in South America rivals that of the United States.

NATIVE AMERICANS. There is no doubt that people from Asia populated the Americas, but which part of Asia is in dispute. Increasingly, the physical evidence suggests a migration of a non-Mongoloid human strain, possibly from Southeast Asia, as being the first significant human incursion into the Americas. Some genetic evidence suggests a relationship between the present-day Amerindians, or Native Americans, of Ecuador and southeast

Asians, Japanese, and perhaps even Polynesians. There is similar genetic evidence for the Native Americans in Chile, Colombia, and Brazil. Some genetic and stone tool evidence points to a European presence, perhaps from France and Spain, around 20,000 and 16,000 B.C.E. However, there is no fossil record to support that idea. Subsequent migrations into the Americas appear, instead, to have come from northeast Asia. This is the dominant theory as to the origins of Native Americans.

As to where the earliest South Americans entered into the continent, two possible areas of initial settlement are likely. One area is located in Colombia and Ecuador, along the eastern slopes of the Andes and in the adjacent tropical lowlands. The other is central Amazonia. Some evidence suggests that initial movement into South America took place along the Pacific and Caribbean coastlines. The Native Americans eventually populated the entire continent.

The native ethnic groups that inhabited South America were diverse. The Arawak and Carib peoples inhabited the northern coastal areas such as present-day Venezuela, Colombia, Guyana, Suriname, and French Guiana. The Inca ruled much of Peru, Bolivia, and Ecuador before the Spanish *conquistador* Francisco Pizarro arrived. In Argentina, Native American

*Incas
Pages 753,
755*

groups included the Diaquita of the Andean northwest, the Querani who inhabited the present-day region of Buenos Aires, the Tehuelche in Patagonia, and the Ona in the Tierra del Fuego. Among the native ethnic groups in Chile when the Europeans arrived were the Atacameños, Picunches, Cuncos, and the Araucanians, who are still extant.

The eventual arrival of the Portuguese and Spanish doomed the Amerindian civilizations and, to some extent, the people. Forced labor and European diseases decimated the native populations. In the coastal tropical areas, only about 5 percent of the native population was left ten years after the first significant contact with Europeans. The rate of population loss was less pronounced in higher, cooler areas, perhaps because disease did not spread so easily there. As a result, the native population in western and northern South America eventually recovered. In Brazil, the Amazonian tribes were almost eliminated by European diseases. In Argentina, Uruguay, and, to a lesser extent, Paraguay, the number of Amerindians was driven to low levels by disease and by being hunted down. The native populations became so small that the European population absorbed their remnants. Argentina and Uruguay have become European with pockets of Native Americans, much as the United States was around 1920.

IBERIANS. Christopher Columbus led the first Europeans to the New World in 1492. He landed on an island in the Caribbean and claimed the lands he found for Spain. Conflicts at the end of the fifteenth century between the Portuguese and Spanish over their overseas claims led the Roman Catholic pope to negotiate the Treaty of Tordesillas in 1494. This treaty divided the New World between Portugal and Spain, with a line drawn such that what became Brazil eventually went to the Portuguese and the rest of the New World to the Spanish.

Until the early to mid-nineteenth century, when Iberian domination came to an end, only the Spanish and Portuguese were admitted to their South American colonies. The rigid exclusion of other foreigners had but few exceptions. Most of the Spaniards came from Castile and the southern regions. It is estimated that the total number of *licencias* (authorizations to emigrate) granted by Spain was about 150,000 for the entire colonial period, which lasted from the sixteenth to the nineteenth century. It is possible that the number of illegal immigrants also approached this number. Of these, no more than two-fifths of the emigrants went to South America.

Little is known about the principal regions from which the Portuguese came. As many as one million Portuguese may have emigrated to Brazil, drawn primarily by a gold rush in Minas Gerais in the eighteenth century. Emigration from Portugal to Brazil has continued. Approximately 28 percent of Portugal's net emigration between 1864 and 1973 was to Brazil.

AFRICANS. Sugar production became important in northeastern Brazil in the early to mid-1540's. The Portuguese tried converting Amerindians to Christianity and paying them wages to work in sugar production, but the primary means of extracting their labor was to turn them into chattel slaves.

In the 1560's a major smallpox epidemic broke out among those previously unexposed populations of Amerindians. It has been estimated that thirty thousand Amerindians under Portuguese control, either on plantations or in Jesuit mission villages, died of the disease. This decline in native slave labor led to the beginnings of mass importation of African slave labor after 1570. By the 1620's sugar plantation labor was almost entirely African slaves. The sugar plantations in South America were concentrated mostly in the northeast part of the continent in present-day Guyana, Suriname, and northeastern Brazil.

The Dutch initially dominated the sugar trade in both the Caribbean and northeast South America including that portion of Brazil, but the Portuguese had pushed the Dutch out by about 1660. The Dutch did much of the initial importation of African slaves into the region. Among the Dutch planters in the seventeenth and eighteenth centuries were an important minority of Jews. In Dutch Guiana (Suriname) by the 1760's, Jewish families owned 115 of the colony's 591 sugar estates and formed the largest number of native-born whites. A small free mulatto Jewish community developed and formed its own synagogue in 1759.

By 1780 there were 406,000 freed persons of slave descent and 1.5 million slaves in Brazil. African slaves in Brazil came from West Africa, the Congo, Angola, and Mozambique. The last slaves in Brazil were not freed until 1888. Brazil now contains the largest population of African origin outside of Africa. While African slaves were taken to other areas in South America, their numbers in other locales never approached those of Brazil. In Peru, for example, there were ninety thousand African slaves in the eighteenth century, and that number did not change.

By 1700 the native populations of Peru and other Spanish-controlled areas such as Mexico and Colombia had adjusted to the European disease environment and were in the process of rapid population expansion. The free trade native and mestizo populations met labor needs in agricultural, mining, artisanal, and service areas; African slaves were not needed. In other areas of South America in the late eighteenth century, the African slave popula-

tions were twenty-one thousand in Argentina; twelve thousand in Chile; fifty-four thousand in Colombia; seventy-five thousand in Suriname; eight thousand in Ecuador; and sixty-four thousand in Venezuela.

INDENTURED LABORERS. In the 1830's slavery was abolished in much of the Caribbean and Central and South America. That left a vacuum in the labor market for the sugar plantations. In response to this need, indentured laborers were brought in from China and India. Between 1838 and 1918, 238,909 East Indians, primarily from Bengal, Bombay, and Madras, went to Guyana. From 1853 to 1867, 11,282 Chinese went to Guyana. The numbers for French Guiana and the Dutch Caribbean were similar to those for Guyana. During the 1850's and 1860's, 100,000 Chinese went to Peru. Much smaller groups of Chinese went to Brazil, Chile, and Venezuela. At the same time, poor economic conditions in the Madeira Islands of Portugal caused approximately ten thousand Madeirans to immigrate to Guyana as indentured servants or subsidized labor, as it was often called.

OTHER EUROPEANS. By 1800 Spanish immigration into most of the Americas had ceased. In 1810, because of French control of Spain under Napoleon, almost all of Spanish America declared its independence. Voluntary emigration of the Spanish into much of South America has been limited since the early 1800's.

Spanish governments typically have restricted emigration by controlling the numbers who leave and requiring the issuance of a permit to emigrate from Spain. Portugal, however, has never attempted to control emigration.

Only Brazil and Argentina have had significant immigration in modern times. Argentina is quite European. Between 1857 and 1872, 221,000 immigrants entered Argentina and about 103,000 stayed in the country. Of that number, 63,825 were Italians (61 percent); 21,416 were Spaniards (20.5 percent); 7,055 were French (6.7 percent); and the rest of northwest European stock such as 2,604 English (2.5 percent). While Brazil has a strong African and even now an Amerindian presence, it also has had significant European immigration. Brazil is somewhat similar to the United States in its ethnic complexity and has a better history of race relations, despite Brazilian enslavement of Africans. Racial classifications in Brazil are not as sharply defined as in other nations. The Portuguese colonists who settled Brazil had a more relaxed attitude toward interracial relationships than other Europeans and often intermarried with Africans and Amerindians.

ARGENTINA: PRESSURE-RELIEF VALVE OF EUROPE. Argentina, in particular, became a haven after World War II for anticommunists of all stripes, including Nazis and Nazi sympathizers. Argentina opened its doors to Italian immigrants on a large scale, with almost half a million arriving in the late 1940's. In opening its doors to immigration from Italy, Argentina became a haven for Ukrainians, Croats, and Yugoslavians living in Italy who were unable or unwilling to be repatriated after World War II. They were anticommunists, and a large percentage were Nazi collaborators.

The United States Department of State also intervened on behalf of some fifteen thousand Yugoslavians who could not return to Josip Tito's Yugoslavia because they had fought under the promonarchist general Dragoljub Mihajlovic or were suspected of collaborating with the Nazis. Argentina was asked by the United States to take in five thousand of them. The British government requested that Argentina absorb a group of Polish soldiers who had fought to liberate Italy under the anticommunist general Wladyslaw Anders. Argen-

tina complied in both cases, thereby bringing into the republic thousands of newcomers, many of them openly anti-Semitic. On October 18, 1948, Argentina signed an agreement with Spain, which was a preferred source of immigration like Italy. The agreement brought 140,000 Spaniards into Argentina during the next five years.

MODERN SOUTH AMERICA. Neither Colombia nor Venezuela had much net immigration in the last half of the twentieth century. Colombia does not encourage immigration. While Venezuela has had great influxes of people due to its petroleum economy, few have stayed. Bolivia has seen little immigration since the early 1800's, other than small groups of Japanese and Okinawan farmers who arrived in the 1950's and 1960's.

Paraguay has seen little immigration— its people are almost entirely mestizo. Around the beginning of the twentieth century, small numbers of displaced eastern European Jews and Christian Syrians and Palestinians fleeing the Ottoman Empire arrived in Chile. There was an unusual official encouragement of German and Swiss colonization in the Lake District of Chile during the second half of the nineteenth century. Ecuador has had immigration from a variety of foreign countries, including Lebanon, China, Korea, Japan, Italy, and Germany. Most modern censuses in Ecuador have not inquired about ethnicity, language, religion, or origin. Thus, the number of individuals in each different group is not precisely known.

Bolivia has had an interesting small-scale influx of Europeans. Between the outer edge of the Amazon and the heart of the Chaco desert is a vast plain with some of the richest soil in the world. In eastern Bolivia, the jungle gives way to agricultural flatlands reminiscent of the American

Midwest. Since the 1950's these plains have been colonized by the poor and religiously persecuted from all over the world. During the 1950's the Old Order Mennonites of German and Russian descent came to Bolivia from neighboring Paraguay in covered wagons. More recently, Mennonites from Canada, Mexico, and Belize have arrived to develop new colonies. The number of Mennonite colonies on the Bolivian frontier has been continually growing, with seven new colonies breaking ground in 1996, bringing the total to more than thirty.

Dana P. McDermott

FOR FURTHER STUDY

Avni, Haim. *Argentina and the Jews: A History of Jewish Immigration.* Tuscaloosa: University of Alabama Press, 1991.

Bialy, Samuel L. *Immigrants in the Lands of Promise: Italians in Buenos Aires and New York City, 1870-1914.* Ithaca, N.Y.: Cornell University Press, 1999.

Conrad, Robert Edgar. *World of Sorrow: The African Slave Trade to Brazil.* Baton Rouge: Louisiana State University Press, 1986.

Dillehay, Thomas D. *The Settlement of the Americas: A New Prehistory.* New York: Basic Books, 2000.

Howard, David A. *Conquistador in Chains: Cabeza de Vaca and the Indians of the Americas.* Tuscaloosa: University of Alabama Press, 1997.

Klein, Herbert S. *African Slavery in Latin America and the Caribbean.* New York: Oxford University Press, 1986.

Lesser, Jeff. *Welcoming the Undesirables: Brazil and the Jewish Question.* Berkeley: University of California Press, 1995.

CENTRAL AMERICA

Central America's first inhabitants were various groups of indigenous peoples later popularly known as Indians. Originally thought to be migrants from the Asian continent, records of them have been found from Mesoamerica, now known as Mexico, to present-day Panama. The isthmus of Central America acted as a bridge for the migrations of peoples from South America and for the movement southward of peoples from North America.

EARLY HISTORY. Central America's most famous precolonial settlements were the Mayan city states. The Maya had developed a complex society, skilled in astronomy and agriculture, and devoted to a complex set of religious practices. They settled in modern Guatemala, Honduras, and El Salvador.

Another powerful Indian society, the Pipiles, came from Mexico to occupy western Central America, chiefly in modern El Salvador. They are believed to have been descendants of the Aztec peoples and spoke Nahuatl, a language common to both societies. Less-advanced Indian cultures existed further south, in modern Nicaragua, Costa Rica, and Panama.

Christopher Columbus, the Italian navigator in the service of the Spanish crown,

Maya ruins
Page 758

731

THE MAYA

The Mayan people inhabited much of Central America from the third to the ninth centuries C.E. Archaeologists believe that during the height of their power, in what is called the Classic Period (around 1,800 to 1,200 years ago), the Maya flourished throughout most of Belize and Guatemala, the northwestern portion of El Salvador, northern Honduras, and much of southern Mexico, including the Yucatán.

The political geography of the Mayan world revolved around city-states, such as Tikal in Guatemala. Their architecture is some of the most impressive of any prehistoric peoples. Mayan culture began to deteriorate around 1,150 years ago, and when the Spanish entered their homeland in the 1500's, the Maya reflected but a shadow of their past glory. Today, over eight million modern Maya inhabit the homeland of their ancestors, and continue to be a dynamic part of the region's human mosaic.

opened up Central America to European exploration at the end of the fifteenth century. Afterward, Hernán Cortés, conqueror of Mexico, sent his lieutenant, Pedro de Alvarado, to invade Central America and claim the lands therein for the king of Spain. Alvarado moved south, defeating any Amerindians who attempted to oppose him, and established claim over much of the isthmus as part of New Spain, as Mexico was called during the sixteenth century.

SPANISH COLONIZATION. As the Spaniards began to colonize Central America, they introduced African slaves from the Caribbean to aid in the development of sugar plantations in Guatemala and Nicaragua. The slaves proved to be a source of effective and dependable labor. The Amerindian population was much less inclined to perform the demanding work in the fields and sugar mills that was involved in producing this cash crop. The Spaniards also brought in Africans to work in the mines in Honduras. Because of the high cost of African slaves, Indian labor was used instead wherever possible.

SLAVE LABOR. In the seventeenth century, the British introduced African slave labor into British Honduras, which later became the independent country of Belize. The British had seized the area from Spain and began the export of hardwoods. Belize remained a British colony, despite claims to the territory by Guatemala, until it achieved independence in 1981. English is still the official language of the country, although its population has begun to become more latinized. Peasants from Guatemala and El Salvador have moved into western Belize to escape political unrest of those two countries. Belize, with a population of approximately one million people, has more open land than any other Central American nation.

"LOS TURCOS" IN CENTRAL AMERICA

During the late eighteenth and early nineteenth centuries, the countries of Central America experienced an influx of Near Eastern peoples, mainly from present-day Lebanon and Syria. Most practiced the Christian faith but came from the Turkish Empire, a Muslim state. Because they carried Turkish passports, they came to be identified as "Los Turcos," or "the Turks." Many immigrated to escape Turkish rule and to be able to practice their religion without interference. Descendants of these immigrants live throughout contemporary Central America. To some degree, they continue to maintain their ethnic heritage, socially and economically.

INDIVIDUAL NATIONS. Guatemala, Central America's largest and most populous country, is also the most ethnically Indian. The capital, Guatemala City, contains the majority of the country's ladinos—the people who adhere to European culture. In the highlands, tribal languages and customs prevail over Spanish. A continuing civil war during the 1980's and 1990's led to a steady, substantial emigration of Indian peasants from their traditional villages north toward Mexico and the United States.

Honduras, Central America's third-largest country, has a population of 5.5 million. Primarily an agricultural area, its major commercial operation is the United Fruit company, a North American enterprise. The country's major crop is bananas for export. Job opportunities on the banana plantations also have attracted a small minority of Caribbean blacks. Substantial vacant land on its western border with El Salvador, as well as an ill-defined border, have caused a heavy immigration from El Salvador to Honduras in the twentieth century

In 1969 an attempt by the Honduran government to expel thousands of Salvadorans led to the so-called Soccer War, which lasted only a few days. The Organization of American States persuaded the smaller country to withdraw its forces from Honduran soil. The Salvadorans dispossessed by the war were precluded from returning, however. Relations between the two countries later were restored and the borderline more carefully drawn.

El Salvador, the smallest of the Central American countries, with only a Pacific coastline, has never had a major influx of

The ethnic mixes of Central America vary from country to country, but Guatemala has the highest proportion of Indians. (Clyde L. Rasmussen)

blacks. During colonial times, the mountains dividing eastern and western Central America, together with the high costs of shipping, discouraged their use in agriculture. Political oppression on the part of the government in the 1930's deterred the retention of Indian cultures; therefore, little evidence of the pre-colonial society exists. During one episode in 1936, government troops massacred thirty thousand Indians, leading the latter to abandon tribal organization.

El Salvador's population exceeded six million people in the late 1990's, although civil wars had driven nearly 20 percent of the population out of the country during the 1980's. The United States received the largest number of these immigrants.

Nicaragua's Mosquito Coast also became the object of Caribbean African colonization. Although the country's population is heavily concentrated in the Pacific Coast and is predominantly Spanish-speaking, the more isolated Atlantic Coast has been influenced by the proximity of the island culture of the Caribbean. The central government in Managua has tradi-

*Bananas
Page 816*

*Migrant
worker
Page 755*

Costa Rican children welcoming an international sporting competition.
(Coco Van Opens/mercurypress.com)

tionally had a difficult time imposing its authority over the eastern shore. Nicaragua's population was 4.25 million in the 1990's.

Costa Rica, with a 1990's population of 3.5 million, is unusual in that the majority of its inhabitants are Caucasian. When Europeans arrived, they found an area sparsely settled by indigenous peoples. Costa Rica is a country of self-sustaining small farms as well as commercial agriculture. There has been an influx of blacks from the Caribbean into the country's eastern port area, around Puerto Limón. They work in Costa Rica's commercial agricultural industry, for the most part. The country produces bananas, coffee, sugarcane, rice, corn, and livestock for export.

Central America's southernmost country, Panama, came into existence in 1903, securing its independence from Colombia with help from the United States. At issue was the soon-to-be-built Panama Canal, a shortcut between the east and west coasts of the North and South American continents. The canal, built and operated by the United States, reverted to Panamanian sovereignty in the year 2000.

Panama's population, Caucasian, mestizo (mixed blood), and Indian at its inception, received a substantial influx of black workers from the Caribbean when construction on the canal began. Panama's modern population reflects that pattern of immigration.

At the end of the twentieth century, Central America represented a kaleidoscope of different races and ethnic backgrounds. Although primarily Latin in social structure, minorities from throughout the world have made these countries their home. In many cases, native Central Americans have returned to their countries of origin after spending years in political or economic exile. They have brought back ideas and practices from the countries that had furnished them with refuge, further broadening the social bases of their respective societies.

Carl Henry Marcoux

FOR FURTHER STUDY

Bean, Frank D., Jurgen Schmandt, and Sidney Weintraub, eds. *Mexican and Central American Population and U.S. Immigration Policy.* Austin, Tex.: Center for Mexican American Studies, 1989.

Capa, Cornell, and J. Mayone Stycos. *Margin of Life: Population and Poverty in the Americas.* New York: Grossman, 1974.

Pebley, Anne R., and Luis Rosero-Bixby, eds. *Demographic Diversity and Change in the Central American Isthmus.* Santa Monica, Calif.: Rand, 1997.

Rodríguez, Mario. *Central America.* Englewood Cliffs, N.J.: Spectrum Books, 1965.

POPULATION DISTRIBUTION

Maps Pages 756, 757

The region of South and Central America is home to approximately 475 million people, about 8 percent of the world's total population. Its total land area is 7.1 million square miles (18.4 million sq. km.), giving the region a population density of about 70 people per square mile. In contrast to the world population density of approximately 105 people per square mile, the region appears to be relatively uncrowded. However, population density figures can be misleading.

There are few places in the world, and none in South and Central America, where populations are spread evenly throughout an entire country. The actual distribution of people within a defined area is much more important than its numerical density. In South and Central America, population distributions are uneven. Some areas support extremely high densities, whereas vast areas have few people.

Many factors influence the distribution of people. The physical environment plays

POPULATION, AREA, AND DENSITY IN SOUTH AND CENTRAL AMERICA

Country	Population	Area		Density	
		Kilometers	Miles	Per sq. km.	Per sq. mi.
Argentina	36,000,000	2,780,000	1,073,000	13	34
Bolivia	8,100,000	1,098,000	424,000	7	19
Brazil	168,000,000	8,547,000	3,300,000	20	51
Chile	15,000,000	756,000	292,000	20	51
Colombia	38,600,000	1,140,000	440,000	34	88
Ecuador	12,400,000	283,000	109,000	44	113
French Guiana	200,000	91,000	35,000	2	5
Guyana	700,000	215,000	83,000	3	8
Paraguay	5,200,000	407,000	157,000	13	33
Peru	26,600,000	1,285,000	496,000	21	54
Suriname	400,000	163,000	63,000	3	7
Uruguay	3,400,000	176,000	68,000	19	49
Venezuela	23,700,000	912,000	352,000	26	67
Belize	200,000	23,000	9,000	11	28
Costa Rica	3,600,000	52,000	20,000	70	182
El Salvador	5,900,000	21,000	8,000	278	721
Guatemala	12,300,000	109,000	42,000	113	293
Honduras	5,900,000	111,000	43,000	53	136
Nicaragua	5,000,000	130,000	50,000	39	100
Panama	2,800,000	75,000	29,000	37	96

Source: Population Reference Bureau, *1999 World Population Data Sheet.*

an important role in population density. In South and Central America, climate, land features, soils, and water strongly influence where people do, or in many cases do not, live. Cultural factors also are involved. For example, populations tend to cluster in places that offer at least the hope of achieving a better quality of life, and to avoid those places where living can be difficult.

CHARACTERISTICS OF POPULATION DISTRIBUTION. Population distribution in South and Central America has three primary characteristics: People are unevenly distributed, with most settlements bordering, or standing close to, coasts. The region is highly urbanized, with nearly three of every four people living in cities. Finally, recent migrations have changed the population density of some areas.

Santiago
Page 885

Perhaps the most obvious feature of the region's settlement is its uneven distribution. Some areas have high population densities, while others support few people. In South America, only Uruguay has nearly all of its territory settled and reached by road or rail. In Central America, the same can be said only for Costa Rica and El Salvador. All other countries in the region have large parts of their territory that remain relatively isolated and thinly populated.

SOUTH AMERICA. The highest population densities in South America generally occur near the edge of the continent. Nearly 90 percent of that continent's people live within 100 miles (160 km.) of the coast. Densities ranging from 125 to more than 250 per square mile occur in several locations. The continent's greatest cluster of population is in southeastern Brazil. Major cities include São Paulo, a huge center of industry, agriculture, trade, commerce, and services; Rio de Janeiro, until the 1960's the capital of Brazil, and still its center of culture and tourism; Santos, the

São Paulo
Page 819

port for São Paulo; and Belo Horizonte, a regional center for agriculture, mining, and industry. A thriving economy and pleasant environment attract people to this area.

South America's second largest cluster of people is in east central Argentina and southern Uruguay. There, the fertile soils and favorable climate of the Argentine Pampas and the rich grazing lands of Uruguay support one of the world's most productive agricultural regions. Buenos Aires (population, eleven million) is one of the continent's major centers of manufacturing and trade.

Secondary centers of high population density in South America occur in central Chile, central Colombia, northern Venezuela, and coastal Brazil. More than half of Chile's population is located in a large valley near its capital and primary economic center, Santiago. A mild Mediterranean climate and fertile soils help make Chile's Central Valley a productive agricultural region. Because it is in the Southern Hemisphere, Chile can grow summer crops for export to North American winter markets. The area's industry and agriculture are served by the coastal port city of Valparaiso.

In the northern Andean area, higher elevations give relief from the hot, humid conditions of the tropical lowlands. In Colombia, an area of high population density is clustered in mountain and river valleys in an area roughly outlined by a triangle linking the capital, Bogotá, and the cities of Medellín and Cali. Historically, agriculture has been the primary source of income in this region.

A final area of high population density occurs in eastern coastal Brazil, from Rio de Janeiro, northward to the cities of Salvador (Bahia), Recife (Pernambuco), and Fortaleza (Ceara). Fertile alluvial (stream-deposited) soils and a humid tropical climate have helped make this a productive agricultural region. Early Portuguese settlers, using African slaves as laborers, developed a plantation economy based on sugarcane. The narrow coastal strip has continued to be a major area for growing sugar and other tropical plantation crops.

Approximately half of South America has a population density of fewer than two persons per square mile. Vast areas are without roads, electricity, communications, or services. Such areas are not attractive to potential settlers. Geographers often refer to such areas as being outside the realm of effective national control. They contribute little to the national economies and, because of their isolation, are difficult to control.

"TOO LANDS." The concept of "too lands" can help to explain the areas of low population density both in South and Central America. Such areas are places that are too high, too low (subject to flooding), too cold, too dry, too isolated, too infertile, or in some other way too difficult to inhabit and develop. The largest such area is the Amazon Basin, which spans nearly half the continent. Many factors explain why the region supports such a low population density. Brazil's Portuguese settlers avoided the interior at first. They were a coastal people and had come to the New World to grow sugarcane on the fertile soils of the narrow, tropical, Atlantic Coastal Plain.

When Brazilians finally turned their attention to the Amazon Basin, they learned that the rain forest ecosystem presented many problems in terms of potential development. The humid tropical conditions were uncomfortable. Dense tropical rain forest was difficult to penetrate and clear. Most tropical soils, they soon learned, were infertile because their nutrients were leached by the region's high rainfall. Much of the area bordering the Amazon River and its many tributaries floods each year. Only recently has the vast Amazon frontier been opened by roads; as roads penetrate the interior, settlement and economic development follow.

To the south, in the continent's midlatitudes, Argentina's Patagonia region is a dry, cold, windswept plateau. Streams running from the Andes to the Atlantic Ocean have carved steep valleys that make north-south travel difficult. Livestock grazing is the primary economic activity of the region. Settlements and transportation routes are few and far between. To the west, in Chile's southern Andes Mountains and Pacific coastal region, elevation, cold, ruggedness, and lack of access make much of the area uninhabitable.

CENTRAL AMERICA. The population of Central America is also distributed unevenly. Only Costa Rica and El Salvador have most of their territory settled. Although there are some exceptions, most of the region's population and larger cities are in the cooler, more comfortable interior uplands. Hot, humid coastal plains are poorly developed, with low population densities and few communities. Exceptions are Panama's Canal Zone, with the coastal port cities of Colón and Panama, and Managua, Nicaragua's capital and largest city, which is on the shores of Lake Managua, near sea level. Elsewhere in Central America, most cities and their surrounding population clusters—such as San José, Costa Rica; Tegucigalpa, Honduras; San Salvador, El Salvador; and the city of Guatemala—are located in the interior uplands of their respective countries.

URBANIZATION. South and Central America stand apart among the world's regions in that they are highly urbanized, yet still are not well developed industrially. Nearly three of every four people in the region live in a town or city. Two of the world's four largest cities, Mexico City and São Paulo, Brazil, both with populations of about sixteen million, are located in Latin America. Buenos Aires, Argentina, and Rio de Janeiro, Brazil, both with populations of ten to eleven million, rank among the world's ten largest urban centers.

Geographers use the term "primate city" in reference to one city that is much larger and more important than other cities in a country. In Latin America, most countries have one urban center that not only is much larger than others, but also serves as the country's economic, political, and cultural center. Exceptions include Belize, with Belize City the population, economic, and cultural center, and Belmopan the capital; Brazil, with population and economic functions, government, and culture served by São Paulo,

Favela
Page 809

Brasília, and Rio de Janeiro, respectively; and Ecuador, which has the Andean city of Quito as its capital and cultural center and the coastal port of Guayaquil as its largest city.

Because industry and commerce are not well developed in much of South and Central America, many urban people live in poverty. The cities in which they live lack a well-developed economy and enough jobs to support such large populations. As a result, huge slums—called *barrios* in Spanish-speaking countries and *favelas* in Brazil—surround nearly all Latin American cities. It is estimated that as many as 50 percent of the people in some cities live in poverty. Despite their size and the hardships that many residents endure, urban populations continue to swell throughout the region.

Favela *neighborhood in Recife, Brazil.* (Clyde L. Rasmussen)

RECENT PATTERNS OF MIGRATION.

When people make a decision to move, two factors come into play: those that push, and those that pull. In South and Central America, as elsewhere in the world, the desire to improve one's economic well-being has been the major factor influencing a decision to move. Much of rural Latin America is poorly developed. Jobs are scarce, living is difficult, and such important things as electricity, clean water, and social services are unreliable or nonexistent. Cities, despite the hardships often faced by first-generation migrants, offer many poor rural peasants at least the future hope of a better living standard. During the twentieth century, millions of people have moved to cities, making rural-to-urban migration the single most important cause of the region's changing distribution of population.

Other patterns of migration have influenced population distribution in both South and Central America. In Brazil, the government has taken deliberate steps to encourage population growth in the isolated and sparsely populated interior. In the 1960's, Brazil's capital was moved from Rio de Janeiro to a new city, Brasília, designed and built 900 miles (1,450 km.) inland. In 1966 the interior Amazon city of Manaus was made a free port in which trade can be conducted without tariffs. A recently built network of roads has made it much easier to reach large areas of the once-isolated Amazon Basin. Many settlers, particularly from the poor and densely populated northeast of Brazil, have followed these routes into the interior. The population boom in the Amazon has caused much concern about its environmental consequences. The Amazon rain forest is being cut and burned at an alarming rate. Scientists fear that many plants and animals native to the region will disappear altogether.

In the central and northern Andean region, from Bolivia northward to Venezuela, many people are moving from the highlands into the eastern wet tropical lowlands. Here, in the once almost impenetrable upper basins of the Orinoco and Amazon Rivers and their tributaries, the lure of land and opportunity has attracted people to the hot, humid, isolated, rain forest region. Only Venezuela, however, has experienced major population growth and urban development in its tropical lowlands. Rich deposits of iron ore and bauxite (the ore from which aluminum is made) near the Orinoco River have helped this once-remote area to grow in importance. In Peru, a terrorist movement centered mainly in the mountains drove perhaps a million people from their Andean homes to the country's capital and primate city, Lima, and to other coastal cities during recent decades.

Most Central American countries have experienced internal migrations resulting primarily from economic influences or, in some instances, civil unrest. For the region as a whole, the major migration of recent decades has been northward to the United States and Canada, in search of jobs and a better life.

FUTURE POPULATION DISTRIBUTION.

A population distribution map of South and Central America shows huge areas of low population density. Some areas of low population can be explained by their harsh natural environment, but environment alone cannot fully explain the region's distribution of people. History and culture both played an important role. Brazil's early European settlers, for example, were a coastal, seafaring, people who came to raise sugarcane. Plantations and later cities flourished on the fertile alluvial coastal plains. There was little desire, or need, to explore, develop, and settle the country's remote interior. The tropical

*Manaus
Pages 681,
754, 883*

rain forest environment presents many difficulties to settlement.

Not all economic and population growth is influenced by climate, soil, and rain forest. Manaus, located nearly 1,000 miles (1,600 km.) up the Amazon River, grew from a small town to a booming city with more than one million people after it was made a free port in 1966. By allowing international trade to be conducted without payment of tariffs, the Brazilian government was able to overcome environmental obstacles and encourage population growth in this remote location.

Elsewhere in Latin America, Spaniards came in search of mineral wealth, particularly gold and silver. Partly because of the region's distribution of precious metals, and partly because of the Spaniards' desire to have easy access to the sea, their settlements rarely occurred more than 100 miles (160 km.) from the coast. The Spanish settlers strongly preferred city living, so once the urban centers were established, they grew at the expense of rural development. Outside the cities, vast outlying areas remained remote and poorly developed.

Many areas of South America are capable of supporting much greater populations than they have today. For much of the region, the problem is not an impossible environment. Much of the continent's empty area has environmental conditions that support large populations elsewhere in the world. To attract settlers to areas of potential development, many things will have to be done.

The areas must be made accessible: Transportation and communication linkages must be built. Utilities and other public services must be provided. New communities must be built, and they must provide the kinds of things that young and old alike have become accustomed to having in the twenty-first century. Of greatest importance, economic growth and development must take place, providing jobs and an acceptable standard of living. If these goals for rural development can be reached, the existing flow of migration from country to city can be reversed. Should this happen, the region's existing cities will become more livable. There will be a more even distribution of population and development throughout the region. Areas that today are of little importance will begin to make valuable contributions to the economies of their nation and the region.

Charles F. Gritzner

FOR FURTHER STUDY

Clawson, David L. *Latin America and the Caribbean: Lands and Peoples.* New York: McGraw Hill, 1999.

Collier, Simon, et al. *The Cambridge Encyclopedia of Latin America and the Caribbean.* Cambridge, England: Cambridge University Press, 1992.

Hudson, John C., ed. *Goode's World Atlas.* 20th ed. Chicago: Rand McNally, 2000.

CULTURE REGIONS

SOUTH AMERICA

The cultural patterns of South America might appear to be simple reflections of Iberia. Portuguese and Spanish are the official languages of almost every nation, Roman Catholicism is the dominant faith, the buildings in most urban areas have a distinctive Mediterranean style, and the landscape is filled with reminders of colonial links with Europe. First impressions can be misleading, however.

The cultural patterns of South America are the result of a complex mixture of many elements derived from several ethnic groups over centuries. In some areas, the mixing has resulted in a blended culture with contributions from various sources. A man playing the *carioca* on the streets of Rio de Janeiro, for example, is predominantly of an African racial background; he speaks Iberian Portuguese; his religion is probably a form of Christianity laced with animist symbolism; his samba music is local, but with foreign melodies and rhythms; and his independent spirit and easygoing style are considered by many to be inherited from indigenous ancestors. However, the *carioca* player will claim to be nothing other than Brazilian.

In other regions of South America, the landscape is occupied by ethnic groups that have not mixed. They coexist side by side, accommodated to each other and the physical environment. A town in the highlands of Ecuador or Peru, for example,

may include an upper class of people who trace a pure-blood ancestry directly back to Europe. The type of work they do, their family relationships, prevalent patterns of courtship, traditions of land ownership, the style of their clothing, and many other features may be similar to those of distant Spanish cousins. In contrast, not far away on the outskirts of town, Amerindians till the soil and live out their lives in ways little different from the ways of their Incan ancestors. Although the present European and indigenous cultures occupy the same geographical region, the traditions remain separate.

CULTURAL REALMS. Four principal ethnic groups have contributed to the cultures of South America: Amerindians, colonial-era Europeans, Africans, and postcolonial immigrants. These groups have intermingled and merged to different degrees throughout the continent, creating a multispectral ethnic tapestry with great diversity. Although conditions can vary significantly over a small area, South America exhibits four broadly generalized cultural realms. The first is the Amerindian/mestizo highlands of Colombia, Ecuador, Peru, and Bolivia. There, the descendants of the Amerindians and Spanish, usually mixed in a racial type referred to as mestizo, are prevalent. Predominantly Amerindian communities occupy rural and highland areas while the cities and coastal regions have a greater proportion of colonial European descendants.

The second cultural realm is a discontinuous set of African/mulatto coastal settlement regions, including Esmeraldas in northern Ecuador; Cartagena, Barranquilla, and Santa Marta in coastal Colombia; north-central Venezuela; Northeast (Nordeste) Brazil; and Bahia and Rio de Janeiro in coastal east central Brazil. In some of these areas, large numbers of slaves were brought from Africa, and many of their cultural traits have persisted. In other areas, especially along the Carib-

An enduring cultural image of South America is that of the swaggering cowboys of the pampas of Argentina and Uruguay—the gauchos. Recognized by their black, broadbrimmed hats, billowing pants, blankets, and bolas, they symbolize the cattle-rearing culture of the region. (AP/Wide World Photos)

bean coast, the prevalence of black racial groups and cultures spread from the islands to mainland northern South America. The racial composition is dominated by Africans from sub-Saharan tribes, often mixed with European blood in a racial type identified as mulatto.

The third cultural realm is focused in the southern nations of the continent: Uruguay, Chile, Argentina, and southeast Brazil. In these areas, the population has been most heavily influenced by the large number of immigrants who arrived well after the colonial period, during the late nineteenth century. Many came from southern Europe to work in the alfalfa fields of Argentina or the coffee plantations of Brazil, providing labor that was no longer available from slavery. Throughout the region, the traits of the new immigrants, mostly Europeans, have interacted with traditions from the older colonial European culture. This interaction has led to new and unique lifestyles. At times, such as when the Peronistas wrestled political power from the conservative groups in Argentina, the interactions have caused conflict and violence.

Finally, a broad interior region, occupied by a diverse mix of Amerindians, mestizos, mulattos, and "zambos" (persons of mixed Amerindian and African blood), includes dispersed peasant farmers scattered across the land. They herd cattle on the savannas or move about the forest practicing subsistence-level shifting cultivation much as earlier Amerindians did; clearing the land, burning the debris, planting and harvesting crops, and moving on when the nutrients of the field were exhausted. These people often present a variety of cultural traits that can be traced to each of the principal ethnic ancestral roots of South American society.

Continued on page 759

Climate Regions Of Central America

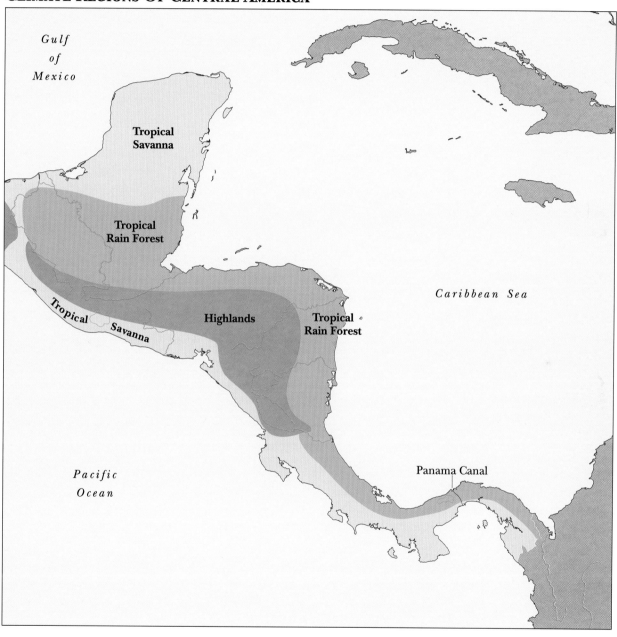

Gulf
of
Mexico

**Tropical
Savanna**

**Tropical
Rain Forest**

*Tropical
Savanna*

Highlands

**Tropical
Rain Forest**

Caribbean Sea

Panama Canal

*Pacific
Ocean*

Selected Resources of South America

North
Atlantic
Ocean

Petroleum
GUYANA
VENEZUELA
SURINAME
Gold
Diamonds
Bauxite
FRENCH GUIANA
Bogotá
★
Aluminum
Platinum
Iron Ore
COLOMBIA
Hardwood
Emeralds
Quito★
ECUADOR
Amazon Basin
Water
**Galápagos
Islands**
Gold
Forests
Uranium
Diamonds
Tin
Zinc
BRAZIL
Tungsten
PERU
Iron Ore
Lead
Atomic Power
Lima★
Gold
Silver
Water
Tungsten
Tin
Diamonds
Brasilia
★
Diamonds
★ La Paz
Iron Ore
Copper M
Uranium
Manganese
Arica●
BOLIVIA
Fisheries
Nitrates
PARAGUAY
O
Copper
Rio de Janeiro
U
Softwood Forests
Asunción
★
CHILE
ARGENTINA
South
Pacific
Ocean
N
Uranium
URUGUAY
T
Santiago★
Copper
Atomic
Buenos Aires★
Montevideo
A
Power
I
Uranium
South
Atlantic
Ocean
N
S

Falkland Islands

744

In mid-2000 the Angra 2 nuclear power plant began operation in the Brazilian rain forest, about one hundred miles from Rio de Janeiro, to help meet the country's growing energy crisis. By 2000 Brazil and Argentina were the only South American nations with nuclear power plants. (AP/Wide World Photos)

In late 1998, Hurricane Mitch destroyed this Honduran banana plantation, while ravaging much of Central America. (AP/Wide World Photos)

Honduran boys clean shrimp boats in Guapinol. Crustacean fishing is an important part of the economies of both Honduras and El Salvador. (AP/Wide World Photos)

SELECTED RESOURCES OF CENTRAL AMERICA

Gulf
of
Mexico

Caribbean Sea

Pacific
Ocean

BELIZE

Silver
Oil   Lead
★
Belmopan

Mercury

GUATEMALA

Geothermal
Power

Guatemala
City ★Hydroelectric
Power

San Salvador ★

EL SALVADOR

Antimony   Gold

Tin   Zinc   **HONDURAS**

Tegucigalpa
★
Manganese   Rio

Sea Salt

Hydroelectric
Power

Limestone

Nickel   Iron Ore

Copper

NICARAGUA

Lake
Managua

Managua
★

Lake
Nicaragua

Lumber

★San
José

COSTA RICA

Oil

Lumber

Fish and
Aquatic
Products

Fish and
Aquatic
Products

Panama
Canal

Colon

Gatún
Lake

PANAMA

Panama City

Lake
Bayano

Rio Cocoosigoria

747

Habitats and Selected Vertebrates of South America

GALÁPAGOS ISLANDS

Marine Iguana

Giant Land Tortoise

Coatimundi

Giant Anteater

Anaconda

Vampire Bat

Boa Constrictor

Sloth

Puma

Toucan

Giant Otter

Peba

Piranha

AMAZON RAIN FOREST

Vicuna

Capybara

Tapir

Jaguar

Peccary

Quetzal

Wooly Tree Porcupine

Ocelot

Llama

Spectacled Bear

Crab-Eating Zorro

EASTERN HIGHLANDS

Coypu Rat

Gray Fox

COASTAL REGION

Andean Condor

Bushmaster

Alpaca

Plains Viscacha

Condor

James Flamingo

GRASSLANDS

Agouti

Chinchilla

Rhea

Guanaco

Armadillo

Maned Wolf

ANDES MOUNTAINS

Great Anteater

COASTAL REGION

Patagonian Weasel

Cavy

Cormorant

Sea Lion

Penguin

North Atlantic Ocean

South Pacific Ocean

South Atlantic Ocean

One of the most beautiful varieties of snakes in the world is the emerald tree boa, which is found in South America's rain forests. (PhotoDisc)

The marine iguanas of the Galápagos Islands are unusual examples of terrestrial animals that have returned to the sea. (Clyde L. Rasmussen)

749

Giant water lilies of the Amazon Basin. (Clyde L. Rasmussen)

Hygrophyte. Water lilies are hygrophytes, plants adapted to living in wet conditions, usually with their roots permanently wet. (Digital Stock)

HABITATS AND SELECTED VERTEBRATES OF CENTRAL AMERICA

Gulf
of
Mexico

Spider Monkey

RAIN FOREST

Macaw

Peccary

Jaguar

Puma

Tapir

Hummingbird

Caribbean Sea

Spider Monkey

Harpy Eagle

HIGHLANDS

White-Tailed
Deer

Warthog

Ocelot

Howler Monkey

Macaw

Sloth

Boa Constrictor

Anaconda

GRASSLANDS

Butterflies

Pacific
Ocean

Toucan

Quetzal

Armadillo

Guatemalan women selling flowers in Chichicastenango. (American Stock Photography)

Among the many brilliantly colored flowers that grow in Central America is the hibiscus. (Digital Stock)

Costa Rica forest. (Clyde L. Rasmussen)

In 1999 well-preserved Inca mummies were discovered atop Mount Llullaillaco in the Argentine Andes. (AP/Wide World Photos)

Open-air market in Manaus, a Brazilian town on the Negro River that was one of the country's biggest and most prosperous cities during its nineteenth century rubber boom. (Clyde L. Rasmussen)

Mayan women participating in an event called the March of Mayan Resistance in Guatemala City in October, 2000. (AP/Wide World Photos)

Both civil conflicts and weather disasters force migration among Central America's nations. This Nicaraguan construction manager picking coffee beans in Costa Rica in late 1998 was forced to leave his own country because of the devastation left by Hurricane Mitch. (AP/Wide World Photos)

Modern female Inca priests make offerings to the sun god in a ceremony at Cuzco, Peru, in mid-2000. (AP/Wide World Photos)

POPULATION DENSITIES OF CENTRAL AMERICAN COUNTRIES
(BASED ON MID-1999 ESTIMATES)

Gulf
of
Mexico

BELIZE

★
Belmopan

GUATEMALA

Quezaltenango
●

Guatemala
★ City

San Salvador ★

EL SALVADOR

HONDURAS

Tegucigalpa
★

NICARAGUA

Lake
Managua

Managua
★

Lake Nicaragua

Pacific
Ocean

● Liberia

Puntarenas
●

★San
José

COSTA RICA

Caribbean Sea

**Panama
Canal**

Colon ●
●

Gatún
Lake

PANAMA

Lake
Bayano

Panama City

	Fewer than 30 persons/sq. mi.		301–500 persons/sq. mi.
	30–100 persons/sq. mi.		More than 500 persons/sq. mi.
	101–300 persons/sq. mi.		

POPULATION DENSITIES OF SOUTH AMERICAN COUNTRIES
(BASED ON MID-1999 ESTIMATES)

North
Atlantic
Ocean

GUYANA

VENEZUELA

SURINAME

FRENCH GUIANA

Bogotá

COLOMBIA

Quito

ECUADOR

Galápagos
Islands

Belem

Amazon Basin

PERU

BRAZIL

Lima

Brasilia

La Paz

Arica

BOLIVIA

PARAGUAY

Rio de Janeiro

South
Pacific
Ocean

Asunción

CHILE

ARGENTINA

URUGUAY

Santiago Mendoza

Buenos Aires Montevideo

South
Atlantic
Ocean

Falkland Islands

Fewer than 10
persons/sq. mi.

10–20
persons/sq. mi.

51–100
persons/sq. mi.

21–50
persons/sq. mi.

More than 100
persons/sq. mi.

Colorful houses are a tradition in Brazil's old colonial port of Salvador. (Clyde L. Rasmussen)

Located in what is now Honduras, Copan was a major Maya center about 1,400 to 1,200 years ago. (AP/Wide World Photos)

AMERINDIANS. When Christopher Columbus arrived in the New World, he found that the region was already occupied by humans. These people were identified as "Indians," because leaders of the expedition were certain that the goal of reaching the Far East (Indies) had been accomplished. Furthermore, the native people exhibited racial features similar to those of Asiatic groups.

Although already present when Columbus reached the New World, the Amerindian peoples were themselves relatively recent arrivals in the Western Hemisphere. The estimated span of humans, or humanlike creatures, on Earth stretches back at least four million years, but the Amerindians of North and South America probably arrived no earlier than twelve to fourteen thousand years ago. Traditional theories regarding the populating of the Americas postulate a migration from northeast Asia into North America across the Bering Strait during a glacial period around 11,500 years ago. This was followed by a slow diffusion into the rest of the northern and southern portions of the continent. Recent evidence from archaeology sites at Monte Verde, Chile, and Pedra Furada, Brazil, indicates that these South American sites are probably older than any so far discovered in North America. Theories regarding the method of penetration and settlement have been revised, and many modern scientists support the idea that people moved from Asia along the seashore or in boats rapidly all the way into South America.

By 1492 numerous cultural groups had emerged in South America, ranging from simple hunting and gathering societies in the extreme south to the sophisticated civilizations of the Incas and Chibchas of the Andes. The bulk of the territory in South America was occupied by simple farming communities, such as the Tupi-Guaraní of Southeast Brazil or the Arawak linguistic communities of central and northern South America. They survived by cultivating their crops using a slash-and-burn technique and supplementing the food supply with protein from hunting or fishing. Many of the Amerindians, mestizos, and mulattos continued the practice throughout the rain forest into the twenty-first century.

At the time of European contact, the most important communities lived in the mountains of the west. In Colombia, the Chibchas dominated the Cundinamarca Basin where Bogotá is presently located. Further south, the Incas controlled the land from southern Colombia to northern Chile. Although it is difficult to estimate, the Incas may have numbered from nine to thirteen million around 1500. They had made remarkable advances in farming technology, crop domestication, irrigation, metallurgy, and social organization, but their military capability was far inferior to that of the Spaniards.

Following their conquest by Spain, the Amerindians of the Andes experienced centuries of subjugation to Spanish rule, great loss of life from the introduction of Old-World diseases such as smallpox and influenza, backbreaking work in the fields and mines under the *encomienda* and *mita* systems, and continued oppression even after the South American nations gained political independence. Nevertheless, the cultural fabric in the rural highlands of South America still reflects Incan traditions. Large numbers of people speak Quechua, the language of the Incas; many in southeast Peru and northwest Bolivia use the even older Aymara tongue. Religion, the style of dress, music, farming methods, and many other cultural traits are dominated by the Amerindian and mestizo traditions of the ancient groups in the Andes.

Amerindian groups have left their mark in other areas. Jesuit missionaries

Incas
Pages 753,
755, 873,
882

759

In response to growing sensitivity to Peru's Indian population, Lima's city council voted to get rid of the city's monumental statue of Francisco Pizarro, the conqueror of the Incas, so people would not be reminded of their ancestors' humiliating defeat. (AP/Wide World Photos)

brought European ways to the Guaraní tribes of the upper courses of the Paraná and Paraguay Rivers in a region known as Misiones. Although frequently raided by Portuguese expeditions and later slaughtered in the Paraguay War of the 1860's, the Guaraní continue to influence Paraguayan society. Their language is still widely spoken in that country. In isolated pockets throughout the interior of the continent, remnants of the many South American tribes can still be found. Some governments have offered modest protection through agencies devoted to preserving indigenous culture, but most of the Amerindians continue to suffer as a result of contact with the outside world. Many die when exposed to diseases against which they have little immunity, and the

people are heavily exploited by local ranchers, miners, and farmers.

COLONIAL EUROPEANS. The second group to leave its mark on South America is perhaps the most obvious: Iberian Europeans. From the initial contact in 1492 until the conclusion of the wars of independence in the 1820's, Spain and Portugal maintained political control over most of the lands of South America. During this period, the Amerindians were forced to adopt European customs, religion, and languages. Africans were imported to work in the fields and also were compelled to take on European ways.

Migration from Iberia to the New World during the early colonial period was composed primarily of men seeking adventure and fortune. In Spain, the armies that had recently defeated the North African Moors were available to launch new conquests for god and king. Estates in Spain were inherited by the eldest son, so siblings born later were left without land. This provided manpower for the conquest of the Americas. Tales of El Dorado, the legendary city of gold, enticed others, as did the hope for recognition and land grants in payment for heroic deeds. Portuguese men also arrived in America, and, more accustomed to contact with foreign races, the Europeans in Brazil readily accepted sexual relations with Amerindian and African women. Racial mixture in Brazil began very early, therefore, so that the Brazilian population is one of the most genetically intermingled groups in the world.

The modern influence of the colonial European culture is most evident in cities and in areas of early and continuous Spanish or Portuguese settlement. For example, the Spanish came to the Cauca Valley of Colombia in significant numbers during the early colonial period. Here they multiplied, maintained a conservative political and religious outlook, and established farms and towns that have become among the most productive in the nation. Throughout the continent, the Spanish and Portuguese mixed with the Amerindians and blacks to form the pervasive mestizo and mulatto groups. In the south, colonial Europeans also have mixed with recent immigrant arrivals.

While some of the legacy influences of the Europeans from the colonial period are obvious, others are not readily evident. Among the more visible are the official languages—Spanish and Portuguese—of almost every country; the prevalent Roman Catholic religion; the street layout of cities (especially in Spanish-speaking countries); the coastal orientation of the transportation systems that were used to ship minerals and farm products to the coast; and a peripheral population pattern by which most large cities are located near the coast, where there was easy access to ships from Europe.

Other effects are real but less obvious. The mercantile economic system created export economies in the New World, and those patterns have persisted. Elements of the Iberian patriarchal society, where men dominated, were transferred and have persisted, although they are disappearing in many areas. Paternalism also helped to produce political traditions of authoritarian leadership, whereby the actions of the president or *caudillo* were not subject to question, just as those of the *hacienda patron* were beyond dispute. The traits of colonial Europeans are probably best preserved among the mestizo and mulatto peasants of highland and backcountry communities. They are part of a traditional way of life that is often resistant to change.

AFRICANS. Blacks were brought to South America as slaves at the beginning of the sixteenth century. The earliest arrivals were household servants of Portuguese aristocrats, but soon shipments were made for purely economic reasons. Slavery was authorized by Spain for the first time in 1518, and the heaviest concentrations served the plantations of the Caribbean region. The largest numbers of blacks in South America, an estimated four million, came to Brazil. This was more than the estimated three million who came to Spanish America (including Central America and Mexico) and was approximately two-fifths of all of the slaves brought to the New World.

Several conditions in Brazil contributed to the heavy influx. The Portuguese became involved in hot-weather plantation agriculture in the northeast, and many African societies were well adjusted

761

to hard farm work. The Amerindians discovered by the Portuguese in eastern Brazil were not adaptable; most of those who did not escape died soon after capture. This was in contrast to the native populations in Spanish South America, where the people were capable of providing the required labor. Finally, by the time of their arrival in Brazil in 1500, the Portuguese had a long history of contact with Africans resulting from the efforts by Prince Henry the Navigator's sailors to discover a passage to the Indies. For decades, ship captains sailed along the coast of Africa, so the cultures of African socities to the south were familiar to the Portuguese.

Slavery persisted in the New World until 1888, when the final emancipation declaration was issued by Dom Pedro II, Emperor of Brazil. By the second half of the nineteenth century, slavery was a dying institution around the world, and it persisted in Brazil longer than elsewhere because of the considerable political power of the landed elite. The use of African slaves in Brazil was concentrated in the coastal northeast and center-east regions, stretching from the states of Piaui to Espirito Santo and Rio de Janeiro. Throughout these areas, the cultural influence of Africans has been great. The Portuguese language is altered into local dialects that include a large number of words from the Angolan and Guinea regions of Africa. Food preferences in places such as Recife and Salvador reflect African cuisine, and the local visual arts express African themes. The samba, frevo, and other forms of traditional Brazilian music have roots in Africa.

Salvador
Page 758

Religion in Brazil also has been affected by African culture. Sects such as Macumba and Candomble incorporate the worship of traditional spirits into traditional Christian beliefs. Much of the activity of these faiths focuses on establishing

contact with spirits that can be made to temporarily take possession of the physical bodies of the ceremony participants.

Outside Brazil, African influences have not been as significant and are restricted to regional pockets of northern South America and a few southern urban enclaves. Poor blacks in Montevideo and Buenos Aires are credited with inventing the tango, Argentina's best-known contribution to music and dance. Around the city of Esmeraldas in northwest Ecuador, blacks of African descent have farmed the forest lands for many years. They comprise the most important racial element in the area. Similarly, the northern coastal regions of Colombia and Venezuela reflect heavy influence of African culture. Although slaves were brought to these areas, much of the impact has been due to the proximity to black-dominated areas of the Caribbean region.

RECENT IMMIGRANTS. The latest contributions to the culture of South America were introduced by several immigrant groups during the late nineteenth and twentieth centuries. The majority were Europeans attracted to agricultural regions of southern Brazil, Uruguay, and Argentina; but Asians and North Americans were also among the arrivals. The largest cluster, including approximately six million Italians, Spanish, Germans, and other Europeans, settled in Argentina, where most became tenant farmers on the rich soils of the Pampas. They raised alfalfa to feed the cattle of the landowners and produced wheat, corn, and flax for their own profit. Following the collapse of meat prices in the 1920's, most moved to Buenos Aires and other large cities, where they gained employment in factories and shops.

The immigrant population had a tremendous impact on Argentina, and at one time three-fourths of the total population was either born overseas or was a first-generation descendent of an immigrant. From the Spanish language, which is spoken with a definite Italian-sounding accent, to clothing styles, Argentine culture reflects the recent European heritage. The architecture of Buenos Aires is reminiscent of stately cities of southern Europe, and the picturesque Boca area near the port preserves the Italian urban landscape.

Though less dominant than in Argentina, European immigrants also had a strong influence in Uruguay, southern Brazil, and Chile. In southeast Brazil, Italians were attracted by work opportunities on the coffee *fazendas*, and as in Argentina, many accumulated wealth that was later invested in factories or other businesses. In extreme south Brazil and in the regions of Chile south of the Bio-bio River, German influence has been strong. Fair-skinned children grow up in cities named for locations in Bavaria, and the modest-size, family-operated farms of these areas contrast with the larger plantations and ranches of São Paulo and Middle Chile.

Other immigrant groups have left their mark in South America. The Guiana region, later occupied by French Guiana and the independent nations of Guyana and Suriname, received additional settlers from the colonial and former colonial powers France, Great Britain, and the Netherlands. In order to support farming activity, the British imported large numbers of laborers from South Asia (referred to as East Indians) into Trinidad (an island off the coast of Venezuela) and British Guiana (later Guyana). In some areas, including Trinidad, South Asians comprise over half of the total population.

Chinese immigrants have been a significant presence in several of the large cities, and Levantine (Palestine, Lebanon, and Syria) groups have established themselves in commercial enterprise. A large number of Japanese colonized several rural areas of interior south Brazil during the early twentieth century, and they have had an important presence in the Amazon region as well.

Mennonites from the United States and Canada were drawn to the forbidding Chaco of Paraguay near the remote city of Filadelfia, and Americans from the U.S. South moved to interior southeast Brazil following the U.S. Civil War. There, near the city that would eventually take on the name of Americana, they established an enclave that had a remarkable influence on local Brazilian society. They introduced new farming technology and contributed toward the establishment of mainline Protestant religions in that country.

The cultural panorama of South America is diverse and reflects inputs from several different sources. In many areas, the races and cultures have mixed and blended to create a way of life that is uniquely South American. In other areas, much of the original culture of the dominant groups has been preserved. As communications technology increases the contacts between South Americans and people from other areas of the world, the cultural mixing will likely accelerate. Especially evident is the modern influence of the United States and other modern Western societies. Terms like "software" and "e-mail" are part of the everyday language, and North American music competes for air time with traditional styles. Regardless, South America will remain an area of great cultural diversity.

Cyrus B. Dawsey

Buenos Aires Page 813

FOR FURTHER STUDY

Blouet, Brian W., and Olwyn M. Blouet. *Latin America and the Caribbean: A Systematic and Regional Survey.* 3d ed. New York: John Wiley & Sons, 1997.

Clawson, David L. *Latin America and the Caribbean: Lands and Peoples.* New York: McGraw-Hill, 1999.

James, Preston, and C. W. Minkle. *Latin America.* 5th ed. New York: John Wiley & Sons, 1986.

Preston, David. *Latin American Development.* Essex, England: Longman, 1996.

CENTRAL AMERICA

Like the rest of Latin America, Central America has a culture that is stratified according to perceived racial background. Although many societies have subdivisions within races, the primary races for the inhabitants of these lands are European, Amerindian, mestizo (mixed European and Amerindian), mulatto (mixed European and African), zambo (mixed African and Amerindian), and African. In general, the more European one appears to be, the higher one's status is. The culture that has developed in these regions is a blending of the diverse traditions of the cultures of origin of these peoples.

The blending of the cultures is evidenced in a number of areas. One obvious area is that of religion. The dominant religion in the region, except in Belize, is Roman Catholicism. However, the Catholicism practiced varies greatly. The role of saints in Catholic theology was adapted by the indigenous populations to include the worship of some of their primary deities; thus, feast days to these gods have crept into the calendars of most Amerindian societies. The church initially allowed the practice, given that the process of conversion was underway. These syncretistic events have now become the core of festal days for most societies. The Mayan practice of offerings to the gods is preserved in the practice of erecting cave shrines to saints, who are given fruit and flowers as offerings. African elements have crept into the Catholicism practiced by the Caribbean descendants of the region.

EUROPEAN CULTURE. Latin America's cities and larger estates are the areas that traditionally have been populated primarily by Europeans and mestizos. Europeans came to those areas to exploit the resources of the region, primarily the volcanic soils of the mountains. Estates were situated on the foothills, river valleys, and along the coasts of these lands. Only in Nicaragua and Panama can more than 10 percent of the population be unambiguously classified as European. However, Europeans generally form the core of the elite in any of these societies, including in Belize, where Europeans comprise less than 1 percent of the population. The perceived homogeneity of Costa Rica, where 96 percent are European or mestizo, although most claim to only be the former, has led to a society in which the majority has enjoyed a more egalitarian existence, because a middle class emerged here long before anywhere else in the region.

MESTIZO AND LADINO CULTURE. This category represents the majority of the population in every country in the region with the exception of Belize; there, it is the largest racial group, at 44 percent. A sizable number of mestizos in Belize are refugees from Guatemala. Mestizos make up 94 percent of the population of El Salvador, 90 percent of Honduras, 70 percent of Panama, 69 percent of Nicaragua, and 56 percent of Guatemala.

The classification "ladino" is found in the cities and larger villages of Guatemala, Honduras, and the southern Mexican state of Chiapas. Ladinos are mestizos who consciously deny their Amerindian heritage. They practice more normative Roman Catholicism and tend to shun traditional medicine and dress. Despite this bias, the Mayan imprint upon these areas and this class is unmistakable.

AMERINDIAN CULTURE. Every Central American country has a significant population of Amerindians. Most live in either the marginal agricultural areas (the better soils having been reserved for European *encomienda* or for mestizos) of the hills or in tropical rain forests. The largest Amerindian ethnic group is the Maya, numbering over six million, distributed in southern Mexico, Guatemala, Belize, Honduras, and El Salvador. Indigenous groups of sizeable numbers inhabit the coasts of Honduras, Nicaragua, and Panama.

The key to the preservation of these cultures has been their ability to maintain a continuous homeland. Many of the governments in the region have attempted to set aside these traditional lands as preserves. The Maya have survived due, in part, to isolation. One group in southern Mexico (the Lacandon, numbering about two hundred) have never been Christianized. In many isolated villages throughout the region, the "day keepers," or priests, still exist, responsible for keeping track of Mayan rituals and other events of the Mayan calendar. Cultural awareness among the Maya has led its leaders to try to resist assimilation to European culture.

The preserves of the tropical rain forest that have been established by govern-

ments for the Maya, Garifuna, Kuna, Embera, and other ethnic groups is a means of preserving the forests themselves. The peoples who inhabit these regions live in symbiosis with the land. To abuse nature is to lose resources for the people. Their lifestyles promote uses for plants that have yet to be employed by Western cultures.

Many of the indigenous people still engage in horticulture or hunting and gathering (although most now hunt with shotguns and rifles) when they not doing menial labor for outsiders who are exploiting the resources of the forests. In any economic scenario, they are not integrated into the overall economy of Central American nations.

MULATTO CULTURE. Mulatto regions are generally found on the Caribbean coasts. This classification results from Caribbean migrations onto the mainland. The mulatto population of Belize comprises 30 percent of the population, while 14 percent of Panama's population is mulatto. Lesser numbers are found in most Central American countries. The similarities of these communities with mulatto regions in South American countries evidences the impact this group has had on their host cultures.

ZAMBO CULTURE. The primary region of zambo culture is in the Atlantic coastal areas of Honduras and Nicaragua. The most prominent group is the Miskits—the offspring of escaped slaves, mostly from Jamaica, and a number of local indigenous peoples, who assimilated other nearby groups. The Amerindian groups that escaped assimilation by moving inland into the forests are known collectively as the Sumu, a group that formed (as did the Miskits) two and a half centuries after the arrival of Europeans.

AFRICAN CULTURE. African culture comes by way of the Caribbean, having undergone a cultural transformation before

Mayas
Pages 754,
758

entering Central America. Most Africans were subsumed into mulatto status. Sizeable populations still remain in Nicaragua and Belize. Africans often endure more prejudice than other cultures, given that lightness of skin color often is a prerequisite for prestige. For example, the Costa Rican port of Limon is nearly 24 percent African (who make up about 1 percent of the population as a whole), the descendants of late nineteenth century railroad workers. By a presidential order put in effect in 1936, Africans are not allowed to leave the region.

Mark Anthony Phelps

FOR FURTHER STUDY

Blouet, Brian W., and Olwyn M. Blouet. *Latin America and the Caribbean: A Systematic and Regional Survey.* 3d ed. New York: John Wiley & Sons, 1997.

Herlihy, Peter. "Panama's Quiet Revolution: Comarca Homelands and Indian Rights." *Cultural Survival Quarterly* 13, no. 3 (1989): 17-24.

Klak, Thomas. "Globalization, Neo-liberalism, and Economic Change in Central America and the Caribbean." In *Latin America 2000: Globalization and Modernity,* edited by Robert Gwynne and Cristobal Kay. London: Edward Arnold, 1999.

Place, Susan, ed. *Tropical Rainforests: Latin American Nature and Society in Transition.* Wilmington, Del.: Scholarly Resources, 1993.

West, Robert, and John Augelli. *Middle America, Its Lands and Peoples.* 3d ed. Englewood Cliffs, N.J.: Prentice-Hall, 1989.

EXPLORATION

Europeans were first drawn to South America during the so-called Age of Exploration, a part of the broader cultural movement known as the Renaissance. Initial contact and exploration stemmed from several often contradictory motives: desire to find a sea route to Asia, greed for native wealth, the Christian mission to convert non-Christians, conquest and colonization for national expansion, curiosity, and a desire for adventure. As Europeans staked their claims, competition for territorial control sparked further exploration and colonization. The early exploration of South America cannot be viewed apart from its attendant activities of conversion, colonization, and exploitation. More recent exploration has been accompanied by economic development and ecological destruction.

PROBING THE EASTERN COAST. On his third voyage for Spain, Christopher Columbus landed on the mainland near the mouth of the Orinoco River, in 1498. He coasted along westward to Margarita Island and returned to Hispaniola. At about the same time, the experienced Portuguese captain and scientist Duarte Pacheco Pereira may have been the first European to sail along Brazil's coast, for he reported a vast continent stretching from 70 degrees north to 28 degrees south latitude. His later accounts of Portuguese exploits are valuable records of his adventures in Africa and India, as well as the western Atlantic.

Between May, 1499, and June, 1500, the Spanish navigator Alonso de Ojeda and Florentine businessman Amerigo Vespucci landed in what would become French Guiana and sailed south to the mouth of the Amazon River, which they described for the first time. They then moved farther south to Cape St. Augustine (about 6 degrees south latitude), then north and west to the Magdalena River. As Spain's chief navigator, Vespucci was responsible for preparing the official maps of newly discovered and surveyed areas.

In January, 1500, Vicente Yanez Pinzon, the Spaniard who had captained Columbus's ship *Niña*, explored around Cape St. Roque and coasted north and westward. He probed the Amazon estuary and sailed up to the Gulf of Paria. Diego de Lepe, also from Spain, at about the same time traveled south from Cape St. Roque to near 10 degrees south latitude. Portuguese captain Pedro Cabral, with a fleet of thirteen caravels, landed and formally

*Map
Page 807*

*Cabral's
ship
Page 809*

THE CARAVEL AND EXPLORATION OF THE NEW WORLD

The caravel is the ship most commonly associated with early Spanish and Portuguese exploration in the New World. A caravel typically measured between 65 and 100 feet (20-30 meters) long and weighed less than 140 tons. It evolved from a two-mast ship with lateen (triangular) sails to one of up to four masts, with a lateen sail on the aftermast only. Square sails added the speed and maneuverability necessary for long voyages. Caravels were light enough to sail up river and sturdy enough to mount over fifteen cannon. However, as transatlantic traffic increased, the caravel was soon replaced with the larger Spanish galleon.

took possession of Brazil for the king of Portugal, following the provisions of the Treaty of Tordesillas of 1494. He was on his way to India on a trading voyage and stayed only ten days, naming the region Tierra de Santa Cruz.

Ortelius's maps Page 808

Amerigo Vespucci sailed again in May, 1501, this time for Portugal, and reached Guanabara Bay (Rio de Janiero), the Rio de la Plata, and somewhat farther south. His published account of this adventure led German mapmaker Martin Waldesee-muller to name the region "America," a name that eventually encompassed both continents. From the Panamanian Isthmus, Rodrigo de Bastidas explored the coast southward to Port Manzanilla (1500-1502). Vicente Pinzon may have sailed down the coast from the Bay of Honduras to the easternmost tip of Brazil in 1508.

LA PLATA REGION. The La Plata River region was first explored by Juan Díaz de Solís of Spain, who was inspired by the reports of Vespucci to seek a passage to the Pacific Ocean. He left Spain in October, 1515, with three ships and about seventy men. He charted the coast from near Rio de Janiero to La Plata, naming the river's mouth the "Sweet Sea" (Mar Dulce). They sailed up the Uruguay River and disembarked, only to be killed and eaten by the native Charrúa Amerindians in 1516. The lone survivor told his tale to Sebastian Cabot, who returned in 1526. Convinced that the area held a wealth of silver, Díaz named the river La Plata, as in "silver-plate."

On his famous circumnavigational voyage (1519-1522), Ferdinand Magellan first reached Brazil near Pernambuco, then sailed into La Plata estuary. This was formally charted by Sebastián del Cano. Convinced that this was no passage to the Pacific Ocean, Magellan wintered at Port St. Julian, proceded through the straits that now bear his name, then up the Pacific

coast to about 40 degrees south latitude. From there he headed westward to Guam and the Philipines, where he was killed by the local people.

In 1525 a group of Sevillian merchants hired the adventurous Sebastian Cabot to lead three ships to establish trading ties with Molucca in the Indian Ocean. Rather than proceed directly, he explored South America's Atlantic coast (1526-1529), in search of the "City of the Caesars." He was drawn by the promise of silver that Díaz de Solís posthumously held out to him. His men probed La Plata, as well as the Paraná and Paraguay Rivers, establishing a small colony on the lower Paraná River that he named Sancti Spíritu. This was abandoned in September, 1529. Upon his return to Spain, he was banished to Africa for his failure to carry out his original mission.

Within a few years, Portuguese developments in Brazil and Spanish successes in Peru persuaded Spanish authorities there was a need for an official presence in the area that would become Argentina. In 1535 the Spanish crown sent Pedro de Mendoza with thirteen ships and two thousand men to establish formal colonies in the region. In La Plata estuary, he founded a settlement that he named Santa Maria de Buen Aire. After less than a year, the colonists were moved to a fort at Asunción; Buenos Aires would be refounded by Juan de Garay in 1580. Mendoza oversaw a number of expeditions inland that finally succeeded in linking with the Spanish presence in Peru.

MOVING INLAND. Early exploration resulted in few European settlements, since few resources of interest to the explorers were found. Even the attempt by Bartolomé de las Casas—famed for his religious work among the people of Mexico—to establish a nonexploitative religious colony at Cumaná failed. Beginning in 1529, greed resulted in a better record of colonial success. Spanish king Charles I (also known as Emperor Charles V) was in debt to the Welser family of bankers in Augsburg, and provided them with a broad concession to explore, colonize, and exploit the region of the Orinoco River and beyond. Their colonists pushed through the *llanos*, up the river, across the Apure and Meta Rivers, and into the Andes, establishing a presence so violent that King Charles revoked their rights between 1546 and 1556.

In New Granada, the earliest permanent settlement was Santa Marta, founded by Rodrigo de Bastidas in 1525. From here and Cartagena, established by Pedro de Heredia in 1533, the Spanish could rule and explorers could move inland. Gonzalo Jiménez de Quesada proceeded up the Magdalena River onto the Bogotá Plateau, where he founded Santa Fé de Bogotá in 1538.

CONQUEST OF PERU AND THE WEST COAST. Spanish exploration and expansion down the west coast from Panama began in the early 1520's under Pascual de Andagoya, who penetrated the northern regions of Biru (Peru) in 1522. Pascual fell ill, but intrigued Francisco Pizarro with tales of the great wealth of the region, something the Europeans had failed to find elsewhere on the continent. Pizarro initially pushed to the San Juan River, and in another trek, as far as the Gulf of Guayaquil and Túmbez. Convinced now of Pascual's claims, he obtained from the Spanish crown titles of captain general and governor and permission to conquer up to six hundred miles south of Panama. In 1531 he set off with 180 men, twenty-seven horses, two cannons, and his two brothers, seizing the Incan ruler Atahualpa in his capital city of Cuzco on November 16, 1532.

After the Incan ruler was executed in 1533, Spanish authority and exploration stretched out from Cuzco through the An-

Cartagena map Page 877

Francisco Pizarro. (Library of Congress)

des. Lima was founded in 1535, and the rich silver mines of Potosí were worked by native slaves for Spain from 1545. Sebastian Belalcazar, one of Pizarro's lieutenants, moved through the Quito region and further north, founding Cali and Papayán (1535-1536). He pushed onto the Bogotá Plateau in 1539, and linked with the followers of Jiménez de Quesada.

In 1539 Pizarro, now governor of Quito, led an expedition across the Andes to the headwaters of the Amazon. From here Francisco de Orellana and his followers worked their way down the Amazon River to the sea. He encountered a great wealth of resources, and fierce female warriors after whom he named the river. He died on his return trip to Spain, and no claims for Spain were made by his men.

Diego de Almagro spearheaded Spanish movement south from Peru into Chile (1535-1537), reaching the Maule River valley. Pedro de Valdivia, with 150 followers, explored the Maule Valley further and established Santiago in 1541. Fierce opposition from the local native peoples halted further expansion until the late 1550's. Between 1557 and 1561, Hurtado de Mendoza reached the Strait of Magellan and moved into the Cuyo region. He founded the town of Mendoza.

EXPLORATION AND THE NATIVE PEOPLES. Early explorers learned from the indigenous people to survive on native foodstuffs that were often strange to them and to travel in native canoes where their larger vessels could not penetrate. Contact with Europeans often resulted in demographic catastrophes, as smallpox, measles, and influenza ran unchecked through the local populations. Peru's population dropped by 90 percent and Brazil's by perhaps 60 percent in the first century of contact. Since exploration usually meant settlement and control by Europeans, road-building and deforestation for agriculture often altered the local landscape.

The establishment of plantation economies in the secured territories of the north required slave labor: native at first and where possible, later augmented by huge numbers of enslaved Africans. Christian missionaries, especially the Jesuits, sought to protect the native peoples from the explorers and created huge settlements for their charges. In Brazil, slave-hunting expeditions called *bandieras* began early in 1628 under Antonio Raposo Tavares from São Paolo. These were controlled by wealthy entrepreneurs and might sweep deep into uncharted jungle. The *bandieras* also preyed on the undefended mission villages, which forced the Jesuits and their followers further into unexplored territory. As many of these peaceful Europeans were men of learning and curiosity, they made excellent observations and valuable discoveries.

OTHER PATTERNS. The coastal region of Guyana, known then as "the wild coast," was generally avoided by explorers, but Dutch settlers began moving up the rivers beginning about 1580. By the seventeenth century, they had large sugar plantations worked by African slaves. The Pacific coast of South America is far more forbidding than the Atlantic coast, and coastal exploration developed only after the wealth of Peru had been discovered.

EXPLORATION FOR SCIENTIFIC DISCOVERY. The earliest attempt to disclose the nature of the South American interior apart from the river valleys resulted in the *Relaciones geográficas* of 1579-1585. In the seventeenth century, Jesuit missionaries were noted for their record keeping as they moved through the mountains and jungles and established villages for converts. They and their followers surveyed and charted the entire Paraná River Basin. In the 1630's, the Portuguese Pedro Teixeira explored the Amazon Basin from Belem to Quito.

Although the Spanish and Portuguese authorities kept a tight control on access to South America in the eighteenth century, two men managed to make important expeditions of discovery and research. In 1743 the French scientist Charles-Marie de la Condamine traveled down the Amazon River, from Quito to its mouth, on rafts for four months. He took copious notes on both the natural plant and animal life, and the native cultures he encountered in the Andes and the Amazon Basin. He made the first serious observations on the uses of rubber by indigenous people. He published his findings both in an official scientific form and in a more popular work entitled *Journal of a Voyage to the Equator Made by Order of the King*.

At the end of the eighteenth century, the Prussian naturalist and explorer Alexander von Humboldt sailed from Marseilles with the French botanist Aimé Bonpland on a self-financed expedition of research and discovery in northern South America. Well prepared to conduct sophisticated research—even by the standards of the Enlightenment—Humboldt had obtained the support of the Spanish prime minister Mariano de Urquijo. Between 1799 and 1804, the pair traveled over some 6,000 miles (9,650 km.) of the roughest mountain and jungle terrain on earth. Beginning in Caracas, they explored and mapped the drainage network of the northern Andes, discovering that the upper reaches of the Orinoco and Amazon systems were connected by the Casiquiare River. After a feverous rest in Cuba they continued into the Andes range, traveling from Bogotá to Trujillo, Peru. Poking into volcanoes and climbing extraordinary peaks, they eventually ended up in Quito at the end of 1802.

The remainder of their time was spent in Central America. Collation and publication of the data they gathered on plant and animal life, geology, climate, and the effects of high-altitude oxygen-deprivation on the travelers occupied Humboldt from his return to Paris in 1804 to 1827. Eventually, thirty well-illustrated volumes presented his immense range of findings to the world.

With independence from Spain and Portugal in the early nineteenth century, new national boundaries between the former colonies needed to be surveyed, and restrictions on access by scientists were loosened. Among foreign visitors of a scientific bent one should include Charles Darwin, who explored the natural world of the various anchorages along the Pacific coast that his ship visited, and Henry W. Bates, the English entomologist. Beginning in 1848, Bates spent eleven years crisscrossing the Amazon Basin collecting various species of insects, eventually accumulating 14,712 specimens, of which nearly 8,000 were newly discovered. He published his findings in London, supporting Darwin's ideas of natural selection.

RECENT TIMES. The Amazon Basin is the largest drainage system in the world and covers about 2.3 million square miles (6 million sq. km.). It continues to draw modern explorers who seek to understand its mysteries and exploit its vast resources. Expeditions are funded by many sources, including regional governmental agencies; international organizations, such as the United Nations Educational, Scientific and Cultural Organization (UNESCO); private foundations, such as the National Geographic Society; and multinational private industries, such as pharmaceutical companies researching new materials for medicines. The great diversity of life forms—both plant and animal—draws scientists from around the world, who seek to understand better the area's ecology and the threats to it.

Since World War II, all the region's nations have sought to increase exploitation of their portions of the Amazon Basin for economic development. Private companies in Brazil and surrounding countries extend human activity ever deeper into the rain forest of the basin. At the same time, indigenous peoples move further west and south to maintain a buffer between them and civilization—the alternative is destruction of their culture.

Mining companies stretch pathways deep into the forest in search of lucrative ores, and governments create networks of roads to integrate towns and villages. Cattle grazing, oil exploration, timber exploitation, the demand for natural rubber from the native trees, and even cultivation of the coca leaf for cocaine production have all served to push back the boundaries of the unknown territories. The building of the Brazilian capital city of Brasilia, beginning in 1956, and the gold rush of the 1980's both were accompanied by an increase in human understanding of the area and by tragic destruction of its natural elements. As in centuries past, exploration today is a complex phenomenon with many motivations and even more consequences.

Joseph P. Byrne

FOR FURTHER STUDY

Campbell, John. *In Darwin's Wake: Revisiting Beagle's Anchorages in South America.* Dobbs Ferry, N.Y.: Sheridan House, 1997.

De Cieza de Leon, Pedro, et al. *The Discovery and Conquest of Peru: Chronicles of the New World Encounter.* Durham: University of North Carolina Press, 1998.

Gonzalez Garcia, Pedro, ed. *Discovering the Americas: The Archive of the Indies.* New York: Vendome Press, 1997.

Goodman, Edward J. *Exploration of South America: An Annotated Bibliography.* New York: Garland Press, 1983.

_____. *The Explorers of South America.* Norman: University of Oklahoma Press, 1992.

Lockhart, James, and Stuart Schwartz. *Early Latin America: A History of Colonial Spanish America and Brazil.* New York: Cambridge University Press, 1983.

Smith, Anthony. *Explorers of the Amazon.* Chicago: University of Chicago Press, 1994.

Varon Gabai, Rafael. *Francisco Pizarro and his Brothers.* Norman: University of Oklahoma Press, 1997.

Whitehead, Neil, ed. *The Discovery of the Large, Rich, and Bewtiful Empyre of Guiana.* Norman: University of Oklahoma Press, 1998.

POLITICAL GEOGRAPHY

SOUTH AMERICA

South America's approximately 330 million people live in twelve independent nations and one French-ruled colony. Brazil dominates the continent in land area, size of its economy, and population. The remaining nations, in descending order of population size, are Colombia, Argentina, Peru, Venezuela, Chile, Ecuador, Bolivia, Paraguay, Uruguay, Guyana, and Suriname. French Guiana, the last European colony on the continent, has the smallest population.

CULTURAL DIVERSITY. South America's great cultural diversity is complex and causes much political injustice and sometimes violence. Throughout the continent's history distinctions in race and culture have determined a person's prestige and access to political power, land, military rank, and business resources.

After founding their first colonies in the sixteenth century, the Spanish and Portuguese soon controlled most of the wealth and had nearly all the political power. Their descendants still consider themselves the ruling elite. Later immigrants, especially European Christians, have been next in status, followed by mestizos, people of mixed white-Amerindian parentage; people of African descent; people of mixed racial heritage; and Amerindians.

REVOLUTIONS. By the mid-eighteenth century there existed a large number of South American-born whites, known as Creoles. European officials and military officers often denied Creoles the same status and political power as European-born whites. This discrimination caused jealousy and led to revolts in which the Creoles allied themselves with mestizos and mulattos in their common hatred of native Europeans.

Spain and Portugal successfully repressed the revolts until the early nineteenth century. Then, led by brilliant Creole military leaders, such as Simon Bolivar and José de San Martín, the Spanish colonies gained independence. By 1825 the political map of the continent was divided into essentially the same countries that exist today, although the borders were somewhat different. Brazil became technically independent of Portugal in 1822 but remained close to the parent country and had its own Portuguese-based monarchy until 1889.

During the new nations' early years, their leaders tried to imitate the democracy of the United States or modified parliamentary systems, like that of Great Britain. In fact Bolivar dreamed of uniting South America under one large federal government, a United States of South America. However, democracy never took a firm hold.

Regional rivalries over land and resources among wealthy Creoles prevented continental union. Led by economic and

El Niño
Page 694

Venezuelan president Rafael Caldera lays a wreath before the statue of Venezuela's national hero, Simon Bolivar, in 1995. (AP/Wide World Photos)

military strongmen, called caudillos, the elites ruled their territories like private clubs; nonwhites had few rights. Revolutions occurred, but until the late twentieth century they usually only replaced one group of elite white rulers with another. Small communities of Amerindians in remote areas were free to follow their tradiional ways of life. Most, however, lived as peasants on large estates or in segregated villages.

INTRA-AMERICAN WARS. South American countries have fought several wars over disputed territory. For example, Paraguay lost the War of the Triple Alliance (1865-1870) to the combined forces of Argentina, Brazil, and Uruguay. The War of the Pacific (1879-1884) pitted Chile, the eventual victor, against Peru and Bolivia. Bolivia and Paraguay fought each other to a bloody draw in the Chaco War (1932-1935), in which each sought to gain control of a valuable oil field that had not been correctly mapped.

A long quarrel between Peru and Ecuador over their eastern border erupted into a brief war in 1941. Ecuador repudiated its border treaty with Peru in 1960. Another war between them broke out in 1981, which Ecuador also lost. In 1995 the two countries skirmished over a small territory, but after a cease-fire was arranged by other countries, the dispute remained unsettled. Tensions between Peru and Ecuador finally subsided in 1998 when El Niño-spawned storms devastated both countries, and their leaders pledged to help each other recover.

Brazil and Argentina, long major commercial rivals, have sometimes issued warnings to each other over international trade policies. In 1997, when they quarreled over the export price of sugar, political tensions between them rose. However, a 1996 military pact between them almost guaranteed there would be no battles. Moreover, negotiations in 1994 and 1998 for a trade treaty covering the entire Western Hemisphere, the Free Trade area of the Americas, reduced the chance of military conflict because of trade disagreements throughout the region, even though the treaty was not scheduled to take effect until 2005. Also, membership in the Organization of American States (OAS) and in regional trading pacts has encouraged member countries to negotiate their disagreements rather than go to war.

REBELS AND INSURGENT STATES. Until the mid-twentieth century, it was nearly impossible, or difficult, for outsiders to win their way into the ruling elites who controlled the economies and politics of South American countries. Indians, African Americans, and poor people of all ethnic groups had especially hard times. They were the disenfranchised peoples with no meaningful roles in political decision-making. One way for the disenfranchised to gain some control over their own destinies was to rebel against established governments.

South America has a long history of rebellions, most of them unsuccessful. It has been typical for left-wing intellectuals to gain support of the disenfranchised by promising them more social services and greater participation in government. Leftists formed guerrilla armies, manned largely by the poor, and battled the right-wing elements in the government. The latter have usually controlled the national armies and wanted to keep the traditional power structure. When leftist guerrillas have won and taken over governments, right-wing forces have often formed guerrilla groups of their own, starting new cycles of rebellion.

Between 1956 and 1998 twenty-eight major revolutionary organizations conspired to overthrow one or more of the South American governments. Nearly all these organizations were left-wing and wanted to create socialist or communist states. Most relied upon support from the underprivileged and disenfranchised. During the 1990's, almost all South American guerrilla activity occurred in Venezuela, Colombia, Bolivia, and Peru.

SOCIAL UNREST AND ETHNIC CONFLICT. According to sociologists, social conflict is nearly inevitable in a class-divided society. Moreover, when a society's largest class is impoverished, as is the case

throughout South America, the chances for conflict are still greater. Even in prosperous times, such as the 1990's, the income of more than half of South Americans remains below the poverty line. Many South Americans are desperately poor, and 130 million were homeless or lived in unfit housing during the 1990's.

Large numbers of rural poor have migrated to South American cities in hopes of finding jobs. Rings of slums have grown up around industrial cities, especially Lima in Peru and São Paulo and Rio de Janeiro in Brazil. Because of high unemployment rates and low incomes among the working poor, poor South Americans often turn to crime, such as theft and drug dealing, to support themselves. Police forces in major South America cities are hard pressed to control it. As a result police have grown repressive, even murderous, in some countries.

Rio slums Page 809

MILITARY COUPS. South American nations have had hundreds of coups in their history, many by right-wing leaders and some by left-wing leaders. Paraguay, an especially unstable country, has had more than 250 coups, but not a single peaceful and constitutional change of government in its entire history. Between 1950 and 1990 coups put military officers in power at least once in almost every South American country.

At issue in most coups has been the question of how to develop national economies and who should control them: whether to have free-market systems, as in the United States and Western Europe, or to have centralized economic control under a socialist or communist system. During the period of military dictatorships, juntas suppressed political opponents, often arresting and jailing them without trial.

Coups have been most likely to occur in countries whose economies are small, crippled by inflation, or threatened by strikes. South American countries all suffered high rates of inflation during the 1980's, but most brought the problem under control during the 1990's and raised the standard of living. Political analysts thereby expected there would be less chance of successful coups after 1990. Nevertheless, a large portion of South American society stayed poor, and if economies should worsen and social and political turmoil should occur, military coups remain possible.

Defeated South American political parties routinely claim that the elections they have lost are dishonest and refuse to accept their outcomes. Such was the case in Venezuela, Colombia, Guyana, Suriname, and Paraguay during the 1990's. Another source of potential political conflict comes from unions and political action organizations. Despite the material prosperity of many countries, and Chile in particular, during the 1990's, industrial workers and some professionals believed they did not receive the wage increases due to them.

According to political analysts, democracy based upon free elections is unsteady throughout South America. The key to its survival lies in continued economic growth and a rising standard of living for all citizens. Political leaders hope that the Free Trade area of the Americas treaty will solve economic problems, but many South Americans resent the influence of the United States and fear being dominated. There is significant opposition to the treaty. Unless national leaders can allay the citizen's concerns, the treaty could become another source of political strife.

ENVIRONMENTAL CONFLICT. The governments with territory in the Amazon Basin were under great international pressure to end destruction of the rain forest during the 1980's and 1990's. Brazil, Peru, and Ecuador had difficulty in complying: Each had based much of its economic grown on exploitation of Amazon resources, such as gold, oil, and timber; and each had encouraged colonists, who cut down the forests to clear farmland. The governments' attempts to satisfy the international criticism were denounced as insufficient by environmental groups in the United States and Europe.

Attempts to restrict field burning, logging, and hunting were either ignored or met with harsh opposition by Amazon residents. For example, as much as 80 percent of the logging in the Brazilian Amazon violates laws, according the government. Fur-

Residents of French Guiana—South America's only remaining European colony—gather in Cayenne in late 2000 to demand greater political autonomy. (AP/Wide World Photos)

thermore, South American citizens and foreigners have invaded Amerindian territories to capture rare animals and harvest plants with medicinal properties. If Amerindians fail in trying to enlist government support to keep out these "eco-pirates," the indigenous peoples may resort to violence.

Roger Smith

FOR FURTHER STUDY

Blouet, Brian W., and Olwyn M. Blouet. *Latin America and the Caribbean: A Systematic and Regional Survey.* 3d ed. New York: John Wiley & Sons, 1997.

Box, Ben. *South American Handbook.* Bath, England: Footprint Handbooks, 1999.

Clawson, David L. *Latin America and the Caribbean: Lands and Peoples.* New York: McGraw-Hill, 1999.

Guillermoprieto, Alma. *The Heart That Bleeds: Latin America Now.* New York: Alfred A. Knopf, 1994.

South America, Central America, and the Caribbean. London: Europa Publications, 1999.

Wickham-Crowley, Timothy P. *Guerrillas and Revolutions in Latin America: A Comparative Study of Insurgents and Regimes Since 1956.* Princeton, N.J.: Princeton University Press, 1992.

Williamson, Edwin. *The Penguin History of Latin America.* New York: Penguin Books, 1992.

CENTRAL AMERICA

Most violent conflicts in Central America have resulted from economic issues. These include a long history of unequal land ownership and use, unfair exploitation of workers, and abuses of political power. Political power has derived from combinations of land ownership and control over its use and its workers. The powerful presence of aggressive, profit-seeking foreign companies has also contributed to aggravating local economic problems. Fears of countries such as the United States about the spread of communism caused those nations to support unpopular governments. Opposing groups within Central America have fought civil wars over land reform and resource control, civil rights violations, and political control.

Since the European Conquest began five centuries ago, Central America has never been totally isolated from foreign influence. However, its tropical jungles and mountains make travel difficult or impossible in many areas.

MODERN CULTURES. Central America's peoples are descended from numerous Amerindian groups, as well as people of European, Afro-Caribbean, and Asian roots. A majority of the people in most of the region's countries are mestizos—persons of mixed ancestry. The populations of southern Mexico, Guatemala, and Honduras are heavily Amerindian. Costa Rica's population, by contrast, is mostly European by descent, with many Afro-Caribbeans and Asians living on the country's east coast. Belize, a former British colony, has large numbers of people of British descent.

Many Central Americans deny that discrimination is ethnic or racial. They say that it is economic: the few rich discriminate against the many poor. However, due to historical oppression, disproportionate numbers of poor are of either Amerindian or Afro-Caribbean descent.

ECONOMIC CONFLICTS. Economic problems based on land ownership and use have been a root cause of violent conflicts in Central America since the sixteenth century. Immediately before the Spanish arrived members of many Central Americans societies shared their land and lived simple rural lives. To encourage aggressive exploration and colonization, the Spanish crown granted explorers both huge tracts of land and the right to use forced Indian labor.

Most Amerindians eventually converted to Roman Catholicism, while often retaining elements of their ancestral religious beliefs. Though European and Indian religious traditions blended over the centuries, the socioeconomic practices and the legal system did not foster mixture of the peoples. Central Americans of European descent were clearly favored. Though the Spanish explorers never found as much gold in Central America as they had hoped to discover, the Spanish prospered. They became landowners of huge estates worked by forced Indian labor (and later imported African labor). In general, Central Americans of European descent became wealthy, while those of Amerindian descent remained poor. Racial distinctions were officially fostered by the colonial government.

INDEPENDENCE. The process of winning independence in Central America began in the early nineteenth century and ended when British Honduras gained its complete independence, as Belize, from Great Britain in 1981. The other Central American countries won their independence from Spain more than a century earlier, when virtually all of Latin America rebelled against colonial rule.

Immediately after winning their independence from Spain in 1823-1824, the nations now known as Guatemala, El Salvador, Honduras, Nicaragua, and Costa Rica rejected Mexican rule and attempted to form a union of their own, with a constitution similar to that of the United States. Due to violent uprisings, it failed. Each of the countries then became independent on its own. Since the early nineteenth century, each of them has typically been ruled by a series of dictators.

ECONOMIC ISSUES. Resentment about foreign exploitation of Central American resources and people has led to much violence, both in protest of the exploitation and in attempts to maintain control. Central America's rich land—which is especially good for plantation agriculture—began attracting foreign companies soon after the countries became independent.

Foreign-owned businesses have played an important role in influencing both Central America's governments and U.S. policy toward these countries. In return for monetary gain and political support from the foreign companies and the U.S. government, many local dictators have granted favors to the companies and the United States. The dependence of Central American countries on foreign companies contributed to their being sarcastically dubbed "banana republics."

ECOLOGICAL ISSUES. Ecological destruction threatens much of Central America. A major problem is deforestation, which has caused the land to lose its nutrients and produce fewer crops. Deforestation has been a byproduct of excessive logging—mostly by foreign companies—and the indigenous system of slash-and-burn agriculture, which Central American farmers have long used to clear and fertilize crop land. Honduras and El Salvador face the additional problem of rapidly growing populations and a consequent need for more farm land.

Debra D. Andrist

FOR FURTHER STUDY

Bethell, Leslie, ed. *Central America Since Independence.* New York: Cambridge University Press, 1991.

Blouet, Brian W., and Olwyn M. Blouet. *Latin America and the Caribbean: A Systematic and Regional Survey.* 3d ed. New York: John Wiley & Sons, 1997.

Clawson, David L. *Latin America and the Caribbean: Lands and Peoples.* New York: McGraw-Hill, 1999.

Levinson, David, ed. *Middle America and the Caribbean.* New Haven, Conn.: Yale University Press, 1995.

South America, Central America, and the Caribbean. London: Europa Publications, 1999.

URBANIZATION

SOUTH AMERICA

*Map
Page 811*

*Rio de
Janeiro
Pages 680,
810*

*Incas
Pages 753,
755, 873*

In South America, 270 million people live in cities—a number almost equal to the entire population of the United States. Since World War II, the populations of South American cities have grown rapidly as people have left rural areas to move to cities. By the year 2000, thirty cities, most on or near seacoasts, had more than one million residents each. São Paulo, the largest, has about twenty million people—roughly the size of metropolitan New York. Rio de Janeiro and Buenos Aires are about the same size as Los Angeles (ten million) while Lima, Bogotá, and Santiago are about the same size as Chicago (five million).

The gap between the few rich and the many poor is visible throughout South American cities. There are modern skyscrapers and dismal shantytowns. Outside fashionable restaurants and shops, ragged children sell gum and cigarettes. In the 1980's, the gap between the rich and the poor widened. After several decades of growth, the economies of most South American countries collapsed. Incomes fell sharply and poverty became more widespread. Cities also began to crumble, unable to cope with the pressures caused by rapid population growth and massive poverty.

PRE-COLUMBIAN URBANIZATION. Before Christopher Columbus opened the Americas to the Old World, most of South America was sparsely populated. Only two areas supported larger populations: the dry valleys of coastal Peru, where there were rivers for irrigation; and the high valleys of the Andes, where there was good farmland. The first urban settlements emerged in these two areas more than two thousand years ago.

By the fifteenth century, the high valleys of the Andes were part of the Incan Empire. The largest empire in the Americas, it stretched 2,500 miles (4,000 km.) from southern Colombia down to central Chile. The Incas built a network of cities that served as centers of trade, religion, and government. Spain conquered the Incas in the sixteenth century. In the process, the Spanish destroyed Incan cities, reducing the buildings and monuments to rubble. Afterward, Spain built new cities on top of the old, often using stones from previous buildings.

COLONIAL HERITAGE. The number of cities in South America grew rapidly during the colonial period. Spain controlled most of the native population from their new cities in the Andes. However, Spain needed many more cities to establish trade. The Spanish, and later the Portuguese, added three main types of cities: mining towns to extract gold and other minerals, ports to send and receive goods, and forts to protect their settlements from pirates and from hostile Amerindian groups.

780

THE CITY IN THE CLOUDS

Around 1460, the Incas built a city high on a mountaintop 320 miles (500 km.) southeast of what is now Lima, Peru. They called the city Machu Picchu. Most of the city's two hundred buildings were constructed of huge granite stones. The Incas did not use wheels or draft animals, yet somehow they moved these heavy stones up steep slopes from quarries several miles away.

The mystery of Machu Picchu may remain unsolved forever. Around 1530, smallpox killed half of the city's residents. The rest fled. The city remained abandoned and mostly forgotten until Hiram Bingham, a Yale professor and explorer, rediscovered it in 1911.

(Clyde L. Rasmussen)

The Spanish Laws of the Indies dictated the layout of colonial cities. These laws required a central plaza surrounded by a regular grid of east-west and north-south streets. Regulations controlled the location of most activities, including slaughterhouses. Near the central plaza were churches, government buildings, office buildings, and stores. The homes of the rich were also near the city center, where the rich could easily enjoy the pleasures of urban life. The poorest people lived on the outskirts of town.

Portuguese colonial cities were different. Some had town squares, but they lacked a rectangular street pattern. Early Brazilian cities looked like medieval European cities, with outer walls surrounding cramped buildings overlooking narrow, winding roads.

By the end of the colonial period, population distribution changed in two important ways. The first change was dramatic. The center of population shifted from the high valleys of the Andes to cities on or near the coasts. The largest cities ringed the northern two-thirds of the continent from Santiago, Chile, to Buenos Aires, Argentina. The second change was more gradual. As Europeans seized control, native people lost their land. Without land, they needed work. They could work as peasants for European landlords or they could find work in a city. So began a trickle of rural-to-urban migration that would turn into a flood three centuries later.

INDEPENDENCE AND URBANIZATION.
The number of cities increased sharply after countries in South America achieved independence from the colonial powers. Immigration, the railroads, and changes in exports spurred city building. Between 1880 and 1930, thousands of people migrated to southern South America. They came from southern and eastern Europe, Germany, and Switzerland. Most of these immigrants moved to cities, where they started small businesses and worked as craftsmen and builders.

Immigrants also helped build the railroads. Railroad lines radiated out from port cities toward the interior. Waves of people followed the railroads, establishing new towns and cities along the way. The railroads opened up the interior, making more land available for farming. At the same time, advances in agricultural technology improved yields. Exports of agricultural goods rapidly expanded. Cities like Argentina's Buenos Aires and Uruguay's Montevideo became important agricultural ports. In the interior, new cities were established as service centers for farm communities.

By the late nineteenth century, coal, petroleum, and rubber became major South American exports, prompting new city-building. Maracaibo, Venezuela, was an oil town and Manaus, Brazil, handled rubber. Industrial towns also grew. São Paulo, for instance, became the most important industrial center of Brazil and the largest city of South America.

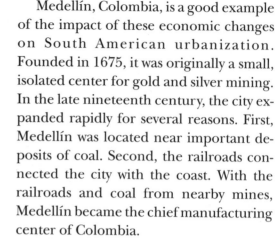

Medellín, Colombia, is a good example of the impact of these economic changes on South American urbanization. Founded in 1675, it was originally a small, isolated center for gold and silver mining. In the late nineteenth century, the city expanded rapidly for several reasons. First, Medellín was located near important deposits of coal. Second, the railroads connected the city with the coast. With the railroads and coal from nearby mines, Medellín became the chief manufacturing center of Colombia.

RURAL-TO-URBAN MIGRATION.
Three out of four South Americans live in cities, and every year the proportion increases as millions of people leave the countryside and move to cities. This is the largest rural-to-urban migration flow in the world. People leave rural areas because there are few jobs there. On modern farms, machines do much of the work that people used to do. At the same time, rural populations continue to grow. The result is too many people competing for too few jobs. Looking for work, young people move to cities where they hope to find jobs.

In the decades after World War II, cities absorbed the new migrants fairly well. Since the recession of the 1980's, however, cities have not been able to provide regular jobs or affordable housing for the flood of new arrivals.

PRIMATE CITIES.
In most South American countries, one city is much bigger and more important than the rest. These are called primate cities. Usually, they are several times bigger than the second-largest city. For example, Lima, Buenos Aires, and Santiago are more than ten times as big as the next-largest cities of Peru, Argentina, and Chile, respectively. In Uruguay, more than half the population lives in Montevideo. Brazil and Ecuador have dual primacy, because their two largest cities are much bigger and more important than

Manaus Pages 681, 754

the third. Only Bolivia, Colombia, and Venezuela do not have primate cities.

The Spanish and Portuguese set the stage for primate cities. The colonies were easier to control from a single large capital, which was often a port. As capitals, they were politically powerful; as ports, they were economically powerful. Their status did not change after independence. The largest cities were favored by government policies and attracted the lion's share of public and private investment.

Primate cities are a sign of uneven economic development. With investment concentrated in one or two cities, other regions of the country fall behind economically. This is a major cause of rural-to-urban migration. A stubborn cycle emerges. Immigrants move to the cities with the best job opportunities. New immigrants require services, which require more businesses, which require more jobs, which require more immigrants. Coping with rapidly increasing urban populations becomes almost impossible.

In the 1960's, Brazil and Venezuela tried to break this stubborn cycle by building new cities in poor regions of the Amazon. Brazil moved its capital to Brasília, and Venezuela built steel and aluminum factories in Ciudad Guyana. Although far from other major cities, both cities grew rapidly. Similar plans in other countries were abandoned during the economic recession of the 1980's.

URBAN STRUCTURE. In contrast to most cities in the United States, the heart of every South American city is the downtown area. There, sedate central plazas have evolved into lively central business districts (CBDs) with modern skyscrapers. People work and play in the CBD. There are commercial offices, department stores, government buildings, fine restaurants, movie theaters, and dance clubs. CBDs do not shut down at six o'clock when businesses close for the day. Activity stretches long into the night as young and old converge on the city center.

A commercial spine extends from the CBD to the outer edge of the city. The spine has gracious, tree-lined boulevards, expensive office buildings, fine shops, and large parks with museums, theaters, golf courses, and zoos. Wealthy neighborhoods lie on both sides of the spine, forming a wedge-shaped residential area that becomes wider farther away from the CBD. The most expensive houses lie farthest from the city center, where lots are large and houses have all the modern conveniences. The city makes sure these neighborhoods have modern plumbing and sewer systems, paved roads, and electric and telephone lines.

Outside the elite wedge, residential areas form concentric rings around the CBD. More than 95 percent of the urban population live in one of these concentric rings. Better neighborhoods lie closest to the CBD. Neighborhood quality gets worse with increasing distance from the

---

BRASÍLIA: A PLANNED CAPITAL CITY

Since gaining independence from Portugal in 1822, Brazilians had wanted to build a new capital in the Amazon. The government finally chose a modern design by Lucio Costa, and construction was begun in 1956. The city was supposed to look and work like a machine. Unlike other Brazilian cities, which have winding, narrow roads, Brasília has wide boulevards and large open spaces. Older cities have mixed land use, with offices, stores, and homes all in the same block; Brasília has a separate zone for each. Critics complain that Brasília is cold and charmless and that the city has not aged well. In spite of these criticisms, Brasília has been a success. Originally planned for a half million people, its population was four times that size by the end of the twentieth century.

CBD. Most cities also have a *periferico,* a ring road similar to the beltways found in the United States. Squatter settlements and large industrial parks generally lie outside the *perifericos.*

SHANTYTOWNS. Squatter settlements ring most Third World cities. The cities of South America are no exception. Shantytowns are called *callampas* in Chile, *barriadas* in Peru, *favelas* in Brazil, and *villas miserias* ("miserable towns") in Argentina. New shantytowns are like refugee camps. Residents clear vegetation for building material and fuel, leaving bare soil. In the dry season, dust coats everything; in the rainy season, unpaved roads are mired in mud. The houses, no more than rickety

Rio favela
Page 809

shacks, do not have access to fresh water, electricity, trash collection, or sewers. Shantytowns have reputations as dangerous places where even the police have no authority.

Shantytowns do not remain like refugee camps. Residents slowly build their own homes on land they rent, buy, or simply take over. At first, houses may be just one room made of cardboard, plastic, or tree branches. Later, as owners save more money, they add rooms or rebuild with brick and concrete. Residents help their friends and neighbors. They start community associations. They demand fresh water, sewers, schools, and health clinics. Eventually, the refugee camps become established neighborhoods.

Rosinha, a *favela* of Rio de Janeiro, is the largest shantytown in South America. More than one hundred years ago, squatters claimed an unwanted mountainside with a beautiful view of the Pacific. Rosinha has 250,000 people, three schools, and two health clinics. Houses in the older sections are made of brick and most have water, sewers, and electricity.

Rosinha is no middle-class neighborhood, however. There is no street garbage collection because city garbage trucks cannot squeeze through the narrow streets. On the upper edge of the *favela,* newer houses have no city services. Trash and garbage accumulate. Sewage runs through the narrow alleys and then down the mountainside. Flies, mosquitoes, and rats flourish in the filth.

URBAN PROBLEMS. Unemployment, homelessness, crime, and pollution are problems in all cities. In South American cities, where poverty and overcrowding worsen every year, these problems are widespread.

Unemployment is one of the biggest problems of South American cities. One-half of the workforce cannot find regular

Caracas shantytown. (Clyde L. Rasmussen)

Lima street vendors. (Clyde L. Rasmussen)

jobs. Poor families often survive by putting everyone, including very young children, to work on the streets. The poor eke out a living shining shoes or picking through garbage for items to sell or recycle. They also work as street vendors, beggars, and prostitutes.

In South American cities, a small but growing number of people are homeless. Many of the homeless are young children. According to the United Nations, there are seven million abandoned and homeless children in Brazil alone. These children lack proper food, health care, and education. Many are prostitutes, drug abusers, and victims of sexual assault. Street children have high rates of HIV/AIDs and other sexually transmitted diseases. Street children are also targets of paramilitary groups. Responding to pressure from businessmen who claimed the children drove away business, groups of soldiers and police murdered several

thousand street children in Colombia and Brazil in the 1990's.

Rising poverty contributes to rising crime. Murder is the number one cause of death among poor men between fifteen and thirty-nine. Many crimes are linked to illegal drugs: People steal to get money to buy drugs; drug dealers fight over territory and business deals. Like the worst inner-city neighborhoods in the United States, in some shantytowns gunshots ring out in the night and children are afraid to go to school.

Rapid population growth means more pollution. Cars and factories pollute the air. Cities dump untreated sewage directly into rivers, canals, and bays. Throughout South American cities, trees and buildings are damaged by acid rain, and respiratory diseases are increasing. While a few countries have passed laws to reduce pollution levels, others countries believe pollution is a necessary part of modernization.

PROSPECTS FOR THE FUTURE. Rapid population growth and increasing poverty contribute to most of the problems of South American cities. Unfortunately, cities cannot effectively eliminate either one. Cities cannot build fences to keep out poor people, nor can they narrow the gap between rich and poor. Improving conditions in South American cities requires healthy national economies and policies aimed at reducing poverty.

National governments must be able to invest in basic infrastructure—schools, hospitals, roads, sanitation measures, and modern telecommunications systems. This is particularly true in rural areas, because the only way to slow rural-to-urban migration is to make rural areas better places to live. The poor need education, health care, and jobs that pay a decent wage. Governments must abandon policies that benefit only the powerful and turn instead to policies that help alleviate poverty.

The general trend for the economies of South America during the 1990's was up,

but there were great fluctuations from year to year and from region to region. In spite of the general upward trend, the gap between rich and poor widened. Based on these two indicators, the future of many South American cities seemed bleak by the year 2000.

Virginia Thompson

FOR FURTHER STUDY

Holtwijk, Ineka. *Asphalt Angels.* Asheville, N.C.: Front Street Press, 1999.

Kent, Deborah. *Buenos Aires.* Chicago: Children's Press, 1998.

_____. *Rio de Janeiro.* Chicago: Children's Press, 1996.

King, David C. *Peru: Lost Cities, Found Hopes.* New York: Benchmark Books, 1997.

Lispector, Clarice. *The Hour of the Star.* New York: New Directions, 1992.

Ness, Immanuel. *Encyclopedia of World Cities.* Chicago: Fitzroy Dearborn, 1999.

Pearce, Fred. "A Shanty Town That's Here to Stay." *New Scientist* 135, no. 1837 (September 5, 1992): 22-25.

*Map
Page 812*

CENTRAL AMERICA

In many rural parts of Central America, living conditions are poor. Therefore, thousands of Central Americans each year migrate to cities in search of better jobs, housing, and education. Since the early 1970's, the region has been a leader in this phenomenon, known as rural-to-urban migration. Rural-to-urban migration is influenced by both push and pull factors. Push factors that persuade Central Americans to leave rural areas include loss of ag-

ricultural jobs and educational facilities, as well as rising poverty. Migrants are attracted to urban areas through pull factors such as new opportunities in industry and education.

Central America's neighbors to the north and south have experienced rapid increases in the number of people living in cities, particularly in the capitals. Mexico's urban population, for example, grew from 66 percent in 1980 to 74 percent in 1998.

Brazil, in South America, experienced an increase in its urban population from 66 to 76 percent between 1980 and 1998. South America boasts some of the highest urban populations in the world. The percentage of people living in cities is extremely large in countries such as Venezuela, Argentina, and Uruguay, whose urban populations are 86-90 percent.

DEGREE OF URBANIZATION. In contrast to these other countries, the percentage of people living in Central America's cities is relatively low. The most urbanized country in Central America is Nicaragua, whose urban population grew from 53 percent in 1980 to 63 percent in 1998. The urban populations of Belize, El Salvador, and Panama barely exceed 50 percent. In the three remaining countries of Central America—Costa Rica, Guatemala, and Honduras—less than half the population lives in cities.

The majority of Central America's people are Native Americans, or Amerindians, who make their living off the land. They may be involved in seasonal work as laborers on large plantations or farms, or they may cultivate their own food and crops as sharecroppers—people who work the land for a share of the crop—or on land that they own or rent. Despite the large number of people living in rural villages, many do not have access to enough cultivable land. This is because the upper classes that make up a small percentage of the total population hold the majority of the land in huge ranches, plantations, or haciendas. The shortage of farmland for the poor in rural areas has been a major factor contributing to urban migration.

A homeless Honduras boy scavenges in a Tegucigalpa dump. As in other Latin American nations, Honduras faced a growing problem of "street children" during the late 1990's. (AP/Wide World Photos)

Dissatisfied with political and economic circumstances, many Central Americans have attempted to migrate, legally or illegally, to cities in other countries. New migrants are often poor and unable to read or write and must compete for limited jobs. Women may find work as domestic servants, and men may find low-skill jobs in construction, maintenance, and small-scale manufacturing. They often depend on day work that is frequently short-term, or earn money through jobs like cleaning or washing cars. Significant numbers of Hondurans, Salvadorans, and Guatemalans in particular continue to migrate to the United States.

Unless poverty diminishes and living conditions improve in rural areas, the trend of rural-to-urban migration is likely to continue. Increasing numbers of migrants flock to cities in both Central America and the United States in search of a better life.

Anne Galantowicz

FOR FURTHER STUDY

Blouet, Brian W., and Olwyn M. Blouet. *Latin America and the Caribbean: A Systematic and Regional Survey.* 3d ed. New York: John Wiley & Sons, 1997.

Ness, Immanuel. *Encyclopedia of World Cities.* Chicago: Fitzroy Dearborn, 1999.

South America, Central America, and the Caribbean. London: Europa Publications, 1999.

ECONOMIC
GEOGRAPHY

AGRICULTURE

SOUTH AMERICA

Map Page 814

Most people of South America, like people of the United States, live in large cities. About 20 percent of South America is considered rural, compared to about 23 percent of the U.S. population. The real contrast is in the number of people who make their living from agriculture. About 23 percent of the population of South America receives most of its income from agriculture, compared to 4 percent in the United States. Only about 40 million acres (96 million hectares) of the continent is farmable (arable)—considerably less than North America's 90 million acres (222 million hectares).

The agricultural economy of South America underwent dramatic changes in the twentieth century. South America became much more urbanized, and industrialization overtook the levels of agricultural incomes. For example, Brazil now contains the ninth largest economy in the world. This presents a tremendous challenge to people in rural communities who have depended on agriculture as a way of life for generations. Because it is so difficult to make a living in the farming areas, more South Americans are leaving their traditional farming areas to live in large cities. As the economy of South America has expanded through its industrial base, poverty has continued to rise. While 20 percent of the richest South Americans control more than 60 percent of the total

wealth of the region, 20 percent of the poorest South Americans control only 2 percent of its total wealth.

In the late 1990's, 70 million South Americans lived in rural areas and about 275 million lived in urban areas. Cities such as Brazil's Rio de Janeiro (population 5.8 million) and São Paulo (9 million) in Brazil continue to grow quickly, but the overall industrialization of South America has not kept up. Miles of squatter communities surround the cities, but people keep coming. The poor migrants come from impoverished rural agricultural areas, where many exist only on what they can grow. This migration to the city has had a tremendous impact on the farmland that is left behind, idle and nonproductive. At the same time, cities are faced with the problems of uncontrolled growth and trying to find jobs for the unemployed.

AGRICULTURE AND THE TROPICAL FOREST. Some of the most remote regions in South America are its fastest-developing areas. The northern interior regions of Brazil in the Amazon Basin face tremendous pressure from development and population growth. This area is covered with the world's largest tropical rain forest, as big as the forty-eight contiguous United States. Within some areas of this rich habitat, gold and huge iron ore deposits have been discovered. Development programs have encouraged mining, hydroelectric projects, ranching, and farming there. This has produced a need for clearing the forests and caused a large migration of people into this otherwise remote, isolated region.

Competition for the land and its resources has been fierce, with the detrimental consequence of thousands of square miles of tropical forest being removed every year. It has been estimated that 30,000 square miles (78,000 sq. km.) of tropical rain forest were destroyed annually in the 1990's.

Although the rain forest might appear to be a highly productive growing region for crops, it is not. Soils in those forests are thin and have few nutrients. To grow crops and grasses for cattle, slash-and-burn agricultural practices are used. Crops such as corn and rice are planted on the newly cleared ground, but after about three years the nutrients have been washed out of the soil by the heavy tropical rains. Farmers and ranchers move on and find a new forest area to cut, and the cycle goes on. Why conserve these forests? Rain forests cover only about 5 percent of the total land area of the earth but contain more than half the different types of plants and animals on earth. These forests provide lumber products, medicines, and food. No one knows what amazing products they might yet hold for human good.

SOUTH AMERICAN AGRICULTURE AS A SYSTEM. Agriculture is a complex system comprising both human and natural vari-

LEADING AGRICULTURAL PRODUCTS OF SOUTH AMERICAN COUNTRIES

Country	Products
Argentina	Wheat, corn, sorghum, soybeans, sugar beets, beef
Bolivia	Coffee, cocoa, cotton, corn, sugarcane, rice, potatoes, timber
Brazil	Coffee, soybeans, wheat, rice, corn, sugarcane, cocoa, citrus, beef
Chile	Wheat, corn, grapes, beans, sugar beets, potatoes, fruit, beef, poultry, wool, timber, fish
Colombia	Coffee, cut flowers, bananas, rice, tobacco, corn, sugarcane, cocoa beans, oilseed, vegetables, forest products, shrimp farming
Ecuador	Bananas, coffee, cocoa, rice, potatoes, manioc, plantains, sugarcane, cattle, sheep, pigs, beef, pork, dairy products, balsa wood, fish
Guyana	Sugar, rice, wheat, vegetable oils, beef, pork, poultry, dairy products
Paraguay	Cotton, sugarcane, soybeans, corn, wheat, tobacco, cassava, fruits, vegetables, beef, pork, eggs, milk, timber
Peru	Coffee, cotton, sugarcane, rice, wheat, potatoes, plantains, cocoa, poultry, red meats, dairy products, wool, fish
Suriname	Bananas, palm kernels, coconuts, plantains, peanuts, beef, chicken, forest products, shrimp
Uruguay	Wheat, rice, corn, sorghum, livestock, fish
Venezuela	Rice, coffee, corn, cacao, sugar, bananas, dairy and meat products

Source: The Time Almanac 2000. Boston: Infoplease, 1999.

Farm on a Peruvian Altiplano slope. (Clyde L. Rasmussen)

ables. Components include the type of landforms, soil, water, and climate, and the human endeavor or technological possibilities that can be applied by humans to an agricultural economy. These variables interact to produce an arrangement of agricultural production specific to the region, in South America as elsewhere.

South America can be divided into three general landform regions: the Andes Mountains, the plateaus of the interior of the continent, and the river lowlands.

THE ANDES MOUNTAINS. The Andes Cordillera reaches from Venezuela in the north to Tierra del Fuego at the south tip of the continent. The Andes are composed of both folded mountains and volcanic peaks, some exceeding 20,000 feet (6,100 meters). The soils there are rocky and are

found on steep grades or hillsides. This makes farming difficult but not impossible. Farmers use terrace-type systems, building up steplike fields carved into the side of a mountain. Because of the limita-

Terraced farms along the shore of Lake Titicaca in the Andes. (Clyde L. Rasmussen)

793

tion of these soils and the difficulty in farming them, the region has only non-commercial, subsistence-type agricultural settlements. Native people in the highlands grow small plots of maize (corn), barley, and especially potatoes on the high-altitude soils. Llamas and alpacas are raised there and are well suited for this rugged terrain.

Highland farms Pages 813, 815

THE HIGHLAND GROWING REGIONS.
In the central eastern region of Brazil are the Brazilian Highlands. To the north of the Amazon Basin lies another plateau region called the Guiana Highlands. Both plateaus, which are not much higher than 9,000 feet (2,743 meters), are old geologic structures with relatively rough surfaces to farm. The Brazilian Highlands is the world's primary coffee-growing region. More than one-third of the world's coffee is grown here, along with soybeans and oranges. The Guiana Highlands, which stretch through southern Venezuela and Guyana, is another plateau of geologically old soils. This area is covered in savanna (grasslands with trees and shrubs). Native people here use the slash-and-burn system of agriculture, cutting down trees and brush on the land, burning them, then working them into the soil. This enriches the soils for a time and allows for limited production of maize and other subsistence crops.

Coffee plants Page 815

THE RIVER LOWLANDS.
The river valleys of South America are some of the largest in the world. The Orinoco river drains the Guiana Highlands and the *llanos* region of Venezuela, flowing out into the Atlantic Ocean. The *llanos* are a large, expansive plain of grassland between the Andes in Venezuela and the Guiana Highlands. Soils are flooded in this area during the rainy seasons, providing for rich grass development and the support of large cattle ranches.

The Amazon River drains the north and western region of Brazil. Although more water moves through the Amazon River than any other river in the world, its location in dense tropical forests under a humid tropical climate makes agriculture there a challenge. Amerindians of the region practice subsistence agriculture, growing yams and bananas and raising some small animals. Manioc (a root crop from which tapioca is made) and sugarcane are also grown here in slash-and-burn fashion.

The Paraná, Paraguay, and Uruguay Rivers, south of the Amazon lowlands, dissect a great grassland region known as the Pampas and a forested region known as the Gran Chaco. The Pampas of Argentina is not unlike the Midwest of North America. It is a huge grassy plain nearly 400 miles (640 km.) long in the central part of Argentina. This is a land of gauchos (cowboys), cattle, sheep, and barbecues. Historically, ranching began in this region because grazing animals did not require a great number of people, and early settlements in the area by the Spanish were few. Also, the products from cattle and sheep, such as hides and wool, could be shipped long distances without damage.

Agriculture is the primary industry in Argentina and encompasses 60 percent of the country's land. Cattle is king here, and large *estancia* (ranches) are common in the region. The soils are well suited to wheat and other grains as well as alfalfa, a grass grown for cattle and horse feed. The level character of the land makes it easy to work, but it is difficult to drain and is prone to flooding.

In the north of Argentina and the Pampas and through the central region of Paraguay lies the Gran Chaco. Paraguay's agricultural zones are divided by the Paraguay River. Tobacco, rice, and sugarcane grow to the east of the river in the more humid climates. To the west, in the drier climates and the Chaco region, the unique growing area of the Quebracho Forest is found. Quebracho is a hardwood that grows only in the Chaco. The wood contains tannin, which is used to produce tannic acid, a chemical used for tanning leather. This area is also suited for cattle, but because of its rocky and steep topography, the population of goats and sheep rises as one moves further west toward the Andes. This region is irrigated with mountain streams from the eastern slopes of the Andes. Grapes also grow well here and are made into raisins and wine.

THE HOT, WET LOWLANDS. The coastal lowlands up to an altitude of about 2,500 feet (750 meters) encompass an area known as the hot land (*tierra calienta*). Temperatures there average between 75 and 80 degrees Fahrenheit (22 and 24 degrees Celsisus), and plantation agriculture

abounds. Plantations are huge commercial farming operations that grow large quantities of crops that are usually sold for export. Because of their easy access to port facilities, coastal lowlands historically have been linked with the markets of Europe and North America.

The banana is one of the best-known examples of a plantation crop. It grows well in the wet, hot climate of this altitude zone and has been cultivated here for U.S. and European markets since 1866. In the 1990's, more bananas were traded on the international fruit market than any other commodity. North America, the third largest importing market for bananas, brings in more than eight billion pounds every year. Even with modern refrigerated vessels and containers, the closeness of the banana-growing regions to the markets of North America is good for North Ameri-

Bananas Page 816

An Argentine worker harvests grapes for a local winery. At the beginning of the twenty-first century, Argentina was hoping to duplicate the success of neighboring Chile in world wine markets. (AP/Wide World Photos)

can consumers, since the bananas can reach the market quickly, eliminating spoilage owing to travel. In South America, Ecuador and Brazil are the leading banana producers, with Colombia third.

Cacao, the bean pods from which cocoa and chocolate are made, are also grown on plantations in this zone. The largest producing area for cacao is Ghana in West Africa, but Brazil and Ecuador are fifth and sixth in world yearly production.

Although sugarcane is grown in almost every country in South America, it does well as a plantation crop in the lowlands of eastern Brazil, the world's largest exporter. There the crop is not used just to produce sugar but also to produce gasohol, an alcohol-based gasoline that fuels more than half the automobiles in Brazil. This type of commercial agriculture has made agricultural business the fastest-growing part of the Brazilian economy.

Yams, cassava (manioc), and other root crops used as staple foods grow well in this humid, hot climate. Cassava is a highly productive native crop of the region, containing more starch than potatoes. Cassava root can be made into bread and tapioca. Some rice is also grown in this zone.

THE TIERRA TEMPLADA. Just above the *calienta* zone lies a zone of cooler temperatures that extends to about 6,000 feet (1,850 meters). Temperatures there range from 65 to 75 degrees (17 to 22 degrees Celsius), and the commercial crop that dominates the landscape is coffee. It is grown on large plantations called *fazendas.* Brazil, the largest South American coffee producer, exports about one-quarter of the world's coffee, producing nearly forty million bags of about 132 pounds each (60 kilograms) annually. Colombia, South America's second-largest coffee producer, produces about ten million bags per year. Coffee was once the leading export from Colombia, but, as a result of a coffee-worm

infestation and lower world prices, other products are taking the lead.

The coffee of the Caribbean is considered to be of a finer quality than Brazilian coffee. Brazilian coffee is harvested late when the bean has already ripened on the tree, giving the coffee a harsh taste, so Brazilian coffees are mixed with other coffees.

Other commercial crops from this zone include fresh fruit. In the central valley of Chile, grape vineyards and apple orchards have begun to emerge. Fresh produce from this region enters stores in the United States and elsewhere as the growing seasons of the domestic products are finishing up. Chilean grapes, apples, peaches, and plums are now sold worldwide.

Corn (maize) and wheat are also grown in this zone. These staple foods are produced for local consumption and sold only at local markets. However, maize production is common throughout South America. In 1998 Brazil and Argentina ranked third and forth in world maize production, but most of this was for domestic consumption.

THE TIERRA FRIA. This is the cold land that extends from 6,000 feet (1,850 meters) to about 15,000 feet (4,570 meters). Average temperatures there range from 55 to 64 degrees Fahrenheit (12 to 17 degrees Celsius). This zone exists throughout the Andes Mountains and can maintain only that plant life that can withstand the limited soils and the cold climate conditions. In this region of subsistence-type farming, crops and animals are grown and raised mostly for family use.

In the lower reaches of this zone, barley grows. Because it requires a short growing season, it grows well at high elevations. In the cooler originated portions of this zone, the potato began. The potato of the Andes is much smaller in size than the potato common in the United States, but

---

HIDDEN AGRICULTURE

Nearly 75 percent of the total world supply of the illegal drug cocaine comes from Peru, Colombia, and Bolivia. This drug is manufactured from the coca plant, which is grown mostly along the east side of the Andes. It grows well in the tropical lowland areas of Peru and Bolivia. The coca plant is historically embedded in the culture of South America. The Incas cultivated this plant and still chew its leaves and drink it as a tea to help them cope with the high altitudes of the area.

Coca cultivation has impacted agriculture in the region. Many peasant farmers, seeing how much money can be made growing coca instead of a conventional crop like maize, leave their traditional farming to raise coca. In this case, the farmer does not leave his farm for the city but changes his crop to make more money. The government has tried to help farmers by giving them funds to help bring up the prices of traditional food crops, but these programs have not worked. So long as markets for high-priced cocaine exist, coca will be grown in these countries.

---

they are relatives. A tuber, the potato can flourish in cold conditions with moderate moisture. The loose soils of this zone are perfect for its production, but it requires a considerable amount of cultivation. Although the potato is used throughout South America, potato production for the continent constitutes only about 5 percent of the world total production.

Alpacas, a type of goat, and llamas are raised here. Throughout Peru, Bolivia, and Chile, flocks of alpaca are commonly found at elevations around 12,000 feet (3,650 meters). Except for their long necks, alpacas resemble sheep. Each year the alpaca is shorn for its fine wool, which is naturally white but can also be black or brown. The fibers are excellent for sweaters and other clothing items. The llama is mainly found in Peru, but its popularity has spread around the world. Llamas make excellent pack animals and also produce a long, smooth coat that is sheared and used for clothing.

POTENTIALS. South America has the potential to develop its agricultural economy even further if it refocuses on dealing with its internal infrastructure challenges.

This is a continent of economic contrasts. Can rain forests and cattle ranches find common ground? Can peasant farmers find alternatives to coca and still make a living? Can the cities survive the onslaughts of population from the rural areas? What about the land the migrants leave behind? The challenge in South America is to find a way to unite the agricultural potential of the land with wise usage and the development that is bound to come.

M. Mustoe

FOR FURTHER STUDY

Booth, John A., and Walker, Thomas W. *Understanding Central America.* 2d rev. ed. Boulder, Colo.: Westview Press, 1993.

Caufield, Catherine. *In the Rainforest: Report from a Strange, Beautiful, Imperiled World.* Chicago: University of Chicago Press, 1991.

Gade, Daniel W. *Plants, Man, and the Land in the Vilcanota Valley of Peru.* The Hague: W. Junk, 1975.

Gonzales, Michael J. *Plantation Agriculture and Social Control in Northern Peru.* Aus-

INFORMATION ON THE WORLD WIDE WEB

A good site for detailed South American agricultural information is that of the United Nations' Food and Agriculture Organization (FAO), which features a searchable database organized by individual country. (www.fao.org)

tin: University of Texas Press, 1985.

Grigg, David B. *An Introduction to Agricultural Geography.* 2d rev. ed. London: Routledge, 1995.

Stanfield, Michael Edward. *Red Rubber, Bleeding Trees: Violence, Slavery, and Empire in Northwest Amazonia, 1850-1933.* Albuquerque: University of New Mexico, 1998.

*Map
Page 817*

CENTRAL AMERICA

Agriculture is generally understood to be concerned with the production of food; however, in Central America, ornamental plants and flowers, forest products, and fibers are also important agricultural commodities. At the end of the twentieth century, the agricultural sector employed about 46 percent of the available labor force in Central America, many of whom were engaged in subsistence agriculture. This percentage is also higher than that of the neighboring developing countries of Mexico (28 percent) and Colombia (30 percent). The Central American percentage is higher than in more developed countries, such as the United States and Canada, each of which is below 4 percent. The percentage of suitable land is about equal to that in Mexico (12 percent) but significantly more than in Colombia (4 percent). Arable land in the United States is about 19 percent.

*Copan
Page 758*

EARLY AGRICULTURE. Considerable archaeological evidence supports the existence of sedentary agriculture in the region for more than two thousand years.

The early Maya farmed raised fields in lowland swamp areas and constructed irrigation systems in areas with a dry season. In highland areas, steep slopes were terraced. The most prominent terrace agriculture in the Americas was in the Andean cultures, but Central Americans also used this practice. Agriculture was based mainly on maize (corn), but other crops were widely grown, including squash, beans, and chile peppers. Nonfood crops such as cotton and tobacco were grown for both domestic use and trade. These two crops continue to be important.

Exactly what group of Central Americans established the various agricultural practices, or when, is debatable. However, it is known that agriculture supported large communities of people early in the first millennium. The cities of Tikal, Copan, Caracol, and others had populations of thirty-five thousand or more.

Raised field agriculture had several benefits. The muck dredged from channel bottoms was added to the fields, raising the surface above the surrounding swamp, creating dry land. This material was rich in nutrients from decaying plant matter and wastes from fish and other aquatic creatures. Channels of water dividing the dry land provided habitat for fish and turtles, which supplied protein to the diet.

Slash-and-burn agriculture was the process of stripping forests and burning the debris in place. Trees too large to be cut with primitive stone implements were girded, that is, a circle of bark was removed from around the tree and the tree left to die. The burned debris added nutrients to the top two to three inches of soil. Because the soil was generally poor, the fields, usually known as *milpas* or cornfields but sometimes referred to as swidden, were abandoned after two or three years of production and left fallow for up to twenty years. This process is still practiced today.

Intercropping or polyculture was a practice that helped ensure a harvest. The planting of several crops and different varieties provided a harvest even if one crop failed because of climatic, insect, or disease problems. This practice is also in use today.

TRADITIONAL AND NON-TRADITIONAL CROPS. For more than a century, certain crops have been raised in Central America as export crops and others principally for domestic consumption. Many of the traditional crops grown for more than a century are not native to the region. Many of the most widely grown crops are termed exotics, that is, plants that are not native to the region but were introduced by Euro-

pean settlers. Bananas, coffee, and sugarcane are three principal exotic crops, with corn being a fourth. Most of the production of introduced plants is grown for export, although native corn is for local use.

Bananas are grown extensively in the Caribbean and Pacific lowlands, but most prominently in the Sula Valley of Honduras, a leading world exporter of this crop. The banana industry flourished under the control of North American growers, especially the United Fruit Company. Beginning in the latter part of the nineteenth century, the banana export business grew and enjoyed large markets in the United States and Europe. The United Fruit Company also exerted strong influence over governmental policies in the region.

Hurricane Mitch, in late 1998, devastated the banana plantations in Honduras.

Bananas Page 816

Hurricane Mitch Pages 746, 822

Most of the bananas sold in North American grocery stores come from Central America. (PhotoDisc)

Chiquita Brands and Dole Fruit, the remaining North American growers, replanted and the industry is expected to recover by the year 2001.

Coffee plants Page 815

Coffee is grown extensively in the highland areas of all seven Central American countries. A slow-ripening crop, coffee requires as much as two months to harvest. Small-scale growers who sell their product through cooperatives produce much of the area's coffee. The best-quality coffee is shade-grown, and so banana trees often are interspersed throughout the small fields.

Sugarcane Page 816

Sugarcane, first introduced by Christopher Columbus to the island of Cuba, is another plant grown over a wide area. Sugarcane is labor-intensive during harvest but requires little attention at other times. The harvest of sugarcane begins with the burning of the fields. This practice reduces the volume of foliage and leaves standing only the stalks, or canes, which are the source of sugar. After the burning—which has the side benefit of chasing out the snakes that inhabit the cane fields—teams of workers with machetes march through the fields cutting the cane.

Corn (maize) is not grown for export. Along with regionally grown rice, it is for domestic consumption. Corn meal is used in the preparation of tortillas, which are eaten at nearly every meal. Rice is commonly served with red or black beans.

Export crops have had peaks and valleys in their economic value to the region. A disease of banana plants nearly ruined the industry in the 1930's. The Great Depression in the early 1930's sharply reduced exports to North America. Import quotas imposed by the United States on sugar and the U.S. ban on importing Cuban sugar provided both a low and a high for Central American sugar producers. Overproduction of coffee by South American producers has led to depressed prices several times. During the late 1990's, the European Union's agricultural import practice of favoring former colonies reduced the value of bananas to growers. In Central America, only Belize benefits from European tariff regulations.

NONTRADITIONAL CROPS. Vegetables, high-value crops, and ornamental plants

---

LEADING AGRICULTURAL PRODUCTS OF CENTRAL AMERICAN COUNTRIES

Country	Products
Belize	Bananas, cocoa, citrus, sugarcane, lumber, fish, cultivated shrimp
Costa Rica	Coffee, bananas, sugar, corn, rice, beans, potatoes, beef, timber
El Salvador	Coffee, sugarcane, corn, rice, beans, oilseed, cotton, sorghum, beef, dairy products, shrimp
Guatemala	Sugarcane, corn, bananas, coffee, beans, cardamom, cattle, sheep, pigs, chickens
Honduras	Bananas, coffee, citrus, beef, timber, shrimp
Nicaragua	Coffee, bananas, sugarcane, cotton, rice, corn, cassava, citrus, beans, beef, veal, pork, poultry, dairy products
Panama	Bananas, corn, sugarcane, rice, coffee, vegetables, livestock, fishing

Source: The Time Almanac 2000. Boston: Infoplease, 1999.

and flowers are being grown at an increased rate. The leading crops are broccoli, cauliflower, snowpeas, melons, strawberries, and pineapples. Palm oil from a nonnative tree is another high-value farm product. Nontraditional crops are labor-intensive and also affect the environment because of the heavy requirements for chemical insecticides and disease control. There are health risks to workers because of these chemical applications, but employment is high. In Costa Rica, the government encourages investment in reforestation using teak from Southeast Asia.

LIVESTOCK. Every country in Central America raises cattle, with swine the second-ranking livestock. Cattle are mostly range-fed; as a result, the beef is of inferior quality compared to North American beef. Most cattle are improved breeds of Cebu (or Zebu), with some dairy herds of other breeds. The dominant area of cattle production is the Guanacaste region of Costa Rica and generally the western slope of the Pacific highlands. Once forest is removed for timber or subsistence agriculture, the area frequently becomes pasture after a few years.

Donald Andrew Wiley

FOR FURTHER STUDY

Cubitt, Tessa. *Latin American Society.* New York: John Wiley & Sons, 1995.

Grigg, David. *Agricultural Geography.* London: Routledge, 1995.

Janzen, Daniel H., ed. *Costa Rican Natural History.* Chicago: University of Chicago Press, 1983.

Kricher, John. *A Neotropical Companion: An Introduction to the Animals, Plants, and Ecosystems of the New World Tropics.* 2d ed. Princeton, N.J.: Princeton University Press, 1997.

McCann, Thomas. *An American Company: The Tragedy of United Fruit.* New York: Crown Publishers, 1976.

Rhoades, Robert E. "The World's Food Supply at Risk." *The National Geographic* (April, 1991): 74-105.

Schwartz, Norman B. *Forest Society: A Social History of Peten, Guatemala.* Philadelphia: University of Pennsylvania Press, 1990.

Thrupp, Lori Ann. *Bittersweet Harvests for Global Supermarkets: Challenges in Latin America's Agricultural Export Boom.* Washington, D.C.: World Resources Institute, 1995

CACAO: A FAVORITE CENTRAL AMERICAN CROP

Cacao (cocoa) beans, from which chocolate is made, have been cultivated in Central America for centuries. Once considered the drink of the gods, chocolate was reserved for royalty. Today, millions around the world enjoy chocolate, especially mixed with sugar and milk.

The beans are actually the berries of the small cacao tree, which grows in shade and is rarely more than 20 feet (6 meters) tall. The tree's football-shaped pods are 6-8 inches (15-20 centimeters) in length. When ripe, the pods can be red, yellow, or orange, depending on the variety. The tree's flowers are tiny, inconspicuous white blossoms that emerge singularly from the lower branches or trunk, not from stem ends. The cacao seeds, or beans, are surrounded by a whitish, gelatinous mass. Cacao beans must be fermented, dried, and cleaned before the chocolate aroma and taste develops.

INFORMATION ON THE WORLD WIDE WEB

A good site for detailed Central American agricultural information is that of the United Nations' Food and Agriculture Organization (FAO), which features a searchable database organized by individual country. (www.fao.org)

INDUSTRIES

SOUTH AMERICA

South America is well known for the number of minerals and other natural resources existing there. It does not have the variety of minerals that are in North America and Russia, but it has some strategic and historically important minerals.

SILVER. During Spanish colonial rule, silver was a major export from the region. In fact, this is why the Spanish were so interested in South America, especially present-day Ecuador, Peru, and Bolivia. The most famous South American silver mine was the Potosí mine in present-day Bolivia. During the sixteenth century, Potosí produced nearly half the world's total supply of silver. In the 1990's, Bolivia still produced a significant proportion of the world's silver, although productivity had dropped off as a result of the difficult conditions of mining in the highlands of the Andes Mountains and the depletion of the silver reserves there.

Another major silver-producing region of South America is located in central Peru. Cerro de Pasco and the surrounding areas have produced a large portion of the world's silver from colonial times to the present. Only Mexico and the United States produced more silver than Peru in the year 2000. Silver mines also are found further south in Chile and Argentina, although most of those deposits were discovered after the importance of silver declined and other industrial minerals rose in importance.

Labor for silver mines was hard to come by in colonial times. Working conditions were terrible, the work itself dangerous, and diseases rampant in the mines. Native Peruvians were not willing to work as wage laborers in great numbers. As a result, colonial mine managers and owners relied on coercion to draw enough laborers. The system used was known as the *mita*, or "turn," whereby local villages were required to supply workers to take their turn in the mines.

GOLD AND DIAMONDS. The other major precious metal, gold, is not as common in South America as is silver, but southeastern Brazil and western Colombia were settled because of the presence of gold. Brazil also mines a considerable amount of diamonds.

The largest area in which gold was found was in southeastern Brazil. Gold was discovered in the highlands of São Paulo and Minas Gerais states in the late sixteenth century by Paulista *bandeiras*, bands of men from São Paulo who were trying to capture native peoples to sell as slaves. Larger deposits were later discovered in Rio de Janeiro state, leading to a gold rush in the early eighteenth century. Further discoveries to the west in Goiás and Mato Grosso do Sul states, and the discovery of diamonds in the same areas, helped establish southeastern Brazil and particularly the city of Rio de Janeiro as the center of Brazilian wealth and settlement.

A minor gold deposit was found in the 1530's in the Cordillera Occidental in Colombia, near the city of Medellín, leading to settlement of that area. Gold and diamonds are also found in the Amazon rain forest in northern Brazil and the Guianas. The exploitation of these reserves has led to significant deforestation and conflicts between independent miners, or *garimpeiros*, and native peoples of the region.

INDUSTRIAL MINERALS. Precious metals and stones are valuable in their own right. Modern mining of industrial minerals, however, depends on factories to which to sell the minerals, since iron ore, petroleum, and bauxite are not useful in their natural state. Some of the most important industrial minerals in the world today are found in large quantities in South America. Many mines are owned and operated by North American, European, and Japanese investors with the main purpose of exporting these minerals to overseas markets.

Petroleum is an essential mineral for modern industry, since it is the raw material for the production of fuels, plastics, and other petrochemicals. The largest petroleum reserves are found in Venezuela, in and around Lake Maracaibo and in the sparsely settled eastern part of that country. Petroleum production peaked in the 1960's and 1970's in Venezuela, but it remains the largest Venezuelan export and has been the basis for development policy in that country. Smaller reserves of petroleum are found in Ecuador, northern Colombia, northeastern Brazil, and Patagonia in Argentina.

Tin traditionally has been associated with South America. Only Southeast Asia as a region produces more tin than South America. South American mines produced just under 30 percent of the world's tin at the end of the twentieth century. Brazil is the largest producer in the region and second only to China in the total number of tons mined, but Bolivia relies on tin exports more than does Brazil. The Brazilian mines are concentrated in the Amazon River valley and the state of Rondônia in the far west. Patinga, the largest tin mine in the world, is located in Amazonas state in Brazil. Bolivian mines are found primarily in the region between La Paz and Sucre. Smaller tin-mining areas include southern Peru and northern Argentina.

Bauxite, from which aluminum is made, is another major mineral found in South America. The leading South American producer and the fourth-largest in the world is Brazil. Bauxite mining is concentrated in the north, especially in Pará state. The largest mine is found at Trombetas, about 150 miles (240 km.) northeast of Manáos. Bauxite also is mined in Suri-

Venezuelan tanker Page 820

MAJOR MINERALS OF SOUTH AMERICA

Mineral	Country and Percentage of Global Production
Bauxite	Brazil (9.6%); Suriname (9.6%)
Chromite	Brazil (2.5%)
Copper	Chile (19.3%); Peru (4.0%)
Gold	Brazil (3.6%)
Iron ore	Brazil (19.1%); Venezuela (2.5%)
Lead	Peru (5.9%)
Manganese	Brazil (10.0%)
Petroleum	Venezuela (3.8%)
Silver	Peru (10.8%); Chile (4.9%); Bolivia (2.0%)
Tin	Brazil (16.3%); Bolivia (8.2%); Peru (2.9%)
Tungsten	Peru (2.7%); Bolivia (2.5%)
Zinc	Peru (8.4%); Brazil (2.0%)

name, Guyana, and Venezuela.

Many other important minerals are found in South America. Copper-mining is important in northern Chile and Peru. Iron ore can be found in Brazil, which is the single largest producer in the world, especially in Minas Gerais state and in Serra do Carajas in Pará state; iron also is mined in Venezuela and Colombia. Coal-mining is an important industry in Colombia, Venezuela, and Brazil, with a smaller role in Peru and Argentina. Uranium reserves are found in Brazil and Argentina, although they have not been exploited to any great extent. Finally, phosphates and nitrates for use as fertilizers can be found in coastal Peru, the Atacama Desert in Chile, and in the Pampas in Argentina.

MANUFACTURING. Modern economies are dependent on manufacturing. In the manufacturing process, minerals and agricultural products, most of which are useless in their original state, are turned into useful goods that human beings can consume. Because of this, manufacturing is said to add value to raw materials by making them into finished products, which are worth more than the raw materials were.

South American industry traditionally has been dominated by the exportation of minerals and raw materials and the importation of finished products. Since most of the value of products is added in the manufacturing process, and since the value of manufactured products has risen as compared to raw materials, South American economies usually have been at a disadvantage in terms of trade—if they sell cheap things and buy expensive things, they get less back than they sell. This disadvantage became more pronounced during the Great Depression, when the demand for South American agricultural products and minerals declined in Europe and North America.

One strategy for overcoming this disadvantage after World War II was the encouragement of import-substituting industrialization (ISI). Import substitution means replacing previously imported finished products with domestically produced alternatives. This was achieved by placing higher tariffs (taxes on imports) on finished products than on raw materials or intermediate goods. Producers were encouraged to import parts and machinery and do final assembly in South American states, which was hoped would provide highly paid manufacturing jobs.

ISI was largely unsuccessful in bringing development to South America and eventually was abandoned for several reasons. First, the domestic industries were too small and inefficient, making the finished products more expensive than their foreign counterparts. This left South American consumers worse off than they had been before ISI. Second, foreign manufacturers moved only the final assembly work to South America, bringing only a few, low-paying jobs. Third, since the manufacturing plants that were built required heavy investment in machinery that had to be imported, South Americans found themselves unable to purchase other imports.

EXPORT-ORIENTED MANUFACTURING. Another development tool used by South American national governments has been the encouragement of export-oriented manufacturing (EOM). It traditionally has been difficult for South American economies to export manufactured goods to the industrialized economies of North America, Europe, and Japan. South American firms could not compete with the efficiency and productivity of North American, European, and Japanese firms. Also, the types and quality of goods that the people of South America demanded were different from the types and quality of goods that North Americans, Europeans, and

Japanese people demanded. Thus, it was difficult for South American economies to develop based on manufacturing, since they could not gain access to major markets.

Two EOM promotion strategies were followed by South American governments beginning in the late 1950's. The first strategy was intended to address the problem that North Americans and Europeans did not purchase the same sorts of goods as Brazilians or Peruvians. Since most South Americans demanded similar types and qualities of goods, if a factory produced for domestic consumption, it could also export its output to places that demanded similar goods. South American governments, therefore, encouraged trade with other South American economies by forming trade agreements and common markets. A factory in Argentina could increase its market beyond the relatively small Argentine population by selling also to Chileans and Venezuelans, becoming more efficient in the process. Although there was some progress, this strategy was not successful in the long run, as disagreements about how to coordinate these development efforts emerged between national governments.

The second and more successful strategy addressed the problem of competing with more industrialized economies. Since South American firms were not as efficient as North American and European firms, they had to concentrate on manufacturing methods that took advantage of their strengths. Wage rates in South America have been significantly lower than those in North America, Europe, or Japan. Therefore, South American firms attempted to use more workers and fewer machines in their factories than a U.S. or German factory would.

South American firms also concentrated on manufacturing goods that

needed a geat deal of labor in the manufacturing process, especially less-skilled labor. Thus, South American manufacturers have concentrated on producing things like textiles and apparel (especially sneakers and underwear), radios and televisions, automobile parts, and toys. Usually, EOM factories use imported parts, and only assembly takes place in the South American factory. The goods produced in many of these factories are too expensive for the local people and workers, who might be paid only the equivalent of one U.S. dollar per day or less. Therefore, EOM goods are produced for the United States and Europe.

MANUFACTURING REGIONS. Despite the plentiful natural resources, South America as a whole has not emerged as a major manufacturing region. Certain regions of South America have developed significant manufacturing, but industry remains concentrated in those regions, while the rest of South America relies on agriculture and mining. One reason for this is that in the colonial period, manufacturing was discouraged in South America by the Spanish and Portuguese governments. Since independence from Spain and Portugal in the first half of the nineteenth century, South American industrial development has been relatively slow and highly concentrated.

SOUTHEASTERN BRAZIL. Brazil is the dominant manufacturing country in South America, producing more than one-third of the total manufacturing output of the continent. The largest area of manufacturing is in the southeast, centered on the cities of São Paulo, Rio de Janeiro, and Belo Horizonte, and the areas in between them. São Paulo by itself is home to more than half of all Brazilian manufacturing.

Before the 1950's, there was little manufacturing in Brazil. Since then, the south-

São Paulo
Page 819

CLEANING UP CUBATÃO

Cubatão, Brazil, is an industrial town 49 miles (80 km.) from São Paulo. In the mid-1980's its air stank and residents complained of headaches and nausea. Each year, two dozen factories released a quarter-million tons of toxins into the air. In nearby shanty-towns one-third of the babies died before their first birthdays and eight out of ten children had respiratory problems. In 1984 an oil pipeline exploded, killing more than five hundred people. The following year, there were mass evacuations when an ammonia pipeline broke. In the face of this environmental nightmare, Brazil passed stricter pollution laws. By 1990, factories in Cubatão had cut emissions by more than three-fourths.

Coffee worker Page 818

Auto plant Page 818

Charcoal worker Page 820

east region has emerged as the center of Brazilian industry for historical and geographical reasons. Historically, the coffee industry, a tremendous wealth-generator for Brazil, has been concentrated in São Paulo state, providing a significant amount of financial capital for investment in factories and also providing Brazil's earliest and most highly developed transportation system. That, combined with the eighteenth century gold rush in the area and the selection of Rio de Janeiro as Brazil's capital (before the capital was relocated to Brasília), tended to concentrate wealth and population in this area. This area is home to a large population that is both labor force and market. Southeastern Brazil also contains important natural resources such as iron ore, and electricity is cheaper and more easily available in this area than other parts of Brazil.

As a result, southeastern Brazil is home to many industries, both heavy and light. Primary among heavy industry is steel and iron production. Brazil is a significant world producer of steel and pig iron, producing about 4 percent of the world's

steel, and given its extensive iron ore reserves, it has the potential to greatly expand that share.

Another important industry in Brazil is automobile assembly, which has produced between 800,000 and 1 million units per year since the early 1970's. Volkswagen is the largest automaker in Brazil, and the original Volkswagen Beetle continues to be manufactured there. Related to this are the aircraft factories in and around São Paulo—Brazil is the sixth-largest aircraft producer in the world. As a result of the many petroleum refineries in the region, there is a growing petrochemical industry. Finally, chemical and pharmaceutical industries are becoming more important in the region. Light industries in São Paulo, Rio de Janeiro, and Minas Gerais states include textiles, apparel (especially footwear), food processing, and light consumer goods.

RÍO DE LA PLATA. Manufacturing in the La Plata River area (including Buenos Aires in Argentina and Montevideo in Uruguay) began as an outgrowth of the agricultural exports from the fertile, productive Pampas region. Argentina and Uruguay are well known for sheep and cattle ranching. These animals are in great demand in Europe and Japan as food. It is difficult to ship live animals, so the meat must be prepared for export. Industry developed around the mouth of the Paraná River, where the agricultural goods would have been loaded for export. Animals first were driven to Buenos Aires or Montevideo or later brought by rail, butchered in slaughterhouses, and prepared for export. At the beginning, the meat was salted in *saladeros*, but when refrigeration was invented in the 1870's, that was no longer necessary, and it now can be shipped frozen. Other related industries that emerged in this time included leather goods and textiles.

Continued on page 823

EXPLORATION OF SOUTH AMERICA, 1498-1547

Two world maps by the Flemish cartographer known as Ortelius (1527-1598). The top map, which he published in the mid-sixteenth century reflected the limits of European knowledge of the Western Hemisphere at that time. His second map, which he published in 1587, shows considerable advances in European knowledge about South America. (Corbis)

A replica of Pedro Cabral's ship Nau Capitania *sailed into the bay of Rio de Janeiro in August, 2000, in preparation for celebrations of Brazil's quincentenary.* (AP/Wide World Photos)

In Rio de Janeiro, gleaming new apartments contrast sharply with the houses of the neighboring favela. (Clyde L. Rasmussen)

Rio de Janeiro, Brazil's second-largest city and the nation's former capital, was the seat of the Portuguese monarchy in the early nineteenth century, while France occupied Portugal. (American Stock Photography)

Major Urban Centers in South America

Galápagos
Islands

North
Atlantic
Ocean

• Medellin
Bogotá ★
Cali •

★ Quito

Amazon Basin

Belem •

Lima ★

Brasilia ★

A
N
D
E
S

★ La Paz

• Arica

M
O
U
N
T
A
I
N
S

South
Pacific
Ocean

Asunción ★

Rio de Janeiro •
São Paulo •

• Porto Alegre

• Mendoza

Santiago ★

Buenos Aires ★
Montevideo

South
Atlantic
Ocean

Falkland Islands

Major Urban Centers in Central America

Gulf of Mexico

Chetumal

Belmopan

Caribbean Sea

Quezaltenango

Guatemala City

Tegucigalpa

Puerto Lampira

Rio Cocoosegoria

San Salvador

San Miguel

Lake Managua

Pan-American Highway

Managua

Lake Nicaragua

Bluefields

Rivas

Liberia

Puntarenas

San José

Panama Canal

Colon

Cañita

Lake Bayano

Gatún Lake

Panama City

Pacific Ocean

Colorfully painted apartments in a Buenos Aires residential district. (PhotoDisc)

Farms in Ecuador's Andean terrain. (American Stock Photography)

SELECTED AGRICULTURAL PRODUCTS OF SOUTH AMERICA

North Atlantic Ocean

GUYANA
VENEZUELA
SURINAME
FRENCH GUIANA

Coffee
• Medellin
Coffee
★ Bogotá
Cali •
Cotton
COLOMBIA

Sugarcane
Cattle
Rice
Bananas
Yams

ECUADOR ★ Quito
Coffee
Bananas

Galápagos
Islands

Bananas
Manioc

Cacao
PERU

Amazon Basin

Belem

Bananas
Oranges
Cotton

BRAZIL
Timber

Coffee

Barley
Lima ★
Potatoes

Soybeans

Alpaca **BOLIVIA**
Llama ★ La Paz

Brasilia ★
Cacao

• Arica

Yams
Cassava
Root Crops

Sugarcane

PARAGUAY
Taunin

Coffee
São Paulo
Rio de Janeiro

CHILE Grapes
Apples

Asunción •
Tobacco
Rice
Sugarcane

• Porto Alegre

South Pacific Ocean

ARGENTINA

Peaches
Sheep **URUGUAY**

Fish

Santiago ★
Plums
Beef
Cattle
Buenos Aires ★
Montevideo ★

South Atlantic Ocean

Wheat

Falkland Islands
Sheep

814

Coffee bean plants. Central America, the Caribbean, and South America are all major coffee-producing areas. However, the Brazilian Highlands are the world's primary coffee-growing region. (PhotoDisc)

Intensive planting on this altiplano peak has given it the look of a patchwork quilt. (Clyde L. Rasmussen)

Banana trees. Central America is one of the world's leading producers of bananas. The banana industry flourished under the control of North American growers, especially the United Fruit Company. Beginning in the latter part of the nineteenth century, the banana export business grew and enjoyed large markets in the United States and Europe. (PhotoDisc)

A day laborer cuts sugarcane in a Guatemalan field. By the late 1990's, sugar ranked as Guatemala's second-leading export, after coffee. (AP/Wide World Photos)

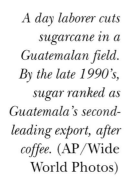

SELECTED AGRICULTURAL PRODUCTS OF CENTRAL AMERICA

Gulf
of
Mexico

BELIZE

★ Belmopan

Coffee

GUATEMALA

Guatemala
City
★

Bananas

HONDURAS

Tegucigalpa
★

San Salvador ★

Corn

● San Miguel

Coffee

Sugarcane

EL SALVADOR

NICARAGUA

Lake
Managua

Managua
★ **Rice**

Cacao

Caribbean Sea

Lake Nicaragua

● Liberia

Pacific
Ocean

San José
★ **Coffee**
Cattle

**Panama
Canal**

COSTA RICA

Gatún
Lake

★
Panama City

Lake
Bayano

PANAMA

Timber

New cars lined up outside the São Paulo, Brazil, Volkswagen factory. (AP/Wide World Photos)

Worker washing coffee beans in Pocos de Caldas, Brazil. Brazil is the world's largest producer and exporter of coffee. (AP/Wide World Photos)

Workers in a Costa Rica factory make Rawlings baseballs for North American major league games. (AP/Wide World Photos)

An overload of commuter traffic brings roads in Brazil's largest city, São Paulo, to a complete stop. In the late 1990's buses were carrying about six million passengers a day in the city. (AP/Wide World Photos)

Charcoal worker in Grão Mogol, Brazil. Most of the charcoal that powers Brazil's steel mills is produced by cheap labor in remote parts of the country. (AP/Wide World Photos)

Venezuelan oil workers stroll past a tanker loading oil at Maracaibo. (AP/Wide World Photos)

Cargo ship moves south through the Gatun Locks of the Panama Canal in late 1998. These locks, which mark the Caribbean entrance to the canal, are located in Colon, Panama's second largest city and principal Caribbean port. (AP/Wide World Photos)

In mid-1998, this old-fashioned Argentine train retraced part of the so-called "convict train" route to Ushuaia, the world's southern-most city, more than two thousand miles south of Buenos Aires. Much of the early railroad was built by convict labor. (AP/Wide World Photos)

The problems of transportation in Central America are aggravated by extreme weather. Here, hundreds of Guatemalans must patiently wait to cross a temporary footbridge after Hurricane Mitch washed away a road near Guatemala City in November, 1998. (AP/Wide World Photos)

Juan Perón (left) campaigning for the presidency of Argentina in 1946. His wife, Eva Perón, whose fame later eclipsed his, stands behind him. (National Archives)

In the 1950's and after, import-substituting industries were established in response to the urging of long-time Argentine leader Juan Perón, who was president from 1946 to 1955, and again in 1973 and 1974. Consumer appliances, such as refrigerators, stoves, and radios, began to be produced in Argentina, primarily in Buenos Aires. More recently, industry has begun to decentralize from Buenos Aires proper into its suburbs, although it remains highly concentrated in the Pampas region. Deconcentration has occured because the types of industries that have developed in the region all require greater space and are "nuisance" industries: iron and steel, petroleum refining and petrochemicals, and automobile assembly.

CENTRAL CHILE. Chile was more dependent on just a few commodities—copper and nitrates—than were most South American economies and thus was harder hit by the Great Depression than most places. As a result, the Chilean government encouraged industrialization in the 1930's and 1940's, earlier than did most governments in South America. Chile now has several well-established industries, including textiles and apparel, construction materials, and food processing. Some attempts at establishing industry have failed, for example, building an automobile assembly industry in the middle of the desert in the north of the country.

OTHER REGIONS. Manufacturing is found in several other regions of South America. Northern Venezuela is dominated by petroleum refining and petrochemicals as a result of its plentiful petroleum in the Lake Maricaibo region. It also has seen the rise of manufacturing for the domestic market in the region from Caracas westward to Valencia. In Colombia, food processing tends to be concentrated around Cali and textiles near Medellín. Similar industries are found near Lima in Peru.

Timothy C. Pitts

FOR FURTHER STUDY

McCarry, John. "Peru Begins Again." *National Geographic* (May, 1996): 2-35.

INFORMATION ON THE WORLD WIDE WEB

A good site at which to begin Internet research on South American industry is Infoplease. Current information on individual countries' exchange rates, gross domestic products, major industries, and history is available.
(www.infoplease.com/countries.html)

The World Factbook 2000 Web site, maintained by the U.S. Central Intelligence Agency (CIA), features industrial profiles of individual South American countries.
(www.odci.gov/cia/publications/factbook)

The Latin American Network Information Center at the University of Texas maintains a Web site with links to resources on South American industry.
(www.lanic.utexas.edu/)

Tenenbaum, Barbara, ed. *Encyclopedia of Latin American History and Culture.* New York: Charles Scribner's Sons, 1996.

van Dyke, Jere. "Amazon: South America's River Road." *National Geographic* (February, 1995): 2-39.

Webster, Donovan. "The Orinoco." *National Geographic* (April, 1998): 2-31.

CENTRAL AMERICA

Central America has exported raw materials and agricultural products to Europe and other countries in the Western Hemisphere from its earliest days as a colonial dependency of the Spanish crown. Its warm weather and rich volcanic soil made the isthmus an ideal environment for raising crops and livestock. In the twentieth century, its exports of coffee, bananas, cotton, and shrimp were the major sources of income for the seven independent countries located in the bridge of land between the North American and South American continents.

This basically agricultural economy benefited only a small segment of Central American society. The majority of its rapidly growing population lived an economically marginal existence. The economies of all of the countries of the isthmus had gradually become stagnant.

In the 1950's, the United Nations Commission for Latin America, led by Raúl Prebisch of Argentina, suggested that groups of countries such as those in Central America should reorganize their economies. The commission recommended a plan to develop local industry and establish trade regulations designed to help one another. Private and public investment in industry in each Central American country would be encouraged, and tariff walls would be erected around the region to protect incipient local industrial development. The result would be an economic trading unit with a population base in the tens of millions rather than one restricted to that of a single country.

Five Central American countries—Guatemala, El Salvador, Nicaragua, Honduras, and Costa Rica—

THE INTRODUCTION OF COFFEE TO EL SALVADOR

After a synthetic indigo dye was developed by German scientists in the mid-1800's, El Salvador looked for a new cash crop to replace indigo, on which the country's agriculture had been based. The coffee bean had already been adopted in Costa Rica, demonstrating that the fertile soil of the Central American isthmus provided an ideal environment for coffee cultivation. The introduction of the coffee bean in El Salvador in the late 1800's changed the whole economic, political, and social structure of the country. It gave rise to a new economic elite and destroyed the system of subsistence farming carried on by the country's majority indigenous population. The tiny country, together with its larger Central American neighbors, became principal participants in the global coffee economy.

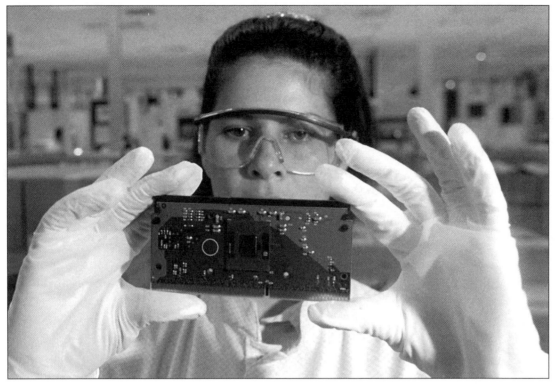

A technician inspects a Pentium III chip in Intel's Belen, Costa Rica, plant. (AP/Wide World Photos)

formed the Central American Common Market (CACM), designed to integrate the economies of its members. In 1960 planners began establishing local industries designed to take advantage of the larger Central American market by reducing or eliminating tariffs among its members. The member countries, at the same time, established tariff barriers on goods from outside Central America that would compete with the newly formed domestic economic units. This process is defined as import-substitution industrialization.

The initial agreement called for free trade within the group of 239 Central American products, as well as a ten-year phase-in on all the remainder of goods produced in Central America. The largest group of commodities that began to flow among the members were consumer goods, mostly processed foods. During the 1960's and 1970's, trade within the CACM increased dramatically. Unfortunately, most of Central America's industrial development remained in the consumer goods sector and did not expand into the area of extraregional exports designed to compete in global markets, initially a major goal for the CACM.

PROBLEMS IN INDUSTRIAL DEVELOPMENT. While the tariff walls set up to protect local industry from foreign competition increased trade among the CACM members, they failed to furnish any incentive for the attempts of Central American industry to break into established markets outside of the isthmus itself. Both the price and quality of their goods faced real competition in open world markets. Capital goods required to establish local industries had to be imported from abroad as well. Again, the countries in the region faced a stagnation of their respective economies as the market within the CACM be-

825

came saturated, and local industry failed to enter the more competitive foreign markets. Only the agricultural exports, broadened to include cotton and seafood, proved attractive to buyers from outside of the CACM.

War broke out between Honduras and El Salvador in 1969, caused by the expulsion of Salvadoran immigrants who had crossed the border to work in the banana industry and take up residence in Honduras. The so-called Soccer War of 1969 was only the first of a series of conflicts, both internal and external, involving Honduras, El Salvador, Nicaragua, and Guatemala. These conflicts compromised the effectiveness of the CACM in the 1970's and 1980's. Honduras resigned from the CACM, claiming that El Salvador and Guatemala derived more benefit from the treaty than did the other members.

Only after the countries involved solved much of their internal and external disorder did the twin concepts of free trade and further industrial development among the Central American countries come into fruition once more. Both Panama and Belize also began to participate in the planning for an integrated Central American trade zone.

THE MAQUILA FACTOR. Globalization has resulted in the expansion of foreign industry into Central America. *Maquiladoras*, in effect assembly plants for unfinished goods brought into the area by foreign entrepreneurs, have been established throughout the region to take advantage of an increasingly large labor pool of

Baseball factory Page 819

skilled workers willing to perform at a competitively low wage level that has existed on the isthmus. Foreign manufacturers have also received favorable tax treatment for the goods assembled in Central America. The arrangement reduces the rate of unemployment locally, decreasing, to some degree, the pressure on Central American governments to solve local job shortages.

TOURISM. The coastal zones of Central America, both on the Atlantic and the Pacific, are home to a wide variety of excellent beaches and sportfishing grounds. Governmental and private organizations have attempted to attract tourists to these areas. There have been modest investments by both domestic and foreign interests to develop beach and fishing resorts on both coasts. However, the continued high domestic crime rate found in many Central American coastal areas has discouraged the development of this industry. Both foreign capital and foreign visitors seek to avoid industrial enterprises that lack security.

Carl Henry Marcoux

FOR FURTHER STUDY

Bulmer-Thomas, Victor. *The Political Economy of Central America Since 1920.* New York: Cambridge University Press, 1987.

Pérez Sáinz, and Juan Pablo. *From the Finca to the Maquila: Labor and Capitalist Development in Central America.* Boulder, Colo.: Westview Press, 1999.

TRANSPORTATION

SOUTH AMERICA

Waterways, highways, railroads, and airways are crucial facilitators of trade, and economic growth is almost always accompanied by an expansion of transportation systems. Unlike North America and Western Europe, South America does not possess fully integrated transportation networks. Goods and people do not move easily to and from the furthest corners of the continent, and many regions can be reached only by circuitous and lengthy routes. Sometimes, several changes in the mode of travel are required. A traveler setting off from the Brazilian metropolitan center of São Paulo, whose destination is a small village of the Amazon region, may first travel on an airline, then ride a bus, switch to a horsecart, and finally complete the trek in a dugout canoe.

HISTORICAL BACKGROUND. The earliest engineered transport systems in South America were footpaths maintained in the Andes mountains by the Incas. These routes included hanging bridges across deep gorges, stone stairways up steep slopes, and well-maintained roadbeds through some of the most difficult terrain in the world. The roads were used by couriers of the emperor and were a vital mechanism by which he exercised his authority over a region that stretched from present-day Chile to central Ecuador. The Spaniards who conquered the Incas had little use for these routes connecting the Amerindian communities in the highlands, so the footpaths were abandoned. The Europeans were more anxious to establish roads from the highlands to the coast.

The colonial period brought an economic system known as mercantilism. Under this system, the function of the South American colonies was to supply Spain and Portugal with raw materials. The Eu-

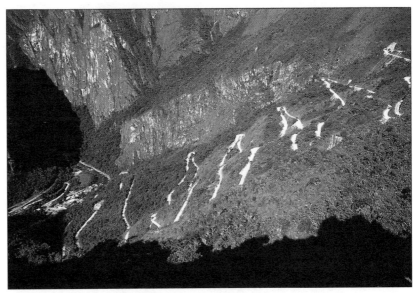

This Inca footpath to Machu Picchu in Peru contains countless switchbacks. (Clyde L. Rasmussen)

827

ropean nations, in turn, were responsible for providing the manufactured items that were needed in the colonies. All trade relationships, therefore, involved connections from each of the South American colonial areas directly to Spain (or Portugal for the Brazilian colony). During the sixteenth and seventeenth centuries, the South American colonies produced gold and silver for the Spanish crown, and sugar and other agricultural items for the aristocracy of Portugal. Later, Brazil also shipped gold to Europe. The colonial areas produced commodities that were desired back in Europe, not items that could be exchanged with each other. There was very little intracontinental trade, therefore.

The transportation routes constructed during the colonial period were designed to accommodate the flow of trade. Most of the mining areas in Spanish South America were located near the Pacific coast, so

This late nineteenth century illustration of steers being loaded onto a ship at Guayaquil, Ecuador, indicates the need for proper port facilities in the region. (Arkent Archive)

roads were built directly from the highlands and across the coastal plains to port cities. Minerals were brought down the mountains on the backs of mules from mining centers such as Cerro de Pasco and Potosi, and when the coast was reached, the cargo was loaded aboard ships destined for Panama. There, the freight was unloaded and carried overland to the Caribbean shore, where it was shipped on vessels in large convoys across the Atlantic Ocean to Spain.

The Portuguese likewise built roads from the cane fields of the northeast and later from the gold mines of Minas Gerais, directly to the coast. Port cities such as Recife and Rio de Janeiro flourished because of the activities linked to loading the sailing vessels destined for Lisbon. As in Spanish South America, trade and the associated economic activity caused roads and paths to link the interior to the shoreline.

IMPACT OF INDEPENDENCE. For most South American countries, the independence movements of the early nineteenth century altered neither the pattern of trade nor the layout of transportation routes. South American republics continued to provide raw materials for the rest of the world, although not necessarily for Spain and Portugal. During the nineteenth and early twentieth centuries, for example, Brazil became the world's major supplier of coffee, Argentina and Uruguay produced meat and grain for Europe, Chile sent nitrate and copper to North America, Bolivia shipped tin, and Peru exported guano. In most areas of South America, this pattern continues to the present.

The majority of the countries derive revenue from exports and use the money to purchase needed manufactured goods from abroad. Only the larger economies—Argentina, and especially Brazil—

have been able to develop a substantial internal industrial base and market for their products. In those countries, transportation networks that interlink important centers within the national territory have evolved. However, much traffic is still focused on moving commodities to the coast.

RAILROADS. The earliest railroads in South America date from the first half of the nineteenth century, and, as with the colonial routes, the railroads were designed to facilitate the exploitation of export commodities. In mining areas such as northern Chile and mountainous Peru, a single line led to the sea; in predominantly agricultural regions such as southeast Brazil and the Pampas of Argentina, a more substantial network was needed because of the dispersed distribution of production. Construction was financed from abroad, especially by British investors.

Several rail lines showcased imaginative strategies for overcoming the engineering difficulties posed by the mountainous terrain. Peru's line from Lima to Cerro de Pasco featured a series of sharp switchbacks, and the climb up the southeast Brazilian escarpment from Santos to São Paulo used of a cable pulley system.

Later lines linked interior Colombia to the coast, and Bolivia to northern Argentina and Brazil. One of the most interesting railroad projects was the construction of a line that provided a detour around the falls of the Madeira River in the heart of the Amazon region. Accomplished with great loss of life owing to yellow fever, the route was built to facilitate the export of natural rubber from regions of northern Bolivia during the rubber boom of the early twentieth century. The railroad was never profitable, and its use was discontinued in the 1960's.

By the early twentieth century, dense rail networks had been laid out in south-

Train station on the Peruvian Altiplano. (Clyde L. Rasmussen)

east Brazil and the Pampas of Argentina. Established to support the export of coffee from Brazil and meat and grains from Argentina, these lines also provided the metropolitan centers along the coast with access to the interior. As the economies of these two countries evolved toward greater self-sufficiency, the rail lines helped support the needs of the manufacturing plants of São Paulo, Buenos Aires, and neighboring centers. For these countries, rail lines played an important role in stimulating industrialization in addition to the traditional function of facilitating commodity exports. Although in modern

Argentine railroad Page 821

times much of the track of the networks has fallen into disuse (as in the United States), Brazil and Argentina still have the densest rail network in South America.

Railroads in South America were plagued by difficulties in the late twentieth century. In Argentina, the decline in the significance of the export economy reduced the importance of railroads. There, and in Brazil, the governments' active program of highway construction and subsidies offered to truck manufacturing have diverted traffic away from the rail lines. Until recently, almost all the railroads in South America were run by government agencies; graft, corruption, inefficiency, and a lack of safety were constant problems. During the 1990's, however, there was a move toward privatization of the rail lines with the hope that management operations would improve.

Venezuelan railroad in the 1890's. (Arkent Archive)

HIGHWAYS. Many of the highways of South America occupy routes that date back to the colonial period and even earlier. During the nineteenth and early twentieth centuries, rail transport took over the bulk of the freight traffic in some areas, but roads continued to support vital local and regional travel. During the second half of the twentieth century, highway construction and traffic increased at an explosive rate while the railroads came to play a secondary role. In some countries, such as Venezuela, railroads never achieved a major role, and highways have always been dominant.

In the densely populated areas around Caracas in Venezuela, the Cauca Valley of Colombia, the Guayas lowland of Ecuador, the Peruvian capital of Lima, middle Chile, the Pampas of Argentina, and southeast Brazil, dense road networks have evolved. Most roads in South America are dirt or gravel, but a significant percentage in the larger and more developed countries has been paved.

The construction of highways and the proliferation of vehicles has led to serious problems in most countries. Though paved, many routes are in dire need of repair. Two-lane highways, clogged with slow-moving trucks and speedy cars operated by inexperienced drivers, combine to create serious safety hazards. South American countries have some of the highest accident rates in the world. Urban areas are seriously congested and polluted by the fumes from buses, automobiles, and trucks. Little urban planning occurs, and vehicles often travel on roads that were built for pedestrian or animal traffic. Dwellers of the larger centers of Rio de Janeiro, São Paulo, and Buenos Aires have access to subway systems, but daily commuters in these and other cities may spend hours traveling to their jobs.

Highways provide the principal access to interurban public transportation for most South Americans. Buses serve most communities of the continent, and travel is relatively cheap. Many of the bus companies offer comfortable accommodations on overnight sleepers linking major cites. Brazil and Argentina have large transportation manufacturing industries that turn out a great variety of automobiles, buses, trucks, and motorcycles.

While most roads are built in response to economic or social need, over the past decades, several South American nations have used highway construction as a tool to try to create economic development.

The first of these efforts was the Pan-American Highway project, initiated after a conference of the American states in 1923. This highway, which links all the nations of the Western Hemisphere over a distance of 16,031 miles (25,800 km.), has been completed with the exception of a 54-mile-long stretch (87 km.) in Central America. The Pan-American Highway has contributed greatly toward interlinking the nations of South America, thus modifying the historical down-to-the-coast orientation of the road and rail systems. Engineering difficulties and environmental concerns have delayed construction through the Darien region of eastern Panama and northern Colombia.

Governments also have used road-building projects to accomplish policy goals. Most of these routes lead directly into the rain forest, and they were established to encourage economic development and establish sovereign control over

Highway into Caracas during the 1970's. (Clyde L. Rasmussen)

remote territory. During the late 1960's, the government of Peru undertook the construction of the Carretera Marginal de la Selva highway, which runs along the eastern flank of the Andes. By 1968 it had been connected with other routes across the mountains, and the project opened large areas of the Amazon rain forest to settlement. Although the grand hope of extending the road from Venezuela to Bolivia and linking with the Brazilian network was not realized because of funding shortages and political unrest, the Carretera has encouraged migration into the forested areas of eastern Peru.

From the late 1960's through the 1980's, the Brazilian government diverted a substantial amount of government funding to the construction of three highways: the Belém-Brasília, the Trans-Amazonian, and the Rondonha. Although initially little more than dirt tracks that were impassible during the rainy season, the paved routes have become heavily traveled by trucks and buses. The first ran directly north from Brazil's new (at the time) capital city to the important port at the mouth of the Amazon River. The second extended over a thousand miles from the overpopulated northeast into the interior forest region, and the third linked the urbanized southeast with the northwest territory of Rondonha. The latter has been especially successful in facilitating the migration of peasant farmers into the heart of the Amazon, where they have contributed significantly to the clearing and burning that endangers the rain forest.

These highways were expected to facilitate the migration of people from overcrowded coastal regions to relatively empty interior areas and facilitate the movement of government forces for political control. They also were designed to provide a network over which newly produced forest products might be shipped to urban areas along the coast. Reducing the cost of transportation was expected to create economic viability for many activities and thus promote development.

Although successful in encouraging migration and the extraction of forest resources, these frontier road-building schemes have not brought growth and development to the region. The most important consequence has been the endangerment of indigenous groups, animals, and plant communities, which are threatened by encroaching civilization. Because of poor soil conditions, limited economic resources, and remoteness from population centers, the interior Amazon region remains one of the poorest areas in the Western Hemisphere.

INLAND WATERWAYS. Traffic on inland waterways is handicapped by several problems. Many regions of South America experience heavy rainfall during the summer months (December, January, and February, south of the equator), followed by dry conditions during the winter, so water levels in the rivers fluctuate dramatically. Many of the streams include rapids, waterfalls, and artificial dams that block navigation. Nevertheless, some of the rivers provide important routes of access.

The Amazon River is wide and deep, so ocean-going ships can easily navigate its course from the mouth to the city of Iquitos in Peru. The Paraná system in the south is not as favorable a channel for shipping, but because the rivers flow through important urban and industrial areas, they are economically more important than the Amazon.

The countries of the Common Market of the South (MERCOSUR)—Brazil, Argentina, Paraguay, and Uruguay—have undertaken two important projects that will improve shipping in southeastern South America. The basin of the Paraná and its tributaries is being dredged and improved to accommodate large vessels from the mouth near Buenos Aires into the interior of southeast Brazil near São Paulo. A substantial amount of the resources are being used to build lock systems that can elevate boats around the massive dams that block several of the rivers.

The second major project involves an attempt to straighten and improve the channel of the Paraguay River from Corumbá on the Bolivia-Brazil border to Cuiabá in the Brazilian state of Mato Grosso. Although beneficial to shipping, the project will jeopardize wildlife in the large wetlands area known as the Pantanal. For this reason, environmental groups are attempting to convince the Brazilian government to change its plans and show more concern for the natural habitat.

Waterborne navigation is also important in northern South America. The streams of Guyana and Suriname are used to transport bauxite down toward the coast, where it is smelted and exported. In Venezuela, the Orinoco River has sustained navigation as far back as the colonial period and is used to ship iron ore to the sea, where it will be loaded on vessels destined for the United States. The Magdalena and Cauca Rivers of Colombia have provided access into the interior, and the Magdalena was the principal route into the central area near the city of Bogotá until the construction of a railroad. Across South America, the rivers of the interior offer a network of transportation routes for peasants, Amerindians, prospectors, and others who travel the streams in canoes, flatboats, and other small craft.

MARITIME TRANSPORTATION. Because of the peripheral distribution of the population of South America and the poor conditions of overland routes, several nations make heavy use of coastal shipping. Ports were developed to service the export economies, but the docking facilities also sup-

port local traffic from one coastal city to another. Some countries have significant merchant fleets. Especially notable is the large fleet of Brazil and the thirteen ships possessed by Paraguay, a landlocked nation. As those of other nations, the ships of the South American countries crisscross the globe with little reference to the home nations. Brazil also has a major shipbuilding industry. Brazilian-manufactured ships make up the bulk of the nation's fleet, and they are sold to many other nations.

AIR TRAVEL. For the more remote areas of South America, air travel is the principal means of access. Communities in the eastern regions of the Andean countries, the central and upper Amazon Basin of Brazil, and the extreme south of Argentina and Chile depend on air connections as links to the outside world. Many villages, *estancias*, *fazendas*, and haciendas include an airstrip. Local air travel has been especially important in Colombia, where the mountainous terrain hampers land travel.

South America is serviced by many commercial airlines. Airports in Buenos Aires, Argentina; Lima, Peru; São Paulo, Rio de Janeiro, and Brasilia, Brazil; Caracas, Venezuela; and Santa Cruz, Bolivia, are major hubs for international travelers. The facilities are modern, and high standards of aircraft maintenance and air traffic control are adhered to. Brazil is one of the world's major producers of aircraft, supplying a substantial portion of the commuter aircraft market in the United States.

Although several areas of South America have developed dense, interlinked networks, many regions remain largely unserved by modern transportation. Some countries still exhibit a pattern that is reminiscent of that of the colonial period, with the major routes connecting interior mining or farming areas directly to the coast.

Cyrus B. Dawsey

INFORMATION ON THE WORLD WIDE WEB

The U.S. Department of Transportation maintains a Web site featuring fact sheets on transportation in South American countries, with overview data and transportation network maps for individual countries. (www.bts.gov/programs/itt/latin/latin.html)

FOR FURTHER STUDY

Blouet, Brian W., and Olwyn M. Blouet. *Latin America and the Caribbean: A Systematic and Regional Survey.* 3d ed. New York: John Wiley & Sons, 1997.

Clawson, David L. *Latin America and the Caribbean; Lands and Peoples.* New York: McGraw-Hill, 1999.

James, Preston, and C. W. Minkle. *Latin America.* 5th ed. New New York: John Wiley & Sons, 1986.

Magnusson, Michael. *Latin Glory: Airlines of Latin America.* Oscela, Wisc.: Motorbooks International, 1995.

Preston, David. *Latin American Development.* Essex, England: Longman. 1996.

CENTRAL AMERICA

The seven nations of Central America cover an area of about 200,772 square miles (520,000 sq. km.), with a highly diverse landscape ranging from coastal lowlands outlined with islands, to uplands, to mountain ranges of active volcanic peaks. Earthquakes and landslides are common. Occasional volcanic eruptions of ash and mud cover towns. Hurricanes, high winds, and flooding also contribute to the challenging environment of Central America. Transportation in this region also is challenged by these conditions.

Central America comprises four physical regions. The Nicaraguan lowlands stretch through the central part of the region for about 250 miles (400 km.) and divide up the rugged highland region running through most of the center of the isthmus. These highland areas are extensions of the mountains in Mexico and exceed 1,000 feet (300 meters). The Caribbean lowland stretches from Belize in the north through Panama in the south and contains some navigable rivers. Cays (islands) fringing the coastline and shallow water ports keep larger ships from entering ports along the Caribbean east coast. The Pacific lowlands is a narrow strip of land bordering the Pacific side of the isthmus. The Nicaraguan lowlands is a passageway between the Gulf of Fonseca on the Pacific side to the Caribbean Sea.

The challenge of transportation has been a key to cultural and political control of this region. The Maya, Carib, and Arawak navigated throughout the area well. They used forest paths and rivers to develop trade routes north to Mexico and perhaps farther. The Caribs of the islands of the Caribbean were skilled at open-water navigation and sailed between islands in boats capable of carrying as many as fifty people. In the seventeenth century, as more Europeans filtered into the region, British pirates knew the eastern coastal waters contained many treacherous barriers for Spanish sailing ships. Pirates hid in the keys and attacked the Spanish as they sailed beyond the reefs and could not enter the shallower safe harbors. In modern times, the region was a battleground for controlling access to the world's great oceans through the Panama Canal.

ROUGH ROADS. Travel continues to be challenging in Central America. It is difficult to construct roads there, not only because of the extreme physical conditions but also because of social issues. Military conflicts, economic troubles, soaring populations, and environmental problems have all contributed to the burden of developing the region.

At the end of the twentieth century, there were nearly 140,000 miles (222,500 km.) of roadway throughout Central America. However, only about 54 percent of that was paved—the remaining roads were unimproved and dirt. The developing Central American countries have not had enough money to invest in roads and railroads, and it is difficult to further develop their economies with such limited transportation. It is not unusual to find one lone automobile traveling on a dirt road next to an oxen cart, a donkey, or a person carrying goods to be sold in a remote local market. After Hurricane Mitch hit in November, 1998, the magnitude of this problem became clear. Transportation on roads that were already in bad condition, and in some cases practically nonexis-

tent, before the hurricane, became an even greater logistics obstacle. Now they were totally wiped out, making it nearly impossible to get aid to victims in remote areas of Honduras.

Hurricane Mitch Pages 746, 822

The Inter-American Highway, also called the Pan-American Highway, is the region's longest roadway. It reaches from the Canadian boarder to the border of Colombia. It stretches 1,500 miles (2,400 km.) through Central America, linking all its countries except Belize.

RAILROADS. Railroading in Central America is tied strongly to its economic development. There are about 4,430 miles (7,130 km.) of track in Central America. Much of this is narrow-gauge track, to help make tighter turns in the highland interior. Some of these railway systems are quite old. Some are operated by electricity; others are conventional diesel electric engines. The upkeep on railroad engines, rolling stock, and track is expensive, and it is difficult for countries with limited resources to keep railroads going. Many of the rail systems in Central America are

Maintaining railroads in the nineteenth century required a constant struggle with luxuriant plant growth. (Arkent Archive)

short lines that were built by sugar, coffee, and banana plantations to haul their commodities to the coast for shipment. As early as 1913, banana companies were building railway systems to haul their products from the fields to the seaport. Many of these are still in use.

Although rail traffic has continually fallen off since the mid-1950's, development is proceeding in cooperative efforts among these countries. Guatemala, El Salvador, and Honduras entered into a free-trade agreement in 1998 to build a new linking railway system with Mexico. It was to involve 1,875 miles (3,017 km.) of track and cost 2 billion dollars. Plans also were underway to refurbish the 143-year-old Panama Canal Railroad. The railway, which runs along the canal for 47 miles (76 km.) is a transcontinental carrier in the free trade zone of the canal.

WATER TRANSPORT. The least expensive means of moving large tonnages of commodities is by water. The closeness to and accessibility of Central American seaports to markets such as the United States and Canada helped to develop the banana, coffee, and sugar trade in the region. Because Central America is a land block between the Atlantic and Pacific Oceans, it is convenient for ships to call on ports there. This blockage was also a hinderance to trade between the two oceans, however. In 1914 that blockage was removed and a new nation emerged in the region as a result.

The Panama Canal was constructed between 1904 and 1914 by the United States. Panama, originally a part of Colombia, was not a sovereign state at the time. After the French attempted but failed to build the canal in the 1880's, the United States

Tanker ship moving through the Panama Canal Miraflores Locks, about six miles (10 km.) from Panama City, shortly before the canal officially passed from U.S. to Panamanian control in December, 1999. (AP/Wide World Photos)

wanted the chance. When petitioned with a treaty by the United States to build the canal, Colombia's government refused. A general uprising occurred in the area of the isthmus. The Panamanians declared their independence from Colombia, and the United States was given full authority to build the canal. The area for the canal was leased from the Republic of Panama. By the 1990's most of the Canal Zone was back in the hands of Panama, and on January 1, 2000, the United States completely withdrew from its operations.

The Panama Canal saves ships traveling crossing between the Atlantic and Pacific as much as 8,000 nautical miles of travel by cutting through the isthmus of Panama, so ships do not have to go around the southern tip of South America. The canal carries ships from the Atlantic side, at Limôn Bay at Colôn, to the Pacific side, at the Bay of Panama at Balboa, and back. The canal is slightly more than 50 miles (80 km.) long. Ships are raised 85 feet (26 meters) through the three locks at Gatun at Limôn Bay, then lowered into Miraflores Lake through two locks, finally going through two more locks to enter sea level on the Pacific side.

It takes ships seven to eight hours to pass through the canal. When the canal was planned, it accommodated the largest ships then made. Many modern ships with deep, wider hulls, supertankers, and similar ships will not fit through the canal, which is only 41 feet (12.5 meters) at its deepest point and 110 feet (33.5 meters) wide. Those ships must pass around the tip of South America. Nevertheless, nearly fourteen thousand ships pass through the canal yearly, many of them tourist ships. About twenty million tourists visit the region each year, about half traveling on tour ships.

WATERWAYS. River transportation in the region is limited to shallow-hulled boats and seasonal water conditions. About 8,050 miles (5,000 km.) of navigable rivers and waterways are found in the region. The Belize River in Belize flows into the Caribbean from 180 miles (290 km.) from the west. It can be navigated almost all the way to Guatemala with small craft. El Salvador's Lempa River can be navigated. In Guatemala, about 155 miles (250 km.) of rivers can be navigated and an additional 290 miles (470 km.) can be used during the high-water season. Nicaragua has two large lakes and over 1,240 miles (2,000 km.) of waterways. Honduras contains about 290 miles (465 km.) of navigable waterways.

AIR TRANSPORTATION. About thirteen hundred developed airstrips are found in Central America. These can handle all sizes of airplanes, but mostly small planes penetrate into the remote regions. In some communities, airplanes are the only link to the outside world. Small airports are prevalent. Air traffic into the larger cities has been increasing, partly because of the tourist trade. About eighteen airline companies serve Central America, with planes from Europe, the United States, and Canada making regular, daily flights to Panama City, Guatemala City, Belize City, and San José.

THE FUTURE. Development in Central America is dependent on growing transportation links. Cooperation among nations to build these links will provide a benefit in the long run. Already a rail link exists between Canada, the United States, and Mexico, and more trade moves across those borders as the North American Free Trade Agreement evolves. Its geographic position gives Central America the potential to take advantage of these adjacent opportunities if it can maintain and improve its links to world markets. Although much of this environment is challenging, with tropical diseases and extreme topography,

*Gatun locks
Page 821*

INFORMATION ON THE WORLD WIDE WEB

The U.S. Department of Transportation maintains a Web site featuring fact sheets on transportation in Central American countries, with overview data and transportation network maps for individual countries. (www.bts.gov/programs/itt/latin/latin.html)

---

the Panama Canal is a good example of the possibilities people have and the progress they can make in further connecting this region to the rest of the world.

M. Mustoe

FOR FURTHER STUDY

McCullough, David G. *The Path Between the Seas: The Creation of the Panama Canal, 1870-1914.* New York: Simon & Schuster, 1977.

McNeese, Tim. *The Panama Canal.* San Diego, Calif.: Lucent Books, 1997.

Zydler, Nancy, and T. Zydler. *The Panama Guide ; A Cruising Guide to the Isthmus of Panama.* Brookfield, Wisc.: Seaworthy Publications, 1996.

TRADE

SOUTH AMERICA

South America historically has played a small role in the global economy. However, the global economy has always played a big role in the economies of South American countries. Whereas the United States exports about 7 percent of what it produces, South American countries usually export twice that proportion. For some countries, that number is even higher; for example, Chile exports 22 percent of its total production.

MAJOR TRADING GOODS. Going back to the sixteenth century, and the beginnings of European colonization of the region, South America has exported primary products to the more industrialized countries of Europe and North America and imported manufactured goods from them. South America still fills this role, though there is a growing importance for exports of manufactured goods from the region.

Raw materials that are typically not used in their original state, such as agricultural goods and minerals, are considered to be primary products. One example is iron ore, which must be smelted and then manufactured into pig iron or steel before it is useful. Another example might be cattle, which must be slaughtered, butchered, and packed before becoming meat that can be eaten. Primary products have always been the major exports from South America.

AGRICULTURE. Argentina and Uruguay are best known for their exports of agricultural products. Argentina is a major exporter of wheat; about 5.5 percent of world exports of wheat originate there, making Argentina the world's fifth-largest exporter. Most of Argentina's wheat goes to Asia, although some is shipped to Brazil. Argentina and Uruguay both export significant amounts of cattle and sheep products, usually after only minimal processing and packaging. Beef exports once went to Europe, the United Kingdom in particular, but after the United Kingdom joined the European Union, Russia and Japan became the major destinations. Cleaned wool is the major product from sheep exported from these countries.

Brazil is a net importer of many agricultural products but is the origin of many

Markets Pages 871, 872

A Brazilian harbor. (PhotoDisc)

tropical crops exported to countries around the world. The most notable crops are cotton, tobacco, and sugarcane. Other crops grown primarily for export from Brazil include cocoa beans, soybeans, and natural rubber. Brazil exports large quantities of orange juice concentrate, primarily to the United States. It is also known for its coffee, shipped to the United States and Europe. Finally, Brazil exports large amounts of wood products, either sawn lumber or wood pulp for paper manufacturing.

Other South American countries export tropical fruits and specialized crops. Colombia is known for its coffee, as is Ecuador to a lesser extent. Ecuador also exports cocoa beans. Both Colombia and Ecuador export bananas. Chile and Argentina are known for apples, grapes, and wine. Fruits are shipped to Northern Hemisphere destinations during South America's fall (March through June).

MINERALS. Many major industrial minerals are exported from South America. One of the most important is bauxite, the ore from which aluminum is made. Brazil, Suriname, Guyana, and Venezuela all export large amounts of raw bauxite. Since aluminum smelting requires heavy inputs of electricity, the process tends to take place near cheap hydroelectric power.

SOUTH AMERICAN EXPORTS AND MAJOR MARKETS

Many South American economies rely on exports for the bulk of their economic activity. Compare how much they make and where their exports go.

Country	Total Exports (in billions of U.S. dollars)	Major Markets
Argentina	25.4	EU, 30%; Latin America, 23%; North America, 14%; Eastern Europe & former USSR, 12%
Bolivia	1.4	Latin America, 58%; EU, 22%; North America, 17%
Brazil	53.0	North America, 28%; EU, 28%; Latin America, 7%; Japan, 7%
Chile	16.9	EU, 37%; North America, 21%; Latin America, 13%; Japan, 13%
Colombia	11.4	North America, 45%; EU, 26%; Latin America, 16%; Japan, 4%
Ecuador	3.4	North America, 61%; Latin America, 18%; EU, 9%; Japan, 3%
Guyana	0.5	Latin America, 53%; EU, 20%; North America, 14%; Japan, 4%
Paraguay	1.1	Latin America, 49%; EU, 35%; other Western Europe, 8%; North America, 4%
Peru	5.9	North America, 31%; EU, 23%; Latin America, 18%; Japan, 10%
Suriname	0.4	EU, 39%; North America, 26%; other Western Europe, 18%; Latin America, 14%
Uruguay	2.7	Latin America, 28%; EU, 26%; North America, 12%; Eastern Europe & former Soviet Union, 8%
Venezuela	20.8	North America, 56%; Latin America, 17%; EU, 17%; Japan, 5%

Source: Instituto del Tercer Mundo. *The Third World Guide 93/94.* Bogota, Colombia: Garamond Press, 1994.

Therefore, Canada, the United States, Europe, and Russia import most of South America's bauxite.

Another important industrial mineral is iron ore, used to produce steel. Brazil is the world's largest exporter of iron ore, most of which is shipped to Europe and Japan. Chile is the only other country in South America that exports a significant amount of iron ore. Petroleum is found in Venezuela and Ecuador and in smaller amounts in Colombia. Most petroleum exports go to the United States.

South America exports several other minerals. Precious metals are gold from Brazil and silver from Peru and Bolivia. Lead, zinc, and tin come from Peru and Bolivia. Raw and refined copper are exported from Peru and Chile.

MANUFACTURED GOODS. Few South American countries export significant amounts of manufactured goods; most import them. Major imports include high-tech products such as computers, televisions, and VCRs; capital goods and machine tools; and parts requiring assembly in South America. Few manufactured consumer goods and appliances are imported, however. Of all the South American countries, only Argentina, Brazil, and Venezuela export significant amounts of manufactured goods.

Argentina is the second-largest exporter in South America in terms of total monetary value, but most of its exports are in the primary sector. In the secondary sector, Argentina exports automobiles, often to other South American countries. Some textiles, mostly leather from the large livestock industry, are also shipped out. Steel products represent most of the remaining manufactured exports.

Brazil is the major exporter of manufactured goods in South America. One of its most important products is steel. Steel exports from Brazil find their way primarily to Southeast Asia, although Nigeria and the United States also import Brazilian steel. Brazil also exports other iron products, plus some aluminum and other processed ores.

Textiles, apparel, and automobile parts are important exports from Brazil, as well. Brazil is well known for making shoes and sneakers. Most products of this type are made to be exported to North America or Europe.

Brazil has tried to expand its export sector to help bring development to the poorer and depressed regions of the country. The most successful attempt has been around Manáos in the Central Amazon River valley. Manáos, the former center of the rubber industry when rubber was extracted from rubber trees, declined after synthetic rubber from petroleum replaced natural rubber. It was declared a free-trade zone, meaning that goods can be imported and exported from the region without tariffs being paid. This has brought some well-paying factory jobs to the people of the region. Similar attempts have been made in the northeast of Brazil, but without the same promising results.

The last major exporter of manufactured products in South America is Venezuela. Since it has large fields of petroleum, its major manufactured exports are petroleum-based products. Chemicals and plastics made from petroleum are among the major exports. Venezuela also exports some steel and aluminum.

SOUTH AMERICA'S MAJOR TRADING PARTNERS. Historically, the countries in the north of South America have had close ties with the United States, while those in the southern portions have had closer ties to Europe. Colombia, Ecuador, Peru, and Venezuela all count the United States as their largest trading partner. However, the United Kingdom was a major destination for goods from Argentina and Uruguay

Venezuelan tanker
Page 820

until the 1970's. Since then, Europe has become more integrated because of the European Union, and trade with South America has declined. Nevertheless, Europe is still the largest destination outside South America for exports from places such as Argentina, Brazil, and Chile.

The United States has increased its role as a trading partner with all of South America in recent years. There has also been a growing role for Japan in trade with the region, especially with countries such as Peru and Brazil. Other developing countries, especially in the Middle East and East Asia, have begun buying South American goods. Finally, other South American countries are rising in importance as trading partners. The landlocked countries and the smaller countries such as Bolivia, Paraguay, and Guyana have traded with their neighbors for many years. However, most South American countries have historically looked to the outside world, at least in part because they have difficulty interacting with their neighbors, given the tall mountains, thick jungles, and poor roads in the interior of the continent between them. By the end of the twentieth century, South American countries had begun trading among themselves, and that trend is expected to continue with the rising importance of regional trading blocs. Brazil and Argentina claim each other as major trading partners, for example.

U.S. TRADE WITH SOUTH AMERICA. South America is a big source of imports into the United States and a bigger destination for exports from it. Brazil and Venezuela are the two biggest trading partners, in that order, but Colombia and Argentina also have a big share of the United States' trade.

Major U.S. exports to South America include telecommunications equipment, office machines and computers, and various types of industrial machinery. South American countries are largely self-sufficient in the production of consumer goods. However, the production of consumer goods requires machinery for the factories that produce those goods. Since South America does not produce enough of this machinery, it must import it from abroad. Machines that are used to make any goods are known as capital goods, and they often come from the United States, Canada, Europe, or Japan.

However, the United States imports a significant amount of products from South America. Brazil supplies a great deal of iron and steel and also shoes and sneakers. Venezuela and Colombia sell petroleum to the United States. Other products that the United States gets from South America are coffee, tea, spices, and other types of apparel.

TRADE ASSOCIATIONS. South American countries, because of their reliance on exports, have a long history of participating in trade associations. That participation expanded as new organizations were being developed and older associations strengthened. In 1960 many South American countries, along with Mexico, formed the Latin American Free Trade Association (LAFTA), whose stated purpose was the lowering of tariff barriers among member states. By 1967 the members included Argentina, Bolivia, Brazil, Chile, Colombia, Ecuador, Mexico, Paraguay, Peru, Uruguay, and Venezuela.

Unfortunately for LAFTA, its members were all following import-substituting industrialization policies that tried to keep out foreign goods and encouraged the manufacture of domestic alternatives instead. Since a free trade agreement requires members to open their markets, those policies were completely incompatible. In addition, the far-flung members shared few things in common and found it difficult to agree on tariff levels. Thus, trade barriers were lowered on only a few goods, and LAFTA generally failed. While LAFTA continued to exist, it seemed unlikely that it will be an important factor in South American trade or economic development.

ANDEAN GROUP. In 1969, after it was evident that LAFTA was not working, five countries in the Andes—Colombia, Ecuador, Peru, Bolivia, and Chile—formed a customs union and tried to integrate development strategies. Venezuela later joined what became known as the Andean Group, and Chile eventually withdrew. In a customs union, members agree to reduce tariffs on goods being shipped to or from other member states and have a common tariff on goods shipped to or from nonmember states. The member states neither could agree on such basic things as where the boundaries between their countries were nor could they agree on more complicated issues, such as the tariff levels for a variety of goods. By the end of the twentieth century, the Andean Group had not had much impact on its members. However, many people have held out hope that the framework can be used in the future to integrate these countries' economies and lead to more economic development.

MERCOSUR. The last twentieth century trade association involving South American countries was the Common Market of the South (Mercado Común del Sur, usually shortened to MERCOSUR), founded in 1991, and including Argentina, Brazil, Paraguay, and Uruguay. A common market is a trade organization that incorporates lower trade barriers between members (like a free-trade association) and common trade barriers with nonmembers (like a customs union), and places no restrictions on the movement of workers and money between its members. As a result, trade between the four member countries increased dramatically in the 1990's

NAFTA. On the surface, the North American Free Trade Agreement (NAFTA) appears not to be an organization that would affect South America. However, there is potential for it to do so. Chile for many years linked its fortunes to its trade with the United States. During the 1990's, there was talk of Chile's joining NAFTA as a full member, along with Canada, Mexico, and the United States. By the end of the decade, Chile was not yet a member, but the potential remained for the future. In the longer run, people have speculated on the potential for a larger-scale Western Hemisphere Free Trade Association incorporating North, Central, and South America.

FOR FURTHER STUDY

McCarry, John. "Peru Begins Again." *National Geographic* (May, 1996): 2-35.

Rosenberg, Jerry M. *Encyclopedia of the North American Free Trade Agreement, the New American Community, and Latin American Trade*. Westport, Conn.:

INFORMATION ON THE WORLD WIDE WEB

Some good starting points for Internet research on South American trade are the Web sites of the International Trade Resources and Data Exchange (www.i-trade.com/), the World Trade Organization (www.wto.org/), and the CIA World Factbook 2000 (www.odci.gov/cia/publications/factbook).

Greenwood Press, 1995.

Tenenbaum, Barbara, ed. *Encyclopedia of Latin American History and Culture*. London: Charles Scribner's Sons, 1996.

Van Dyke, Jere. "Amazon: South America's River Road." *National Geographic* (February, 1995): 2-39.

Timothy C. Pitts

CENTRAL AMERICA

During the early nineteenth century, Guatemala, El Salvador, Honduras, Nicaragua, and Costa Rica briefly joined in a single nation—the United Provinces of Central America, following the region's successful war of independence from Mexico. Bickering broke out among the participants soon after, however, and each country went its separate way. Since that time, there have been several attempts to reunite the original members of the United Provinces, but without any meaningful success.

ECONOMIC UNITY. The attempt on the part of the Central American nations to achieve some form of economic union has proven to be much more popular than efforts to create a political union. Recognizing the need for creating a stronger vehicle for the exchange of goods and services among themselves, the five original nations belonging to the old federation, and—to a lesser extent—Panama, joined together in the early 1960's to form the Central American Common Market (CACM). Under its provisions, goods could move among the signatory nations either without tariffs or with greatly reduced ones. In this manner, a larger market for domestic products could be developed, strengthening the economies of all the members.

The CACM proved to be unsatisfactory to Honduras and Nicaragua, whose leader believed that their countries did not share equally in the benefits that the agreement was supposed to furnish. These complaints, together with the 1969 "Soccer War" between El Salvador and Honduras, led to the dissolution of the formal agreement. Trade relations among Central American countries remained good, however. Through the end of the twentieth century, there had been no erection of prohibitive tariffs walls to impede trade among them.

Central America's principal exports consist of natural resources such as lumber and metals; crops such as coffee, bananas, sugar, and cotton; and livestock, mostly beef. Much of the isthmus is covered with rich volcanic soil providing a fertility to the land that lends itself to the raising of plantation crops. While there is wide variety in the emphasis that each country places on items exported, the countries compete with one another, as well as neighboring countries, in finding markets for their major agricultural produce.

MAQUILADORA INDUSTRIES. The existence of a substantial labor pool of skilled and semiskilled workers, available at comparatively low wage rates, brought business enterprises to Central America. The

THE RISE OF "BANANA REPUBLICS"

Bananas were introduced to the U.S. public by late nineteenth century shipowners, who included small amounts of the fruit as supplements to their regular shipments. Bananas proved to be so popular that some U.S. entrepreneurs decided to expand the trade. Banana cultivation at that time was limited to the small output of a few Caribbean islands, hardly adequate for the presumed demand that existed in the United States. The investors decided to establish banana plantations elsewhere on a much grander scale.

The east coast of the Central American isthmus offered an ideal location for the establishment of extensive banana cultivation, providing a broad geographical production base that could weather the frequent storms that plagued the Caribbean. Central American governments involved eagerly sought potential investors in the largely undeveloped lowlands. Railroad builders in the area saw business opportunities in the development of the new agricultural industry. Soon, swamps were drained, modern harbor facilities built, and large tracts of land put into cultivation. The banana industry provided jobs for native labor and furnished health and educational facilities for their employees.

The banana business became so large and profitable that the major U.S. companies, such as United Fruit and Standard Fruit, could virtually dictate policy to the local Central American governments. Throughout the early twentieth century, the fruit companies dominated the economies of Honduras, Costa Rica, Panama, and, to a lesser extent, Guatemala. After World War II, however, as both the governments and the economies of these countries grew more sophisticated, the economic and political power of the fruit companies diminished. Moreover, the U.S. government ceased to support the claims of private companies to the same degree that it did in the nineteenth and early twentieth centuries.

governments of the isthmus also have been willing to provide tax incentives to encourage foreign business to set up factories for the processing of raw materials into a variety of finished products.

The European Union, which comprises a number of the countries in Western Europe, has adopted what can only be called trade barriers to the importation of Central American agricultural produce. These tariffs are designed to protect certain Caribbean markets—which are dominated by Europeans—from Central American competition. That kind of economic discrimination has caused the Central Americans to seek economic and political aid from the United States, the home base of the United Fruit Company and other U.S. companies with operations in the isthmus. In the late 1990's the U.S. government suggested that it would adopt reciprocal tariffs against European exports in retaliation.

PATTERNS. Central America's trade continues to be dominated by the export of agricultural products. The combination of rich soil and low labor costs have made the sale of bananas, coffee, cotton, and sugar the primary commodities for shipment abroad by the countries of the isthmus. In the case of bananas, particularly, foreign investment has been the major impetus in the production and exportation of the fruit.

Central America's seven republics vary widely in terms of the levels of economic progress. During the 1980's El Salvador, Nicaragua, Guatemala, and to a lesser extent Honduras, had their productive capabilities disrupted by civil strife. In the 1990's, these disruptions were eliminated, making production for foreign trade possible.

Hurricane Mitch Pages 746, 822

Nicaragua and Honduras suffered the most grievous losses to their respective economies as a result of Hurricane Mitch in 1998. Vast areas of both countries suffered extensive flood damage to their economic infrastructures. Nicaragua and Honduras required substantial outside help to resume normal economic expansion. At the end of the twentieth century, El Salvador still suffered from the effects of the brutal civil war waged within the country during the 1980's. A great deal of El Salvador's infrastructure—its roads, bridges, communications system, and transportation equipment—suffered extensive damage.

Costa Rica, Belize, and Panama have not faced the same economic dislocations as their neighbors. Costa Rica has become the most advanced Central American country in economic and political terms. Belize is still seeking to establish itself as an independent democratic nation after centuries of colonial administration by Great Britain. It is the least advanced country in the area. Panama must adjust to the problems and responsibilities of taking over control of the Panama Canal, the international waterway that bisects it.

Future success for Central American trade will depend on each country's ability to improve its economic development. Critical issues include the broadening of trade relations within the area and the successful expansion of the countries' economies to provide greater opportunities for their respective labor forces. Initial planning is underway to incorporate all seven countries into the North American Free Trade Association as well.

Carl Henry Marcoux

FOR FURTHER STUDY

Bulmer-Thomas, Victor. *The Political Economy of Central America Since 1920.* Cambridge, England: Cambridge University Press, 1987.

Karnes, Thomas L. *Tropical Enterprise: The Standard Fruit and Steamship Company in Latin America.* Baton Rouge: Louisiana State University, 1978.

May, Stacy, and Galo Plaza. *The United Fruit Company in Latin America.* New York: National Planning Association, 1958.

Rodríguez, Mario. *Central America.* Englewood Cliffs, N.J.: Prentice-Hall, 1965.

INFORMATION ON THE WORLD WIDE WEB

A good place to find information on trade and economics in Central America is the Web site of the U.S. Agency for International Development. (www.usaid.gov/regions/lac/)

COMMUNICATIONS

SOUTH AMERICA

While most South American countries have more highly developed communication systems than do countries in some parts of the world, particularly Africa, communication systems are less sophisticated and communication devices less prevalent in South America than in Europe, Japan, and North America. Communication systems and devices differ greatly in sophistication and prevalence from one South American country to another, and from the continent's coastal cities to its interior regions.

EARLY HISTORY. During the colonial period, South American cities such as Buenos Aries were likely to have closer communications with Europe than with communities in the interiors of their own colonies. This was because people of the coastal regions were generally of European birth or descent and had a language and cultural background similar to Europeans. The people of the continent's interior were more likely to be Amerindians, and seldom spoke the European languages, primarily Spanish, but also French, Dutch, and Portuguese. Nor did they share the European culture, and it was difficult for people to cross cultural barriers to communicate effectively.

In many ways, it was easier for the people of the coasts to make contact with Europe than with the interior of South America. The Andes Mountains, rising to above 20,000 feet (6,000 meters) on the west, the

Guiana Highlands, rising to nearly 10,000 feet (3,000 meters) on the north, and the Brazilian Highlands, also rising to nearly 10,000 feet on the east, made crossing the continent, or reaching people in its interior, nearly impossible.

Climatic differences from one area to another also made travel and communication between the coastal regions and the interior difficult. The hot, humid climate of the Amazon Basin differs greatly from the cold climate of the mountains and of the Tierra del Fuego near Antarctica. The isolation of people within their own geographic areas and climate zones increased the likelihood of communication barriers.

MODERN DEVELOPMENTS. Certainly, communication from one region of South America to another, from one South American country to another, and from the coastal areas to the interior has improved since colonial times. Modern technology has made communications easier and faster, and education and time have broken down many of the cultural barriers that existed between the various groups of South America. Nevertheless, communication between groups of people in South America is less effective and less extensive than it is between groups of people in North America, for several reasons.

First, the combined gross national product of the countries of South America is significantly lower than the gross national product of the United States or Canada. Therefore, the governments and industries in South America have less money to devote to developing communications technology. The personal income and purchasing power of the citizens of South America also are much lower than those of North Americans.

Nevertheless, there are bright spots in the growth of communications. For example, in the year 2000 technology experts considered South America the fastest-growing market in the world for Internet use. It was predicted that, by 2003, the Internet would reach from thirty to forty million customers in South America, who would make $8 billion worth of on-line purchases per year. There also were indications that South Americans would benefit from the technological revolution brought on by the development of the World Wide Web. Although most Internet service providers charged at least as much in real dollars for their services as did providers in the United States, some free services were available in Brazil, Chile, Colombia, Ecuador, and Peru.

In the year 2000 an international telecommunications company was building a $2 billion fiber-optic network that would encircle and crisscross South America, connecting it with superfast cable lines in Europe, the United States, and Asia by 2001. The America II cable system connected Brazil, the Caribbean, and South America's northeast region to the United States, and a regionwide $1.5 billion Telefonica system also became available there. At the end of 1999, South American business communications were valued at $15 billion and were growing at the rate of 20 percent a year.

OBSTACLES TO DEVELOPMENT. Despite the predicted bright future for Internet use and the strides that communications technologies in general had made in South America, in the year 2000 the continent still had much ground to cover if its peoples were to have as much access to communications technology and devices as the people of North America had. Only about 10 percent of homes had telephone service in the year 2000, compared with 90 percent of homes in the United States. In South America, only about 4 percent of homes had computers and Internet access; in the United States, this number was more than 50 percent. In the United States, there was about one television set per person in the year 2000; no South American country came near to that rate.

In South America, the average monthly income was $350 in 1999; in the United States it was about $2,500. Yet, computers, Internet service, and other communications devices cost the same in South America as they did in the United States. Moreover, it was more difficult to attain these services even for those with the money to buy them. In some areas of South America, customers wait months to get phone service after ordering it.

Of those South Americans who did own computers, 75 percent lived in Brazil, Argentina, and Chile. Experts saw a great divide between those who owned computers and those who did not. Computer owners were generally male, white, well educated, and relatively young.

LANGUAGE BARRIERS. Linguistic diversity has hampered communications within and among many South American nations. Spanish is the official language of most countries of South America, but some, such as Peru and Bolivia, have more than one official language, and many countries have mixes of unofficial languages. This makes daily communications difficult, and formal communications and communication over the Internet become almost impossible. Interpreters are needed for formal face-to-face communication and translators for formal written communication. In the year 2000 only about 15 percent of computer interfaces were a language other than English, and those were not likely to be one of the many languages spoken and written by South America's indigenous peoples. Moreover, much of the communication on the Internet required the ability to use English.

Literacy levels also presented problems in communication. While about 90 percent of the citizens of South America could read and write at the end of the twentieth century, the functional illiteracy rate was high—more than 20 percent in Brazil, for example. This has made it difficult for people to communicate effectively and to use instruments of communication, for example, newspapers, the postal service, and the Internet.

VENEZUELA, COLOMBIA, ECUADOR. Located in northern South America, these three countries are similar in their communications systems and their overall lifestyles. Spanish is the official language of all three countries, but all have many people who use the languages, such as Quechua, of the indigenous people in the area. The mix of languages and cultures affects the overall communication levels. All three countries have high poverty levels, despite their rich resources. In each country, only a small percentage of the population can take full advantage of all the elements of modern communication.

Venezuela had a 1999 population of about 23 million, but there were only about 1.5 million phones in the entire country. However, the phone system was modern and expanding. There was a domestic satellite system with three earth-based stations and one Intelsat station in the Atlantic Ocean. In 1999 there were more than nine million radios to receive the 181 AM stations. No FM stations were available, but there were twenty-six short-wave stations. There were sixty-six television stations with forty-five repeaters, and 3.3 million television sets.

The communications situation in Colombia in the year 2000 was a little better than the situation in Venezuela. Colombia had less diversity of language and culture and a lower poverty rate. In terms of the percentage of citizens who owned communications devices, however, Colombia's situation was not much better than Venezuela's. Of the nearly forty million citizens of Colombia, only about two million, about 5 percent, owned a telephone, about the same percentage as in Venezuela. However, the potential for telephone usage and ownership was greater in Colombia, which had a more modern system. Colombia had a nationwide microwave radio relay system for domestic calls, eleven earth stations as part of its domestic satellite system, and two Intelsat earth sta-

A SOUTH AMERICAN ANOMALY

The approximately three thousand residents of the British-ruled Falkland Islands, which lie off the coast of Argentina, had better access to modern communications technology than most other people in South America. By the late 1990's, the islanders owned twelve thousand phones and had access to a government-operated radio-telephone service that served nearly every point on the islands. Two television broadcast stations, provided by British Forces Broadcasting, provided local television coverage. However, because the islands' official language is English, there are communication difficulties between their residents and those of neighboring Argentina, whose official language is Spanish.

tions in the Atlantic Ocean. Like Venezuela, Colombia had many local newspapers, mostly in Spanish, and several national newspapers. Both Colombia and Venezuela had Spanish-language newspapers available on the World Wide Web.

Ecuador is one of the poorest nations in South America. In 1999, 35 percent of its population lived below the poverty level. Face-to-face communication among its citizens can be difficult, because a variety of languages are spoken there, although Spanish is the official language. The population is 25 percent Amerindian and 55 percent mestizo, a combination of Spanish and Amerindian heritage. Many Amerindians languages are spoken, but Quechua is the most common.

Ecuador had a population of about 12.6 million in 1999 but fewer than 600,000 phones. The phone system was inadequate and unreliable. There were 272 AM radio stations, no FM stations, and 39 shortwave stations. There were fifteen television broadcast stations, including one on the Galapagos Islands. The citizens of Ecuador had slightly fewer than one million television sets.

GUYANA, SURINAME, AND FRENCH GUIANA. These three relatively small countries are located on the northeast coast of South America. Both their historical backgrounds and their cultural makeup are different from most of the rest of the countries of South America. Because the languages used there are different from those spoken in other parts of South America, communication between them and other parts of South America can be difficult. In Suriname, Dutch is the official language, with English being widely spoken. French is the official language of French Guiana, and English is the official language in Guyana, which was formerly British Guiana.

In Guyana in 1999, there were 33,000

phones for a population of 705,000. There was a microwave radio relay for trunk lines on domestic calls; the system for long-distance calls was only fair. Because electricity was in short supply there, citizens could make only limited use of radios and televisions. In 1999 there were about 33,000 television sets in the country, with one public television station and two private broadcast stations. There were also four AM radio stations and three FM stations. Guyana's external debt was so high that it seemed unlikely that facilities to improve communication opportunities and electrical power services would be soon constructed.

Suriname's cultural diversity, with a population of 37 percent Hindustani, 31 percent Creole, 15 percent Japanese, 10 percent Africans, and the remainder Amerindians, creates problems with face-to-face communications among its 432,000 citizens. Nevertheless, Suriname's citizens had more opportunity for communication than did some South Americans. With about 43,000 phones in Suriname, or one phone for every ten people, the citizens of this country had greater opportunities for telecommunications than did people in Ecuador or Guyana. The domestic phone system was based on microwave relay capability, and there were two Intelsat stations. There were about 60,000 televisions to access three television broadcast stations. Suriname had several national newspapers, including the Dutch-language *De Ware Tijd*, which could be accessed on the World Wide Web.

French Guiana is tied economically to France and, therefore, has close business communications with that country. In 1999 the basic literacy rate in French Guiana was very low, affecting the ability of the colony's people to take advantage of modes of communication such as the Internet, newspapers, and the postal service.

In 1999 French Guianans had only limited access to telephone service, as there were only about 31,000 telephones for 170,000 people. Telephone service was only fair.

BRAZIL, BOLIVIA, AND PARAGUAY. Located in the interior of South America, with Brazil having an Atlantic coast, these countries face major communication problems, created by linguistic diversity, cultural differences, and physical barriers. Although French, Spanish, and English are widely spoken in Brazil, Portuguese is its official language. Thus, there are problems with formal communication between Brazil and its neighbors Bolivia and Paraguay, where the official languages are different. In Bolivia, the official languages are Spanish, Quechua, and Aymara; in Paraguay, the official languages are Spanish and Guarani. The Amazon River, located in northern Brazil, the Brazilian Highlands, and the Andes Mountains in Bolivia, contributes to transportation and communication problems.

Brazil, with a population of 172 million, is the largest country in both size and population in South America. About 20 percent of its 1999 population lives below the poverty level. Its basic literacy rate of about 83 percent was also relatively low. In 1999 there were only about 14.5 million phones in Brazil, less than one for every ten people. Despite the low literacy rate, there were many local and national newspapers, including some available on the World Wide Web.

The lack of communications structures and devices in Bolivia is a result of the extreme poverty in that country. In 1999 there were nearly eight million people living in Bolivia, with only about 144,000 phones. Most of the phones were located in La Paz and other cities; little phone service was available to people outside the urban areas. Those who attempted to subscribe to phone service found bureau-cratic problems and long waits for connections. Bolivia had only half a million television sets in 1999, less than one for every ten people.

The citizens of Paraguay also had meager phone service in 1999. There were only about 100,000 phones for its nearly 5.5 million people. Paraguay did have a fairly well-developed microwave radio relay network and one Intelsat station. The people of Paraguay had few other communications devices. There were only about 800,000 radios and 370,000 televisions in the country in 1999. Paraguay had several local and national newspapers, including two, *Diario ABC Digital* and *El Dia Diario*, that could be accessed on the World Wide Web

PERU, CHILE, ARGENTINA, AND URUGUAY. These four countries share communications problems that are common throughout South America. Face-to-face communications are difficult because of language barriers. The development of communications systems within them is difficult because of physical barriers such as the Andes Mountains.

Peru has two official languages, Spanish and Quechua, and several other languages, such an Aymara, that are widely spoken. In 1999 the poverty rate among Peru's approximately 26.7 million people was high, 54 percent. However, some Peruvians are wealthy and enjoyed access to modern communications technology. Many Peruvian newspapers are available on the World Wide Web. Few families of Peru had a telephone in 1999; there were slightly fewer than 800,000 phones in the country. There was a nationwide radio relay system and a domestic satellite system with twelve earth stations and two Intelsat satellite earth stations.

The rugged Andes Mountains of Chile contribute to financial, transportation, and communications problems for its citizens. Isolated areas of the Andes are difficult to reach, and it is not easy for people in those areas to find satisfactory employment. Thus, more than 20 percent of the nearly fifteen million people of Chile live in poverty. It is difficult to provide Chileans with modern communications technology. In 1999 there were 1.5 million phones in Chile and only about 3 million televisions. However, there was the possibility of communications expansion, since the telephone system was modern, based on microwave radio relay and a domestic satellite system. There were 63 television broadcast systems with 121 repeaters.

Argentina has an extensive phone system, but in 1999 most of its families did not have a telephone. Moreover, there were major problems in keeping the phone system operating there. During rain storms, many of the approximately five million phones in the country tend to ground out.

While most people of Uruguay speak Spanish, the official language, there are communication problems on the Brazilian border where many people speak Portunol or Brazilero, a combination of Spanish and Portuguese. Uruguay has modern telephone and television facilities, but they are concentrated in the capi-

tal, Montevideo. People outside the urban area have much poorer access to communication technology. In 1999 the approximately 3.3 million citizens of Uruguay had about 770,000 telephones, or about one telephone for every five people. There were more than one million television sets, about one for every three people.

CONCLUSION. While South America has great potential for development of its communications systems, there are barriers to such development. These barriers include linguistic and cultural differences that create communication problems and physical obstacles that make the delivery of services difficult.

Annita Marie Ward

FOR FURTHER STUDY

Fernandez, Sandy M. "Latin America Logs On." *Time* May 8, 2000.

Krauss, Clifford. "Injecting Change into Latin America." *The New York Times*, March 8, 2000.

Lagario, Juan Jose. "AT&T Latin America to Invest $500 Million in Argentina." *Yahoo Financial News*, July 13, 2000.

Rosen, Jan M. "Data Bank: Latin Stocks Rally in Duke Bid in Chile." *The New York Times*, February 21, 1999.

CENTRAL AMERICA

Central America has the same types of communications systems that the rest of the world enjoys. It has strong radio broadcasts; television has an enjoyable place in society but is not everywhere; telephones are numerous; newspapers are varied and easily available; and the Internet is taking

hold, especially in the cities and urban communities.

RADIO. Central America has 625 radio stations, including 40 shortwave radio facilities. Amplitude modulation (AM) stations are dominant, available in all seven countries. The number of frequency mod-

RADIO AND TELEVISION STATIONS IN CENTRAL AMERICA

Country	AM	FM	Shortwave	Television
Belize	1	12	0	2
Costa Rica	71	0	13	6
El Salvador	18	80	2	5
Guatemala	91	0	15	6
Honduras	176	0	7	11
Nicaragua	45	0	3	3
Panama	91	0	0	9
Total	493	92	40	42

ulation (FM) stations is increasing, but four countries did not have any FM radio stations in 1999. Shortwave radio plays a minor role in Central American society and is slowly losing its place, except in the rural communities.

TELEVISION. Television plays a strong role in Central America's society and has done so for decades. In urban areas, television has been a major source of entertainment, enabling its viewers to become part of the global society. The rural areas of all seven countries have been less affected by television. Forty-two television stations in Central America are operational every day. In addition, there are fifty-eight supportive repeater stations that catch television signals from the original stations and retransmit them. The repeater stations broaden the main signal base out to the people who live in remote areas, especially to those who live in mountainous regions. Television has added global sophistication to Central America and helped make its people more aware of what is going on in the world. There are 2.9 million television sets in Central America.

TELEPHONES. Central America has 1.4 million telephones. The telephone systems in the seven Central American countries differ slightly from one another. Some systems are above-average in operations; others are poorly constructed, maintained, and developed. Most use the microwave system for international calling, with support through the satellite earth station. The various federal governments of Central America have put a priority on upgrading the infrastructure of the telecommunications systems. Government officials have looked to their countries' major trading partners for help in telephone improvement. In each of the seven Central America countries, the United States is the major trading partner.

NEWSPAPERS. Central America has had newspapers far longer than other communications media. There are no less than forty-five recognized newspapers in the seven countries, and several unrecognized (underground) newspapers. Most of the major newspapers come from the capital cities and enjoy a wide circulation in their home country. Guatemala City has the largest circulation newspaper, *Pres Libre*, with a distribution of more than 120,000. All are in Spanish, with just a few having an English-language edition. Each country is concerned about the free press, and councils stress the importance of maintaining a free press for society.

News-papers Page 873

INTERNET. The desire for improved telecommunications for Central America is real. The growth is consistent with the rest of the world's craving for new technologies. The annual growth in the Latin America community was close to 50 percent each year during the last part of the twentieth century. The rapid increase of Internet usage has also driven the market for rapid growth in telecommunications

REBUILDING COMMUNICATIONS IN CENTRAL AMERICA

Hurricane Mitch Pages 746, 822

In 1998 El Salvador, Guatemala, Honduras, and Nicaragua were devastated by Hurricane Mitch, one of the century's worst storms. Almost $6 billion in damage was done, and the communications infrastructure of all four countries was demolished. The destruction, while tragic, gives these countries an opportunity to rebuild with new, modern communications systems on the cutting edge of technology. Various relief organizations have pledged money, skilled technicians, and advanced equipment to replace the systems destroyed by the hurricane.

A house on the coast of La Ceiba, Honduras, is destroyed by Caribbean floodwater pushed ashore by Hurricane Mitch's 120 mile per hour winds. (AP/Wide World Photos)

infrastructure. The government has encouraged Internet use so that Central America will not miss out on benefits of business globalization. Interestingly, Central America has not been supportive of privatization of the network operators.

Mexico has assisted the Central American region in the development of the Web and the delivery of e-commerce data to other Spanish-speaking nations in the Americas, as well as with markets using other languages worldwide.

Initially, it was thought that the Spanish language would cause a problem in doing business with Europe, the Far East, and the United States, but that has proven to be false.

Earl P. Andresen

FOR FURTHER STUDY

Blouet, Brian W., and Olwyn M. Blouet. *Latin America and the Caribbean: A Systematic and Regional Survey.* 3d ed. New York: John Wiley & Sons, 1997.

Clawson, David L. *Latin America and the Caribbean: Lands and Peoples.* New York: McGraw-Hill, 1999.

James, Preston E., and C. W. Minkel. *Latin America.* 5th ed. New York: John Wiley & Sons, 1986.

South America, Central America, and the Caribbean. London: Europa Publications, 1999.

INFORMATION ON THE WORLD WIDE WEB

A good starting place for Internet research on communications systems in Central America is the CIA World Fact Book 2000. (www.cia.gov/cia/publications/factbook)

ENGINEERING PROJECTS

Engineering projects in South and Central America are closely linked to the overall economic growth of the region as well as the individual countries. Economic and political fluctuations have often prevented these countries from undertaking expensive infrastructure projects such as building dams for hydroelectricity generation. In Central America, devastating hurricanes like Hurricane Mitch in 1998 frequently occur. These natural disasters with their destruction of buildings and massive flooding can set a nation's economy back decades. Particularly in the Central American republics, these tragic events undermine development in economies already devastated by years of civil war and bloodshed.

Hurricane Mitch Pages 746, 822

CONSTRAINTS ON INVESTMENT. In the late 1990's, South and Central American countries faced major setbacks from the natural environmental disasters of the 1997-1998 El Niño event, falling East Asian demands for their mineral exports, and uncertainties concerning future international linkages. These countries were just beginning to gain economic stability. Once they win the confidence of foreign investors, expensive projects like dams, canals, and port improvements can be discussed and implemented.

El Niño Page 694

Inflows of capital from foreign countries are closely linked to world economic conditions and internal political events. The countries of South and Central America rely heavily on foreign investment monies. The countries of this region also have low personal savings rates, which means they contribute little toward investment within their own economies. For this reason, this region has been heavily dependent on cash flows from foreign nations. The growing trend toward privatization, or private ownership of businesses and industries, has slowly improved economic conditions in Chile, Peru, and Argentina. As reforms have slowly taken place in banking and finance in these countries, foreign banks and industries have become more willing to invest in development projects, such as building dams and improving port facilities.

The economical development of Bolivia, Uruguay, and most Central American countries has been retarded by civil wars, lack of resources that the world wants, or poor political leadership. Few, if any, engineering works were taking place in these countries around the year 2000. Foreign nations have shown little interest in infrastructure projects in these countries.

HYDROELECTRIC PROJECTS. In August, 1999, the Brazilian government's electrical-power-producing corporation, Electrobras, unveiled plans for a series of large dams in the Amazon Basin. The plans called for a series of large dams on the Tocantins and Araguaia Rivers and the revival of a controversial plan for a dams network on the Xingú River. They were controversial because dams would flood tens of thousands of square miles of tropical forests. They could also displace more than 100,000 people and could flood extensive areas of native Amazonian indigenous reserves, affecting the Xingú indigenous park.

Under the Electrobras plan, eleven large dams were planned to be constructed on the rivers of the Amazon by the year 2015. The planned staircase of six large dams on the Tocantins River would effectively turn the normally raging river into a chain of great lakes. It would also double the capacity of Tucuruí Dam, located in Pará, near where the Araguaia and Tocantins Rivers meet; that dam opened in 1985. Electrobras also proposed building two huge dams on the Xingú River—Belo Monte and Altamira. Belo Monte was to be in a class by itself in terms of capacity. It would be the first large dam to be built in the Amazon rain forest for the national power grid since Tucuruí.

The way in which the Brazilian government handled resettlements of people displaced by its massive projects provoked considerable criticism. There has also been much criticism of the environmental impact of these projects. One of the problems with these large dam projects in Brazil has been the huge numbers of people who have been directly affected. It has been estimated that more than one million Brazilians have had to relocate because of these projects. Many relocated people feel they have not been adequately compensated for their losses. Resettlement provisions have been paid but have rarely been large enough to cover the losses of those relocated to make way for the dams. Spokesmen for the indigenous people and others involved in these resettlements contend that constitutional guarantees of land rights have been violated.

A major power outage in São Paulo (pictured) and Rio de Janeiro—Brazil's two largest cities—in early 1999 underscored the need for new sources of electric power. (AP/Wide World Photos)

Despite these problems, Brazil's government officials have stated that energy alternatives are still some years away from being technically and economically practical. Brazil receives 93 percent of its electricity from large dams and likely will remain dependent on large dams for the foreseeable future. Critics claim Brazil should develop alternative energy sources, such as natural gas, wind, biomass, and solar energy. They believe Brazil should also be more aggressive at managing electricity consumption by electric-intensive industries.

*Nuclear
power plant
Page 745*

OTHER CONTROVERSIES. Controversies surrounding dam construction also occur in Chile, Paraguay, Argentina, Colombia, Panama, and Guatemala. Some opponents of dam projects in those countries have been tortured or have received death threats. Nevertheless, some dam opponents have gotten anti-dam laws passed.

Concern over the effects of dam projects in Central and South America has received technical support by researchers from major research institutions. New research reveals that Tucuruí Dam, the largest ever built in a tropical rain forest, emits the same amount of greenhouse gases annually as that emitted by cars and industries in the city of São Paulo.

Another environmental impact of hydroelectric dams is siltation in the reservoirs behind them. If allowed to go unchecked, silt buildups can greatly reduce water storage capacity and the power-generating ability of the facilities themselves. Many South American dam reservoirs have silted up within twenty to twenty-five years. One of the worst cases of siltation ever documented was that of the Amaluza Reservoir behind Ecuador's Paute River hydroelectric complex. Deforestation and soil erosion were so extreme in the surrounding highlands that the reservoir was virtually filled with sediment by

1992 and had to be dredged in order to remain operational only ten years after its opening.

Other environmental threats posed by hydroelectric projects may include the loss of fish, plant, and animal species owing to downstream water changes brought about by the projects. A greater occurrence of serious diseases such as malaria, yellow fever, and South American sleeping sickness, or Chagas' Disease, are also threats caused by the increased populations of mosquitoes, black flies, snails, and rodents in the areas affected by the dams.

Plans for small nuclear power plants, such as Nuclebras in Brazil, were not going forward in the year 2000 because of technical and financial problems. Because of restricted government investment, Brazil's expansion of electricity production has not kept pace with demand, which quadrupled during the last two decades of the twentieth century. In the mid-1990's, a range of projects was opened to private and foreign investments in an effort to increase the power available.

The main hydroelectric projects in South America include the Itaipú and Yacyreta dams on the Parana River, the Paulo Alfonso and Tres Marias power plants on the São Francisco River, the Guri Dam near Ciudad Guyana, and Ecuador's Rio Paute Project. Itaipú Dam, at Itaipú on the Parana River on Brazil's border with Paraguay, is the world's largest hydroelectricity project. It opened in 1983 and produces one-fifth of Brazil's power and much of Paraguay's.

PERU'S WATER PROJECTS. Peru is another country that was embarking on several large engineering projects in the year 2000. It was undertaking projects to create a cleaner drinking water supply and build additional irrigation projects for its agricultural sector. Only 67 percent of Peru's people have access to a central water supply, and only 20 percent of them receive clean water. Roughly 50 percent of Peruvians have access to public sewer systems. After 1990, when the government of Peru transferred ownership of water and sewer facilities to the municipalities, efforts were begun to update and improve the systems. Those helping in the upgrades of these systems include the World Bank and the Japanese government.

Reforms in the agricultural sector have led to laws improving the establishment of private water rights. Peru has invested a great deal of money in irrigation projects on its coast. Major projects built included: Chira-Piura, Olmos, Chavimochic, Chinecas, Majes, and Pasto Grande. These projects alone have provided water to more than 120,000 acres of coastal farmlands.

PIPELINE PROJECTS IN SOUTH AMERICA. In the late 1990's, work began on a $1.9 billion gas-pipeline project to move natural gas from eastern Bolivia to São Paulo in Brazil, 1,950 miles (3,150 km.) away. It was hoped that this pipeline would attract private foreign firms who plan to drill fifty or more deep wells a year—five times as many as Bolivia's state-owned oil company was already managing. Another huge natural gas pipeline project was being designed to transport Argentina's natural gas to Santiago, Chile. These pipelines were being built by consortiums, or groups of private firms working hand-in-hand with state-owned concerns.

PORTS AND BRIDGES. Many ports in South and Central America need modernization and improvement. Ports in Brazil,

especially, require radical reform and expansion. São Paulo's port of Santos has been widely condemned as the least efficient and most expensive big port in the Western Hemisphere. However, as late as the year 2000 no improvements were being planned because of lack of funding.

Bridges are also among the projects being planned as economies grow. Highway and railroad systems are being improved to provide much-needed transportation links between the countries. In 2000 the Inter-American Development Bank (IDB) and the World Bank were financing some major road improvements that were to include an expensive bridge across the estuary of the Plata River. This would serve as a major link between Rio de Janeiro and Buenos Aires, Argentina. A new road bridge was also under construction over the Uruguay River; it was financed, and would be operated, by private investors.

Carol Ann Gillespie

*Pipeline
Page 874*

FOR FURTHER STUDY

Blouet, Brian W., and Olwyn M. Blouet. *Latin America and the Caribbean: A Systematic and Regional Survey.* 3d ed. New York: John Wiley & Sons, 1997.

Bradshaw, Michael. *World Regional Geography: The New Global Order.* 2d ed. New York: McGraw-Hill, 2000.

Clawson, David L. *Latin America and the Caribbean: Lands and Peoples.* Dubuque, Iowa: Wm. C. Brown, 1997.

Goodwin, Dr. Paul B., Jr. *Global Studies: Latin America.* Guilford, Conn.: Dushkin/McGraw-Hill, 1998.

GAZETTEER

Places whose names are printed in SMALL CAPS *are subjects of their own entries in this gazetteer.*

Aconcagua, Mount. Highest peak in the WESTERN HEMISPHERE, at 22,842 feet (6,962 meters). Located at 32°39 south latitude, longitude 70°1 west, in a group of Andean summits that exceed 21,000 feet (6,400 meters). Perpetual snow and ice cover these extinct volcanoes and provide meltwater for irrigation on both the Chilean and Argentine sides.

Acre. State in NORTH region of BRAZIL. Covers an area of 59,343 square miles (153,698 sq. km.), with a population of more than 500,000. Capital is RIO BRANCO. Land descends in west from foothills of sub-Andean range to eastern lowlands. Has an equatorial climate. Business includes rubber extraction, some agriculture, and ranching.

Alagoas. State in NORTHEAST region of BRAZIL. Total area of 11,238 square miles (29,184 sq. km.), with a population of almost three million. Capital is MACEIÓ. Land descends from high, arid interior in west to tropical Atlantic coast. Lowlands in the south, along SÃO FRANCISCO RIVER. Cattle are raised in upper region scrubland; tropical agriculture is practiced along the coast.

Altiplano. With Lake TITICACA at its center, South America's *altiplano* is a high plain in the ANDES MOUNTAINS of southern PERU and western BOLIVIA. Situated at more than 12,000 feet (3,650 meters) above sea level, this cold, dry, windswept plain is inhabited by farmers who eke out a living cultivating small plots of potatoes and raising sheep and llamas. Spanish for "high plain."

Amapá. State in NORTH region of BRAZIL. Total area of 54,965 square miles (142,359 sq. km.), with a 1990's population of 400,000. Capital is MACAPÁ.

From Brazil's western border with FRENCH GUIANA, land descends gradually eastward to Atlantic Ocean and AMAZON RIVER delta. Mostly equatorial rain forest. Extensive mining for manganese.

Altiplano Page 875

Amazon Basin. Drainage area of the AMAZON RIVER system, covering about 2.25 million square miles (5.83 million sq. km.) of South America. *See also* AMAZONIA.

Amazon River. South American river, almost 4,000 miles (6,500 km.) long. Forms the largest water basin in world, fifth of world's fresh water. Begins in Peruvian ANDES as APURÍMAC RIVER near Lake TITICACA, becomes the Ucyali

Scene in the Amazon River Basin in 1943, during a transport of survey crews with the U.S. Army 311th Air Photo Wing. (National Oceanic and Atmospheric Administration)

River in eastern PERU, then meets the Marañon River and becomes the Peruvian Amazon River. After entering BRAZIL, the river's name changes to Solimões River until it meets NEGRO RIVER, below MANAUS, and becomes the Brazilian Amazon River. its major tributaries are the Negro River to the north; and to the south and progressing downriver, the JURUÁ, PURUS, MADEIRA, TAPAJÓS, XINGÚ, and TOCANTINS Rivers. These tributaries are each more than 1,000 miles (1,700 km.) long.

Amazonas. Largest state in BRAZIL. Located in its NORTH region, with a total area of 604,032 square miles (1,564,443 sq. km.) and a 1990's population of 2.5 million. Capital is MANAUS. It occupies the western half of the Amazon plain, bisected from west to east by the AMAZON RIVER, into which drain waters of the GUIANA and BRAZILIAN HIGHLANDS and the ANDES MOUNTAINS. Equatorial climate and dense rain forest. Rubber extraction, lumber, mining, cattle raising.

Amazonia. Largest rain forest in world, covering more than 2 million square miles (5.5 million sq. km.), two-thirds situated in BRAZIL. Dominates entire northern part of Brazil and extends into eight other countries and territories in South America. Equatorial climate with short dry season in the eastern half. Nutrients are primarily in vegetation, not soil.

Ambergis Cay. See CAYS (CENTRAL AMERICA).

Americas. Collective term for the lands of the WESTERN HEMISPHERE, including North America, CENTRAL AMERICA, South America, and the islands of the Caribbean.

Andes Mountains. Forming the western spine of South America, the Andes rise from the waters of the Caribbean in eastern VENEZUELA and extend southward for 4,500 miles (7,240 km.) to the southern tip of the continent and TIERRA DEL FUEGO. The Andes have twelve peaks over 20,000 feet (6,100 meters), including the highest peak in the WESTERN HEMISPHERE, Mount ACONCAGUA. Climate, vegetation, settlement, and agriculture are highly influenced by elevation. The dramatic vertical rises of the mountain slopes contain almost every climate and environment found on earth, from rain forest at sea level to tundra above tree line. The Andes are part of the Pacific Ring of Fire, a zone around the Pacific Rim that is actively mountain-building. Earthquakes and volcanic activity are common in this zone. The mountains are still inhabited by many Amerindian people, who live by subsistence agriculture. The Andes are the place of origin of potatoes, llamas, and guinea pigs.

Angel Falls. World's highest waterfall, with a vertical drop of 3,212 feet (979 meters), almost the height of three Empire State Buildings and about sixteen times higher than Niagara Falls. Located in southeastern VENEZUELA, at 5°44 north latitude, longitude 62°27 west. Named after U.S. bush pilot and gold seeker Jimmie Angel, who first sighted the falls in 1933.

Angostura. See CIUDAD BOLÍVAR.

Antigua. Colonial city and capital of GUATEMALA, from 1543 until an earthquake struck in 1773 and the capital was moved to GUATEMALA CITY. Population in the 1990's was 20,000. Surrounded by three volcanoes—Fuego, Acatenango, and Agua—evidence of the restless earth on which the city lies. Colonial churches and other architectural displays are remnants of Spain's golden age in the AMERICAS. Casa

K'ojom is a museum dedicated to the culture of the Maya, who have played such a vital role in the development of Guatemala.

Antioquia. Hilly province in northwest CoLOMBIA, known for the high-quality coffee it produces. Settled by Spanish farmers, it is a picturesque area known for conservative, Old World, small-farm traditions, and the largest percentage of residents of European ancestry in Colombia. MEDELLÍN is the capital city and an important commercial and industrial center. The population in the 1990's was 4.5 million.

Antofagasta. The principal port in CHILE for mineral exports, especially copper and nitrate. Located in ATACAMA DESERT 840 miles (1,350 km.) north of SANTIAGO, with a 1990's population of 244,000. The world's largest copper mine, Chuquicamata, is located nearby. Antofagasta was part of BOLIVIA until Chile won it in the War of the Pacific (1879-1884), but it is still the terminus of the LA PAZ/ORURO railway from Bolivia.

Apurímac River. Headwaters of the AMAZON RIVER, the second-longest river in the world and the largest by volume. Beginning in the high ANDES MOUNTAINS of southern PERU, the Apurímac River eventually merges with the Amazon River and flows 4,000 miles (6,440 km.) to the Atlantic Ocean.

Aracaju. Capital of SERGIPE state, BRAZIL, with a 1990's population of almost 500,000. Port city, located on the right bank of Sergipe River and Atlantic Ocean in terrain of dunes and lagoon. City was planned on a grid pattern in 1858. It has textile manufacturing, as well as growing tourism as a result of its beaches.

Arenal Volcano National Park. Park in the northern lowlands of COSTA RICA containing a 4,000-year-old volcano. The perfectly conical volcano rises 5,356 feet (1,624 meters). Arenal remained dormant for 400 years, then erupted in 1968, destroying several square miles of farmland around it. The park preserves eight of the twelve natural life habitat zones found in Costa Rica. Also includes Arenal's sister volcano, Chato.

Arequipa. Second-largest city in PERU, with nearly one million inhabitants. Founded on an Inca site in 1540, at an elevation of 7,636 feet (2,325 meters) in an earthquake zone in southern Peru. Known as the White City because many of the buildings are made of a light-colored volcanic rock named sillar.

Argentina. Also known as the Argentine Republic, a South American nation that occupies most of the southern portion of the continent, along the South Atlantic coast. The eighth-largest country in the world, it covers an area of 1.07 million square miles (2.78 million sq. km.) and has an undulating coastline some 2,900 miles (4,700 km.) in length. In the east, the country is separated from neighboring URUGUAY and BRAZIL by the URUGUAY RIVER. In the west, the ANDES MOUNTAINS separate it from CHILE. Argentina also borders BOLIVIA and PARAGUAY to the north. To an extent greater than was the case in most other South American countries, Argentina attracted immigrants from Europe in the late nineteenth and early twentieth centuries. In 1998 its population was 36,125,000, about 85 percent of whom were European in descent. The country still attracts European immigrants. Its capital is BUENOS AIRES.

Arica. Northernmost seaport and international duty-free trade zone in CHILE. Located in the bone-dry ATACAMA DESERT, Arica was part of PERU until the War of the Pacific (1879-1884) between Chile, Peru, and BOLIVIA. At that time, Bolivia lost access to the Pacific Ocean and became a landlocked country. The population was 180,000 in the 1990's.

Artigas. Capital of the province of the same name in URUGUAY. This small town is Uruguay's northernmost important town. It has excellent road and rail connections with BRAZIL and the cities of ARGENTINA and Uruguay that lie along the URUGUAY RIVER. Remote from the national core, Artigas services a large pastoral hinterland.

Asunción. Capital of PARAGUAY, and its first Spanish settlement. Population in the 1990's was 1 million. Strategically located where the PILCOMAYO and PARAGUAY Rivers meet, both flowing into the PARANÁ RIVER.

Atacama Desert. Located in South America along the coast of northern CHILE and southern PERU, this is one of the driest places on earth and almost totally devoid of vegetation. Some locations go for decades without measurable rainfall. Human settlements are generally situated along rivers that originate in the ANDES MOUNTAINS to the east and transverse the desert to the Pacific Ocean.

Lake Atitlán Pages 669, 876

Atitlán, Lake. Beautiful, famous lake in GUATEMALA. Located 90 miles (150 km.) west of GUATEMALA CITY. Covers 50 square miles (31 sq. km.); more than 11 miles (17 km.) long, almost 8 miles (13 km.) wide, and more than 1,000 feet (305 meters) deep in places. Surrounded by volcanoes and granite cliffs, with deep blue water, it is one of the most impressive sites in CENTRAL AMERICA. Name is Mayan for "abundance of waters."

Avellaneda. Suburb of BUENOS AIRES, ARGENTINA, in South America, with a

densely settled core of half a million people. Originally a slum for the working poor, but modern industries of meat packing, wool, and hides have brought a measure of prosperity. Its factory workers were an important power base for Juan Perón in the 1940's and 1950's.

Ayacucho. Located in the ANDES MOUNTAINS between LIMA and CUZCO, PERU. Famous for its Holy Week religious processions and colorful local market. In the 1980's and early 1990's, it was a center of Amerindian resistance and the antigovernment movement *Sendero Luminoso.*

Bahia. State in NORTHEAST region of BRAZIL. Total area of 216,612 square miles (561,025 sq. km.) with a 1990's population of more than 12 million. Capital is SALVADOR. Dry uplands in west descend to fertile, tropical Atlantic coastal area in east. Cattle are raised in upper region scrubland; tropical agriculture is practiced along the coast. Some manufacturing.

Bahia Blanca. City located at the southwesternmost shore of BUENOS AIRES province, ARGENTINA. Originally settled as a fort to protect the settled cities in the north, this city of 250,000 is an important shipping point for products from the PAMPAS and PATAGONIA. Grain, wool, and fruit are sent here by rail, then shipped to final markets.

Bananal. Largest river island in BRAZIL, comprising 7,600 square miles (20,000 sq. km.). Located in the Araguaia River where MATO GROSSO borders TOCANTINS. Extending on a north-south axis, the island is almost 200 miles (320 km.) long. The island is inhabited by the Carajás people.

Baños. Popular resort on the eastern slope of the ANDES MOUNTAINS in ECUADOR. Known for its hot springs and as a gateway for climbers of the volcanic peak Tungurahua (16,460 feet/5,016 meters) and visits to the AMAZON BASIN.

Bariloche. See SAN CARLOS DE BARILOCHE.

Bay Islands. Three islands off the north coast of HONDURAS: Guanaja, Roatan, and Utila. Located about 31 miles (50 km.) off the coast, they are a continuation of the barrier reefs found off the coast of BELIZE. Christopher Columbus was the first European to land on the islands (Guanaja) in 1502; they were not populated by Europeans until the 1520's, when pirates occupied them. The islands remain Caribbean-like, and their people speak a Caribbean style of English. They are popular tourist destinations because of the excellent diving and snorkeling.

Beagle Channel. Waterway along the southern border of TIERRA DEL FUEGO Island, located at 54°53′ south latitude, longitude 68°10′ west. Charles Darwin passed through this channel on the HMS *Beagle* on his famous scientific voyage in 1832-1834. Observing the perpetual fires built by the scantily clad Amerindians in their attempt to stay warm, he named the place *Tierra del Fuego*, or "land of fire." An ARGENTINE national park is on the channel just west of USHUAIA.

Belém. Capital of PARÁ state in BRAZIL. Located on the eastern edge of the mouth of the AMAZON RIVER, with a population over 1 million. Founded early in the colonial period. Major port and a regional commercial and services area. Noted for annual procession to Our Lady of Nazareth.

Belize. Small Central American nation located at the base of Mexico's Yucatán Peninsula, where its much larger neighbor, GUATEMALA, touches the Caribbean. Belize's land area is 8,867 square miles (22,965 sq. km.). It has a pronounced tropical climate, and 86 percent of its land is covered by forest. Its population was 224,663 in 1997. In contrast to the rest of CENTRAL AMERICA, Belize was colonized by Great Britain—which named it BRITISH HONDURAS—and uses English as its official language. It became independent in 1981, joined the Commonwealth of Nations, and continues to recognize the British monarch as head of state.

Belize City. Largest city and former capital of BELIZE, and the country's economic and transportation hub. Population was 80,000 in the 1990's. A bustling Caribbean coastal city, with brightly colored homes, tin roofs, and hurricane shutters; not a strong tourist destination. The new capital, BELMOPAN, is in the country's interior to avoid damage from hurricanes.

Belmopan. Capital of BELIZE since 1970. Located 41 miles (66 km.) southwest of BELIZE CITY, the former capital, in an interior location less subject to flooding from hurricanes. Had a population in the 1990's of 3,700.

Belo Horizonte. Capital of MINAS GERAIS state in BRAZIL. Located in central southeast of state. Brazil's fourth-largest city, with a population over 2 million. Founded in 1893, this planned city replaced the colonial capital of Ouro Preto. Industrial, commercial, and regional services center.

Bermudian Landing Community Baboon Sanctuary. Animal and bird sanctuary located about 19 miles (30 km.) west of BELIZE CITY in BELIZE. The community of Bermudian Landing has set aside forest land to preserve native species and the endangered black howler monkey. Has a visitor information center to explain preservation efforts.

Bluefields. Town and export center of

Belém
Page 876

Bogotá, Colombia. (PhotoDisc)

NICARAGUA. Located on the Caribbean side of Nicaragua, which was not colonized and remained a British protectorate until the late nineteenth century. A distinctly Caribbean town with a mix of Caribbean blacks, mestizos, and Amerindians; population was about 20,000 in the 1990's. Bluefields can only be reached by taking a boat down the Escondido River, since no roads connect it to MANAGUA.

Boa Vista. Capital of RORAIMA state in BRAZIL. In the 1990's its population was less than 200,000. Formerly located on the right bank of the RIO BRANCO, it lies in the central northeast part of state. Center of cattle-raising district.

Bocas del Toro Archipelago. Islands in the CARIBBEAN SEA that make up the Bastimentos National Park. The islands and park offer excellent snorkeling and diving. Sea turtles use the islands as nesting grounds.

Bogotá. Capital of COLOMBIA; officially known as Santa Fe de Bogotá. Located in the northern ANDES MOUNTAINS at an elevation of 8,563 feet (2,610 meters). Founded in 1538, it is a sprawling city with a population of more than seven million. Built in a long valley beneath the spectacular peaks of Monserrate and Guadalupe, Bogotá's splendid colonial architecture and wealthy modern districts contrast with its vast shantytowns, thieves, and drug dealers.

Bolívar. See CIUDAD BOLÍVAR.

Bolivia. Landlocked country in Andean South America known for Lake TITICACA, people maintaining their traditional culture, llamas, and traditional Andean music. LA PAZ is the seat of government, but SUCRE is the constitutional capital. Bolivia has a land area of 424,165 square miles (1,098,581 sq. km.), approximately the size of Texas and California combined. The population in the 1990's was 8.1 million people, 55 percent of whom were Native Americans. The official languages are Spanish, Quechua, and Aymara. The second-poorest country in South America, Bolivia has a dual economy: Local farmers grow potatoes and other traditional subsistence crops and graze sheep and llamas; the export sector produces minerals (zinc, lead, and tin), natural gas, soybeans, and sugar. It is the second-largest producer of coca leaf, for cocaine production, after PERU.

Branco River. See RIO BRANCO.

Brasília. Capital of BRAZIL, located in the Distrito Federal (FEDERAL DISTRICT), surrounded by state of GOIÁS, except for the southeast tip, which touches MINAS GERAIS. The metropolitan population was almost two million in the 1990's. Inaugurated in 1960 as the new national capital, it represented an attempt to draw population to the center of the country and project modernization and development of Brazil

Bogotá's Plaza Bolivia Cathedral. (Clyde L. Rasmussen)

through images of cultural modernism. The United Nations has declared it a World Cultural Heritage site. Numerous satellite cities also occupy the Federal District.

Buenos Aires Pages 813, 877

Brazil. Fifth-largest country in the world in terms of area (3.28 millon square miles/8.5 million sq. km.) and population (170 million in the 1990's). Capital is BRASÍLIA. Spanning four time zones and occupying the central eastern half of South America, Brazil extends from under 5 degrees north of the equator to more than 30 degrees south of it and 10 degrees below the tropic of Capricorn. Its border is more than 14,000 miles (23,000 km.) long, less than one-third of which is along the Atlantic coast; the rest touches all the countries of South America except CHILE and ECUADOR. Highly humid equatorial climate predominates in upper western half, tropical to semiarid climates in upper eastern half. Coast has tropical Atlantic climate, central south a highlands tropical climate, and far south a subtropical climate. Naturally rich soils for productive agriculture exist primarily along the eastern coast and in the southern interior. The AMAZON RIVER drains waters west to east from GUIANA and BRAZILIAN HIGHLANDS and the ANDES MOUNTAINS; in the south, waters drain north to south through the PANTANAL and the PARAGUAY, PARANÁ, and Plata Rivers. The SÃO FRANCISCO RIVER drains eastern central waters from south to north.

Brazilian Highlands. High plain of the interior of northern BRAZIL, which descends west-northwest from coastal mountains to the AMAZON RIVER floodplain. Together with the central and northern ANDES MOUNTAINS and GUIANA HIGHLANDS, they form the continental semicircular system of eleva-

tions whence waters drain into the Amazon River. Soil varies from *caatinga* to *cerrado* and even *terra roxa*. Cattle raising and agriculture dominate.

British Guiana. Colonial-era name of the South American nation of GUYANA.

British Honduras. Colonial era name of Central American nation of BELIZE, which became independent in 1981.

Buenos Aires. Capital of ARGENTINA, and the nation's cultural, economic, and political core. Population of the metropolitan area in the 1990's was nearly 12 million. So much power is concentrated in one place that the outlying regions suffer. *Porteños,* as the people who live in Buenos Aires are known, tend to regad themselves as cosmopolitan and sophisticated and the rest of their countrymen as rustic.

Cajamarca. Mountain town in northern PERU, with a 1990's population of seventy thousand. The site where Spanish conquistador Francisco Pizarro captured and executed Inca emperor Atahualpa in 1531. Has interesting colonial architecture and a colorful local culture.

Cali. Third-largest city in COLOMBIA, with a 1990's population of 2.1 million. Located in the CAUCA RIVER valley, a rich agricultural region that produces sugar, cotton, coffee, and cattle. The principal urban center in the southwest of the country, Cali is a center for salsa and Caribbean music, and a world center for cocaine trafficking and the Cali cartel.

Campo Grande. Capital of MATO GROSSO DO SUL state in BRAZIL. Located in the center of the state on a level peak of low-lying Serra de Maracaju, lying east of PANTANAL, with a 1990's population of 600,000. Railroad and transportation hub, and a center of agricultural and cattle production.

Continued on page 887

Ecuador street market. (PhotoDisc)

Floating produce market in Manaus, Brazil. (Clyde L. Rasmussen)

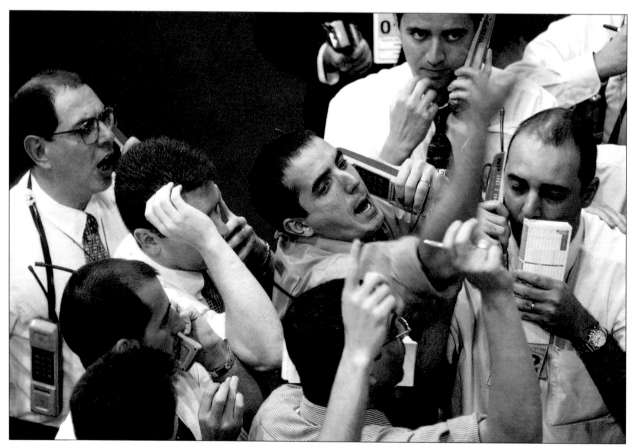

Traders working the floor of the Bovespa stock market in São Paulo—Brazil's financial capital. (AP/Wide World Photos)

Headlines in Costa Rica newspapers report the U.S. Supreme Court decision that enabled George W. Bush to claim victory in the 2000 U.S. presidential election. (AP/Wide World Photos)

South America's first great engineers were Inca builders. Without the help of wheeled carts or iron tools, they built finely dressed stone walls of such precision that many are still in use as the foundations of Spanish-era buildings. (Clyde L. Rasmussen)

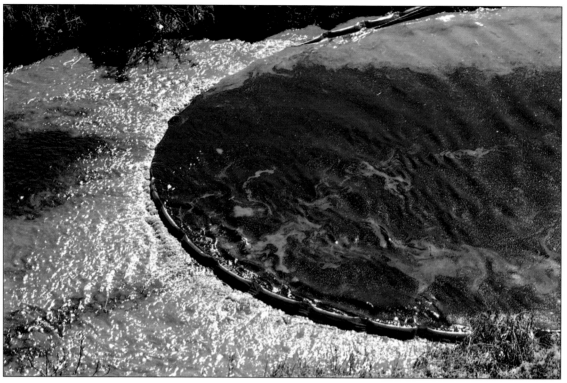

In Brazil's worst environmental disaster in nearly three decades, a refinery pipeline burst in July, 2000, releasing more than one million gallons of crude oil into the Iguaçu River. (AP/Wide World Photos)

In late 1997, Brazil became the first South American nation to attempt to launch its own satellite into space. However, the launch—which took place in northeastern Brazil—failed. (AP/Wide World Photos)

Altiplano region in Peru. (Clyde L. Rasmussen)

Belém, the capital of Brazil's Pará state, is located on the east bank of the mouth of the Amazon River. It is a major port and regional commercial and services center. (Clyde L. Rasmussen)

Lake Atitlán, in Guatemala, is one of the most outstanding scenic sights in Central America. It covers fifty square miles and is as much as one thousand feet deep. (Clyde L. Rasmussen)

876

Buenos Aires is the capital of Argentina and the nation's cultural, economic, and political core. (American Stock Photography)

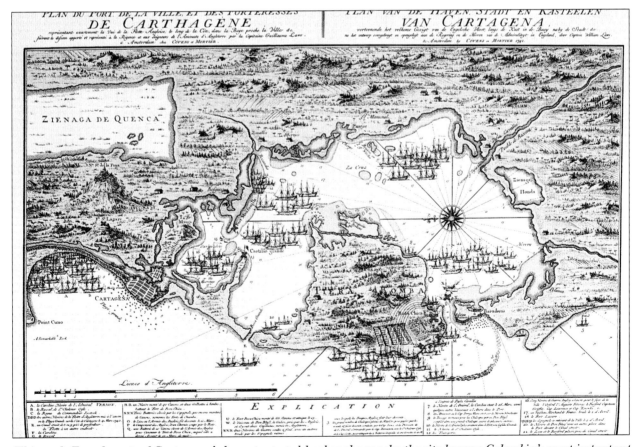

This early French map of Cartagena's large protected harbor shows why the city became Colombia's most important seaport. (Corbis)

The Galápagos Islands of the Pacific Ocean are all volcanic in origin, and their conical shapes are clearly visible in this photograph taken from the shuttle Atlantis *in October, 1985.* (Corbis)

Lake Tagus, on Isabela Island, fills the caldera of an inactive Galápagos volcano. (Clyde L. Rasmussen)

Guatemala City, the capital and leading city of Guatemala. (Isaac Hernández/
mercurypress.com)

*Iguaçu Falls, one of South America's most spectacular scenic attractions. The falls are located in southwest corner of
Brazil's state of Paraná.* (PhotoDisc)

Guyana rain forest. (PhotoDisc)

La Paz, Bolivia, from the air in 1974. (Clyde L. Rasmussen)

Popularly known as the "lost city" of the Incas, Machu Picchu is located near Cuzco in Peru. Built on a high mountain terrace on the eastern flank of the Andes Mountains, it was abandoned in the fifteenth century and was rediscovered in1911. (PhotoDisc)

Manaus, the capital of Brazil's Amazonas state, is a historic town that stands on the south bank of the Negro River, just above where it joins the Solimoes River to form the Amazon. (Clyde L. Rasmussen)

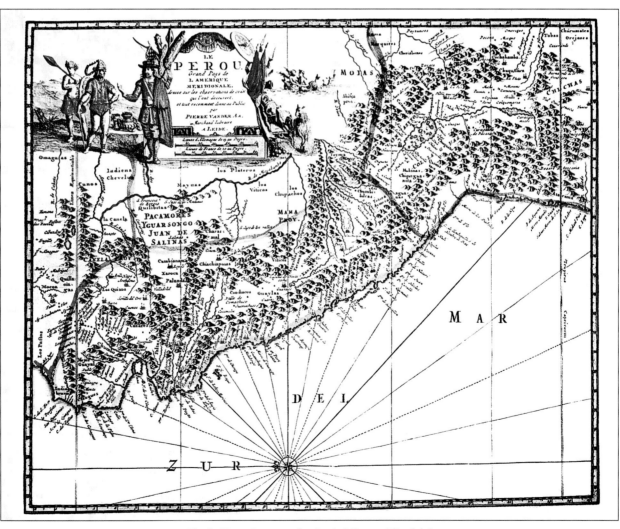

Early French map of colonial Peru. (Corbis)

Rio de Janeiro's Rodrigo de Freitos Lagoon. (Clyde L. Rasmussen)

Rio de Janeiro's famed Copacabana Beach. (Clyde L. Rasmussen)

Salvador, Brazil. Houses built on poles above the water. (Clyde L. Rasmussen)

The capital and largest city in Chile, Santiago is located in a fertile valley below the Andes Mountains. (PhotoDisc)

South America's largest city, São Paulo is the industrial, commercial, banking, and services center of Brazil. (PhotoDisc)

Lake Titicaca, the highest navigable lake in the world. (Clyde L. Rasmussen)

Canal Zone. Territory in PANAMA that includes the PANAMA CANAL. Was acquired by the United States from COLOMBIA, without the agreement of the latter, before the Panama Canal was built. Ceased to exist as a political entity in 1979.

Cape Horn. Southernmost point of South America. Located at 55°59 south latitude in CHILE. Ships prefer to pass through the Strait of MAGELLAN rather than navigate around the treacherous waters of the cape.

Caracas. Capital of VENEZUELA and the country's largest urban agglomeration. Founded in 1567, Caracas has grown to more than 4 million inhabitants, fueled by the oil boom that began early in the twentieth century. Set in the hills at 2,950 feet (900 meters), just 8 miles (13 km.) from the Caribbean coast. Has an agreeable climate with a mean temperature of 70 degrees Fahrenheit (21 degrees Celsius). One of LATIN AMERICA's most modern cities, with high-rise buildings, affluent commercial districts, and a web of highways. Migration has led to sprawling slums and a marked contrast between wealth and poverty.

Caribbean Sea. Portion of the western Atlantic Ocean bounded by CENTRAL and South AMERICA to the west and south, and the islands of the Antilles chain on the north and east. Separated from the Gulf of Mexico on the west by the Yucatán Channel, which runs from the north tip of the Yucatán Peninsula to the southern tip of Florida. Covers about 1.05 million square miles (2.7

Caracas, Venezuela. (PhotoDisc)

million sq. km.) and has a maximum depth of about 25,000 feet (7,520 meters) in the Cayman Trench.

Cartagena map Page 877

Cartagena. Seaport on the northern coast of Colombia, and one of the most beautiful colonial cities in Latin America. Founded in 1533, it was the Spanish empire's most important Caribbean port during the seventeenth century and the gateway to northern South America. The old walled city center has splendidly preserved colonial architecture. It is Colombia's most important petroleum port and processing center. Its population in the 1990's was 660,000.

Cartago. Colonial city and first capital (until 1823) of Costa Rica. Located 35 miles (21 km.) southeast of San José, with a 1990's population of 120,000. Founded in 1563. Plagued by earthquakes over the centuries, the largest occurring in 1841 and 1910, and at times showered with ash from the nearby Irazu volcano. Home of the patron saint of Costa Rica, La Negrita. A small black statue of the saint is housed in the Basilica de Nuestra Senora de los Angeles; every August, Costa Ricans make pilgrimages to pay homage to the sacred statue.

Catamarca. An oasis in the northwest dry belt of Argentina. Founded by colonizers from Chile in 1558. Irrigation from Andean streams enables farmers to grow good crops of grapes, cotton, and fruits; planted pastures are the basis of the cattle industry. Many religious pilgrims visit an old church in the city that contains a revered statue of the Virgin Mary.

Catedral, Mount. Highest point in Uruguay, at only 1,683 feet (513 meters). Located 47 miles (75 km.) north of Punta del Este, it emphasizes the nation's flat terrain. Sweeping grassy plains stretch from the Atlantic seaboard and Uruguay River to the Brazilian border. Cattle raising has been a dominant economic activity since the arrival of Europeans.

Cauca River. Major river in northwest Colombia and a major tributary of the Magdalena River; flows north from its headwaters in the Andes Mountains for 838 miles (1,348 km.). The cities of Cali and Medellín are situated in the Cauca River valley.

Caulker Cay. See Cays (Central America).

Cayenne. Capital, principal port, and largest city of French Guiana. Founded in 1637 by French merchants. Had a 1990's population of about 60,000. Its interesting architecture, colorful outdoor cafes and food stalls, and ethnic diversity give it the feel of "France in the tropics."

Cays (Central America). Barrier reef on Belize's Caribbean coast in Central America; the longest such reef in the Western Hemisphere, at 180 miles (290 km.). Cays (pronounced "keys") on the west side of the reef have clear, warm waters ideal for scuba diving and snorkeling, and they have become a popular tourist destinations. Two of the most popular cays are Ambergis and Caulker. Ambergis Cay, located 36 miles (60 km.) north of Belize City, had a 1990's population of 2,000 people. It is Belize's longest cay, connected to the Mexican mainland to the north, and the site of the only coral atolls in the Western Hemisphere: Half Moon Cay, Turneffe Islands, and Blue Hole. Caulker Cay, 20 miles (33 km.) north of Belize City, is noted for its crystal-clear water, with visibility of up to 200 feet (60 meters).

Ceará. State in Northeast region of Brazil. Total area of 57,147 square miles

(148,000 sq. km.), with a 1990's population of about seven million. Capital is FORTALEZA. Low mountains in south gradually descend to northern Atlantic coast. Ranching is practiced in arid southern interior, tropical agriculture along the coast. There is some manufacturing and growing tourism.

Center-West. Region of BRAZIL, comprising states of GOIÁS, MATO GROSSO, and MATO GROSSO DO SUL, and the FEDERAL DISTRICT. Covers more than 1 million square miles (1.3 million sq. km.), with a population of more than 10 million. Dominating feature in western portion is PANTANAL. Tropical environment.

Central America. Definitions of this region vary, but it is most generally understood to constitute the irregularly shaped neck of land that links North and South America, containing the seven independent nations between Mexico and COLOMBIA: BELIZE, GUATEMALA, HONDURAS, EL SALVADOR, NICARAGUA, COSTA RICA, and PANAMA. These countries collectively cover 228,578 square miles (592,017 sq. mi.) and were home to about 30 million people in the early 1990's. Also sometimes call Meso-America.

Cerro de Pasco. Area of extensive mineral deposits in the central Andean highlands of PERU. Once a major site of Spanish colonial silver mining, it exports copper, lead, zinc, and gold. At an elevation of 14,200 feet (4,330 meters), Cerro de Pasco has some of the highest mines in the world.

Cerro Verde National Park. Home of Izalco and Santa Ana volcanoes in EL SALVADOR. Izalco began to grow more than 200 years ago, until it formed a cone 6,265 feet (1,910 meters) high. It erupted periodically until 1966, then stopped. Adventuresome travelers can hike to the top. Santa Ana volcano is known for its deep blue crater lake, Coatepeque Lake, located on the east side of the volcano. Name is Spanish for "green hill."

Chacaltaya. Highest ski run in the world, at 17,130 feet (5,221 meters) above sea level. Located in the ANDES MOUNTAINS of BOLIVIA just north of LA PAZ. From the peak, one can see Lake TITICACA, the ALTIPLANO, and the volcanic peaks of the eastern range of the Andes.

Chaco. Immense alluvial plain, stretching from just south of the PANTANAL to the middle latitudes of northern ARGENTINA, extending 700 miles (1,125 km.) in a north-south direction. A dry tropical/semitropical region.

Chan Chán. Ruin of the largest adobe city in the world. Located on the north coast of PERU, near TRUJILLO, Chan Chán was the imperial city of the Chimú people who were conquered by the Incas in the late fifteenth century. The city wall encompasses 11 square miles (28 sq. km.) of palaces, temples, royal burial mounds, and ruins of ten thousand other structures.

Chichicastenango. Mayan city in GUATEMALA. Located in a high mountain valley 90 miles (150 km.) west of GUATEMALA CITY. Known for its colorful markets, located in the main plaza on Thursdays and Sundays, selling wares from food to cultural items. In its churches, one can witness the blending of Roman Catholicism and ancient Mayan beliefs. Nowhere is this more evident than at the shrine of Pascual Abaj, which pays homage to the Mayan god of the earth.

Chile. An elongated country in southwest South America bounded by the ANDES MOUNTAINS and the Pacific Ocean. It is 2,650 miles (4,265 km.) long, but never more than 220 miles (355 km.) wide. Its tremendously varied natural environments range from the bone-dry ATACAMA DESERT in the north, to the Mediterranean climate in the center, to the glaciated fjordlike landscape of the far south. Most of the 12 million Chileans live in the temperate central region of the country where the capital, SANTIAGO, is located. At the end of the twentieth century, Chile had the most dynamic economy in LATIN AMERICA and was a major world supplier of fresh fruits (grapes, pears, plums, apples, peaches, and citrus) and the world's largest exporter of copper. In 1970 Salvador Allende became the first democratically elected Marxist leader in Latin America. He was overthrown by the military and Augusto Pinochet in 1973. Chile returned to democracy in 1989.

Chiloé. Island off southern CHILE (42°30′ south latitude, longitude 73°55′ west) known for picturesque forest and farmland and traditional Spanish culture. The descendants of early settlers and Jesuit converts inhabit small agricultural and fishing villages. More than 150 wooden churches dot the island. The island is 155 by 32 miles (250 by 50 km.).

Chimborazo, Mount. Highest mountain in ECUADOR, at 20,700 feet (6,310 meters); once thought to be the highest mountain in the world. In his celebrated work *Kosmos*, German explorer and geographer Alexander von Humboldt described the relationship between elevation and changing vegetation and life zones based on observations on the slopes of Chimborazo and other Andean peaks.

Chocó. Lowland province in the extreme northwest of COLOMBIA, with dense tropical rain forests bordering the

Darién Gap; sparsely populated, mainly by persons of African descent. With more than 160 inches (400 centimeters) of annual rainfall, it is wetter than the AMAZON BASIN and one of the world's richest areas for plants and animals. Gold and platinum mines are also found there.

Ciudad Bolívar. Capital of Bolívar, the largest state in VENEZUELA. Located on bank of the ORINOCO RIVER 250 miles (400 km.) upstream from the Atlantic Ocean, with a 1990's population of 300,000. The jumping-off point for visits to ANGEL FALLS. Originally named Angostura, Ciudad Bolívar is where liberator Simón Bolívar, in 1817, based the military operations against Spanish colonial control in his effort to form Gran Colombia. The state of Bolívar is the site of a major industrial complex based on hydroelectric power and steel and aluminum production.

Cochabamba. Third-largest city in BOLIVIA, with a 1990's population of 500,000. Set in a valley in the ANDES MOUNTAINS at an elevation of 8,430 feet (2,570 meters), it has a pleasant climate and is an important agricultural center for grains and vegetables. The surrounding rural areas are dominated by Quechua-speaking Amerindians.

Colca Canyon. Canyon in southern PERU, near AREQUIPA, that is said to be twice as deep as the Grand Canyon. Both sides are beautifully terraced in agriculture and dotted with traditional villages. The region also contains many majestic volcanic peaks.

Colombia. Country located in northwest South America, bounded by the CARIBBEAN SEA, the Pacific Ocean, VENEZUELA, PANAMA, ECUADOR, PERU, and BRAZIL. BOGOTÁ is the capital. Total area of 439,735 square miles (1,138,914 sq. km.); the population was 38.6 million in the 1990's. Spanish is the principal language. The physical environment is varied: the dissected terrain of the northern ANDES MOUNTAINS, deep river valleys of the MAGDALENA and CAUCA, Pacific coastal lowlands, and the isolated eastern lowlands in the AMAZON BASIN. In the twentieth century, Colombia was plagued by fractious regional divisions, political violence, guerrilla warfare, and drug wars. It is the world's largest exporter of cocaine, and production of opium poppies has increased. Nevertheless, the country has a relatively diversified and prosperous legal economy. Its principal exports are petroleum products, coal, bananas, textiles, leather products, and coffee, of which it is the world's second-largest producer.

Colonia. City in URUGUAY. Located on LA PLATA RIVER ESTUARY across from BUENOS AIRES. Founded in 1680 by Portuguese from BRAZIL to solidify their southern boundary against expansion of Spanish settlements from Buenos Aires. Ferry services link it to Buenos Aires.

Colorado River. River in ARGENTINA, marking the start of PATAGONIA. Its valley has a broad flat bottom and steep banks, because the Andean meltwater has cut deeply into the steplike plateaus that make up most of Patagonia. The region began to be developed near the end of the nineteenth century at the end of the war against the Amerindians. Irrigation was necessary to allow the cultivation of grain, animal feed, and fruit.

Comayagua. Capital of HONDURAS, 1537-1880. Population was 40,000 in the 1990's. Known for its colonial architecture, including numerous churches such as La Merced, built between 1550 and 1558. The first university in CEN-TRAL AMERICA was founded there in 1632, in the Casa Cural, which houses the Colonial Museum.

Comodoro Rivadavia. Seaport in ARGENTINA and center of the oil industry in Argentina's PATAGONIA. Located in Chubut Province, originally as a port to ship the region's agricultural production, it took on new importance when oil was discovered nearby. Tankers and pipelines send the crude oil to refineries near BUENOS AIRES.

Concepción. City in PARAGUAY. Located on the PARAGUAY RIVER, with a 1990's population of 36,000. The most important commercial center for the northern part of the country, and a free port for trade with southwest BRAZIL. Sawmills, flour mills, tanneries, and sugar refineries are major industries.

Concepción. Second-largest city in CHILE and a center for wood products. Located on the Biobío River 340 miles (515 kilometers) south of SANTIAGO, with a 1990's population of 363,000. The surrounding region has a marine west coast climate much like coastal Oregon and Washington. Large tracts of temperate rain forest contribute to expanding exports of timber products. The area has many German and Swiss immigrant families.

Copan. Ruling center of the Maya from about 1,400 to 1,200 years ago. Prehistoric peoples began moving into the Copan Valley, part of present-day HONDURAS, about 2,000 years ago. The Maya and their rulers left behind impressive artifacts depicting their culture. The Acropolis has carved reliefs of the sixteen Mayan rulers of Copan, and the Stelae of the Great Plaza portray these rulers and their reigns.

Córdoba. Second-largest city in ARGENTINA. Located at the eastern margin of the picturesque Córdoba Mountains,

*Copan
Page 758*

with a 1990's population of 1.3 million. Boasting the nation's oldest university, it is an important agricultural and industrial center. A transportation hub between the coast and interior, and a center for leather, textile, glass, automobiles, and food processing.

Corrientes. City in ARGENTINA. Located on the PARANÁ RIVER near the confluence of the PARAGUAY RIVER, with a 1990's population of 260,000 people. Its warm, wet climate allows a diversified agriculture of citrus, sugar, cotton, tobacco, and fruit, as well as cattle and hides. Excellent river, road, and rail transportation link the region with domestic and foreign markets. The 400-year-old city is also a cultural center with a university, museums, and a monastery.

Costa Rica. Central American country bordered by NICARAGUA, PANAMA, the Caribbean, and the Pacific; its area is 19,730 square miles (51,100 sq. km.), with a population of 3,015,000 in 1990. Though within the Tropics, it has mountains reaching as high as 12,530 feet (3,820 meters) at Mount Chirripo, the country's highest peak. Costa Rica differs from other Central and South American countries in having a much smaller gap between its richest and poorest classes. Historically it has shown a greater propensity for social and governmental stability. Its capital is SAN JOSÉ.

Cuenca. Third-largest city in ECUADOR (1990's population 260,000). A pleasant colonial town located at an elevation of 8,300 feet (2,530 meters) in the southern highlands of Ecuador, about 56 miles (90 km.) from Ingapirca, Ecuador's most important Inca ruin. Because of its equatorial location, the climate is springlike. Surrounding region is home to several groups of Native

American peoples, and the place where the original Panama straw hats are woven by hand.

Cuiabá. Capital of MATO GROSSO state in BRAZIL. Located on left bank of Cuiabá River in the central southern portion of state. Population in the 1990's was 400,000. A colonial gold-mining area, a cattle-raising region, and gateway to the PANTANAL. Considered the geographical center of South America.

Curitiba. Capital of PARANÁ state in BRAZIL. Located on east central edge of state at top of escarpment connected by train to coastal port of Paranaguá. Had a 1990's population of 1.5 million. Noted for its exceptional urban administration.

Cuzco. Magnificent Spanish colonial city in southern PERU and the ancient capital of the Inca Empire. Located at an elevation of 10,860 feet (3,310 meters) in the ANDES MOUNTAINS. Most of its 300,000 residents are Amerindians. It has many examples of Spanish colonial architecture and churches, as well as beautifully preserved Inca stonework and ruin sites. Cuzco means "navel" or "center" in the language of Quechua.

Devil's Island. Notorious prison in FRENCH GUIANA that was a penal colony from 1852 to 1945. Located 8 miles (13 km.) offshore on one of the Safety Islands (Iles du Salut), it was nearly impossible to escape from because of shark-infested waters and strong currents. A tourist attraction.

Distrito Federal. See FEDERAL DISTRICT.

Dutch Guiana. Colonial-era name of SURINAME.

Easter Island. Located in the South Pacific 2,350 miles (3,780 km.) off the coast of CHILE. Known for hundreds of monolithic stone figures, it originally was inhabited by Polynesians. The first European to land there was Dutchman

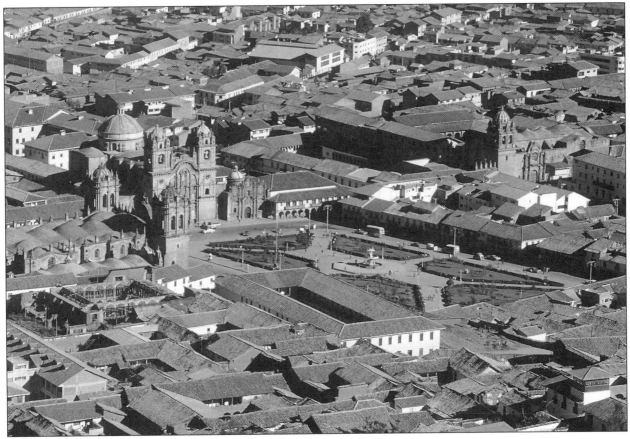

Cuzco from the air. (Clyde L. Rasmussen)

Jacob Roggeveen, on Easter Sunday in 1722. Annexed by Chile in 1888.

Ecuador. Small Andean country located on the equator in western South America. It has an area of 109,483 square miles (283,561 square klometers), about the size of the U.S. state of Colorado. Its population was 12.4 million in the 1990's, 40 percent of whom were Amerindians. QUITO is the capital; the predominant languages are Spanish and Quechua. Ecuador has three geographic regions. The Sierra, located in the ANDES MOUNTAINS, is characterized by large estates and by small farms worked by farmers who raise potatoes and corn and graze animals. The Costa—the lowlands between the Andes Mountains and the Pacific Ocean—is dominated by commercial farms pro-

ducing bananas, rice, cocoa, and shrimp for export. The Oriente is in the AMAZON BASIN in the east of the country. Oil was discovered there in the 1960's. Ecuador is an oil-exporting country and the world's leading exporter of bananas.

El Chapare. A frontier zone in the eastern foothills of the ANDES MOUNTAINS between COCHABAMBA and SANTA CRUZ, and the largest coca-growing region in Bolivia. Most of the coca is processed into cocaine, and the region has been the focus of U.S. crop substitution and eradication programs.

El Salvador. Smallest and most densely populated of CENTRAL AMERICA's seven countries, with a land area of 8,124 square miles (21,041 sq. km.) and a population of 5,487,000 (1992). The

893

only Central American county not to have a Caribbean coast, El Salvador faces the Pacific Ocean and is bordered by GUATEMALA on the northwest and HONDURAS on the east. Its economy is primarily agricultural; its more important crop is coffee. Its capital is SAN SALVADOR.

Encarnación. Second-largest city in PARAGUAY. Located on the PARANÁ RIVER, with a 1990's population of 60,000 people. It has road and rail links with ASUNCIÓN; connections with Posadas, ARGENTINA, are by ferry across the river. A major port on the river, trading yerba maté tea, cattle, timber, hides, and grains.

Esmeraldas. City on the northern coast of ECUADOR, where Spanish conquistadors first landed in Ecuador. Its population in the 1990's was 120,000. Has the terminal point of the trans-Andean oil pipeline, an oil refinery, and a port. Surrounding region is known for shrimp fishing and a Creole population of descendants of African slaves.

Espírito Santo. State in SOUTHEAST region of BRAZIL. Total area of 17,658 square miles (45,734 sq. km.) with a 1990's population of 2.8 million. Capital is VITÓRIA. High mountainous western interior descends to tropical Atlantic eastern coast. Industries include cattle raising, coffee production, tropical agriculture, mining, some industry.

Falkland Islands. Also known as the Islas Malvinas, a windswept archipelago in the South Atlantic Ocean, about 320 miles (500 km.) off the southeastern coast of ARGENTINA, on almost the same latitude as the Strait of MAGELLAN. The archipelago consists of two large islands, East and West Falkland, and more than 340 small islands and islets. Their land area is about 4,699 square miles (12,175 sq. km.)—slightly

smaller than the U.S. state of Connecticut. Most of the approximately 2,500 residents of the islands live on East Falkland, where the capital, Stanley, is located. Great Britain has administered the islands since the 1830's. Argentina's long-standing claims to the islands led to a brief war with Great Britain in 1982 that did not change their status.

Federal District (Brazil). Special administrative district of BRAZIL containing the headquarters of the national government—a territory similar in function to the Mexico's Federal District and the District of Columbia of the United States. Standing on a savanna at an elevation of about 3,300 feet (1,000 meters) above sea level, it has a mild, dry climate. It is located inside the state of GOIÁS in south central Brazil and contains the national capital city, BRASÍLIA. The district and capital were dedicated in 1960.

Fernando de Noronha. Brazilian archipelago more than 200 miles (300 km.) northeast of RIO GRANDE DO NORTE. Largest of islands, comprising tips of ancient volcanoes, is Fernando de Noronha. The territory is an ecological reserve with a small military contingent, administered from PERNAMBUCO.

Florianópolis. Capital of SANTA CATARINA state in BRAZIL. Population in 1990's was more than 250,000. Located on western side of the Atlantic coastal island of Santa Catarina, connected by bridge to mainland. Eastern side of island is dunes and ocean beaches, popular with tourists from BRAZIL, ARGENTINA, and URUGUAY. Formerly named Desterro.

Fortaleza. Capital of CEARÁ state in BRAZIL. Located on Atlantic Ocean, with a 1990's population of 2 million. Growing regional commercial, port, banking, manufacturing, and tourist center. Some fishing; beaches popular with tourists.

Fray Bentos. Major river port in URUGUAY for navigation on the URUGUAY RIVER for oceangoing vessels. An international bridge crosses the river for connection with ARGENTINA. Uruguay's first large-scale meatpacking plant was built here in 1861. With a deep-water port and good rail, road, and air connections, this city of 20,000 people is economically important despite its small size.

French Guiana. Overseas Department (state) of France located on the north coast of South America, bordered by SURINAME to the west and BRAZIL to the east and south. Total area of 35,126 square miles (90,976 sq. km.) with a 1990's population of 200,000. Capital is CAYENNE. Was a French penal colony, including the notorious DEVIL'S ISLAND, from 1852 to 1945. Population is mostly Creole (people of African ancestry), with notable Vietnamese, Indonesian, and European minorities. Most of the settlement is on the coast, with a third of the people living in Cayenne. The interior is largely empty of humans. French is the official language, but a local Creole dialect is spoken. Principal exports are gold, shrimp, rice, and timber. The territory is also used as a launch site for commercial satellites at the Guiana Space Center near Kourou.

Galápagos Islands. Archipelego of nineteen volcanic islands located on the equator 597 miles (960 km.) west of South America, a territory of ECUADOR. Visited by Charles Darwin, sailing on the HMS *Beagle*, in 1835. Darwin's observations on the islands contributed to his theories about evolution by natural selection. With a land area of 5,000 square miles (8,000 sq. km.), the Galapagos are slightly less than half the size of the Hawaiian Islands. In 1979 the United Nations designated the islands as a World Heritage Site, recognizing them as one of the world's most magnificent natural areas and home to many rare and unique plant and animal species, including tortoises, marine iguanas, and blue-footed boobies. Tourism is closely monitored, but the Galapagos are threatened by introduced plants and animals, poorly regulated fishing, and excessive migration from the mainland.

Georgetown. Capital, principal port, and only large city of GUYANA. Located at the mouth of the Demerara River on the Atlantic Ocean, with a 1990's population of 200,000. Founded by the English in 1781. Parts of the city are notable for remnants of old sugar plantations, streets lined with flowering trees, and white wooden nineteenth century houses.

Goiânia. Capital of GOIÁS state in BRAZIL. Population in 1990's more than 1 million. Founded as planned city in 1933 to replace colonial capital of Goiás Velho. Growing commercial and services center for dynamic rural economy.

Goiás. State in CENTER-WEST region of BRAZIL, extending over the central plateau of country. Total area of 131,339 square miles (340,168 sq. km.) with a 1990's population of 4.5 million. Capital is GOIÂNIA. Combines tropical and scrub vegetation; southern half of state productive in agriculture and ranching.

Gran Chaco. Alluvial plain covering western PARAGUAY, northwestern ARGENTINA, southwest BRAZIL, and southeastern BOLIVIA, formed by sediments washing down from the ANDES MOUNTAINS. Covers 95,000 square miles (249,000 sq. km.). Large and small

Galápagos Islands Pages 749, 878

rivers crossing the plain flood in the hot, wet summers, creating vast swamps, and dry out in the cool winters, making irrigation waters scarce.

Guanabara Bay. Major bay off the Atlantic coast of South America, in Brazilian state of RIO DE JANEIRO. Along south edge of bay stretch the port areas of city of RIO DE JANEIRO; along northeast edge is port city of Niteroi. A major bridge spanning the bay connects the two cities. There are many islands in the bay. Its water was once so clean that dolphins swam in it, but it is polluted, especially from oil tankers.

Guatemala. Third largest country in CENTRAL AMERICA; bordered by Mexico on the north and west, EL SALVADOR and HONDURAS on the east, and BELIZE—whose territory it claims—on the northeast. It has a 150-mile-long (240 km.) coastline on its Pacific Ocean side, but its Caribbean coastline is only a small fraction of that length. Guatemala is largely tropical, with low-lying coastlands, but does have some drier areas. Cool temperatures exist at high elevations. Its capital is GUATEMALA CITY. Its land area is 42,042 square miles (108,889 km.). Its population was 9,197,000 in 1990.

Guatemala City Page 879

Guatemala City. Capital and cosmopolitan hub of GUATEMALA. Population in the 1990's was 2 million. Impressive for its size, but little remains of its colonial heritage. The city's retail district is located in the Plaza Mayor, and the central market caters mostly to the needs of tourist.

Guyana Page 880

Guayaquil. Largest city in ECUADOR, with 2 million inhabitants in the 1990's; the country's principal seaport and commercial and industrial center. Located on the ocean near the equator, at the heart of the coastal region that produces bananas, rice, sugarcane, cacao,

and shrimp. Known for its oppressive heat and humidity.

Guiana Highlands. Elevated uplands in north of BRAZIL bordering COLOMBIA, VENEZUELA, GUIANA, and Suriname. Waters from this region drain to the lower AMAZON RIVER. Brazil's highest peaks are located here: PICO DE NEBLINA (about 10,000 feet/3,000 meters), Pico de Trinta e Um de Março (about 9,800 feet), and Mount Roraima (just over 9,400 feet).

Guianas. Region of northern South America comprising GUYANA (formerly BRITISH GUIANA), SURINAME (formerly Dutch Guiana), and FRENCH GUIANA (a territory of France). These territories have interesting colonial histories, highlighted by sugar plantations and imported laborers. This has left them with ethnically diverse populations, including Creoles, Asians (Indians, Indonesians, Chinese, and Vietnamese), and Europeans. Most of the settlement is along a narrow coastal fringe, leaving the undeveloped interior with some of South America's most pristine rain forests. Economies rely heavily on agriculture and mineral extraction.

Guyana. Country on the north coast of South America, bordered by VENEZUELA to the west, SURINAME to the east, and BRAZIL to the south. Total area of 83,000 square miles (214,970 sq. km.), with a 1990's population of 700,000, concentrated on the coastal fringe. Capital is GEORGETOWN. The poorest country in South America. First settled by the Dutch in 1613, became a British colony in 1831 (then known as British Guiana), achieved independence in 1966. The land area is roughly the size of Idaho; approximately 77 percent is covered by dense tropical rain forests and savanna, largely in the undeveloped interior. Its ethnically diverse population is divided between Creoles (people of African ancestry) and East Indians (people of southeast Asian ancestry). English is the official language, but Hindi, Urdu, and Amerindian dialects are spoken also. Principal exports are sugar, gold, rice, bauxite, and diamonds.

Honduras. Republic in CENTRAL AMERICA. Covering an area of area is 43,433 square miles (112,492 sq. km.), it is encompassed by GUATEMALA on the west and NICARAGUA on the east. It has a long coastline on the CARIBBEAN SEA, but EL SALVADOR stands between it and the Pacific Ocean on the southwest, leaving Honduras its only outlet to the Pacific through the tiny Gulf of Fonseca. Its capital and largest city is TEGUCIGALPA. The climate of Honduras is tropical but is tempered by the higher elevations of the interior. Its population was 5,724,515 in 1997.

Huascarán Nevado. The highest mountain in PERU. Located at 9°6′ south latitude, longitude 77°50′ west, at an elevation of 22,133 feet (6,746 meters). Part of the picturesque Cordillera Blanca (white range), it is part of a national park that protects an area of high mountain cloud forest and tundra in the ANDES MOUNTAINS.

Huayaga Valley. Zone on the eastern flank of the ANDES MOUNTAINS in PERU, known for cultivating coca leaf, the raw material for cocaine. Poor peasant farmers there have been caught between U.S. antidrug efforts and Peruvian

antigovernment terrorist activities.

Humboldt Current. See PERU CURRENT.

Iguaçu Falls. Located in southwest corner of state of PARANÁ, BRAZIL, these stunning falls are formed by a deep, semicircular depression in the Iguaçu River as it approaches the PARANÁ RIVER. Rushing down numerous tiers of rock molded in a massive arc, the spewing waters glisten and roar through an ex-

Iguaçu Falls Page 879

Iguaçu Falls. (PhotoDisc)

897

otic subtropical scenario of butterflies, hummingbirds, sunlight, gleaming flowers, and rainbows. Also known as Iguazú Falls.

Iguazú National Park. A favorite tourist destination in ARGENTINA, located along the Iguazú River. One can view tropical vegetation, animals, and spectacular waterfalls where the Iguazú River plunges over the PARANÁ PLATEAU in a series of high cascades.

Ipanema. Famed beach and neighborhood in the Brazilian city of RIO DE JANEIRO, nestled between the Atlantic Ocean and a lagoon. Its sophistication and physical allure are celebrated in the song "The Girl from Ipanema." It is the second of the first three ocean beach neighborhoods of Rio, preceded by the highly commercialized Copacabana and followed by the residential Leblon.

Copa-cabana
Page 884

Iquitos. PERU's most important city in the AMAZON BASIN of South America. Located on the river Marañón, a tributary of the AMAZON RIVER, with a 1990's population of 400,000. Accessible to oceangoing vessels that come 2,300 miles (3,220 km.) up the Amazon River from the Atlantic Ocean. In the late nineteenth century, the region experienced a rubber boom; later, cacao became the dominant crop. Since the 1960's, oil has driven the development of the region.

Isla de Margarita. Venezuelan island in the CARIBBEAN SEA 25 miles (40 km.) north of the mainland. Total area is about 350 square miles (900 sq. km.). VENEZUELA's number one tourist destination for Caribbean atmosphere, white beaches, snorkeling, and visits to nearby national parks.

La Paz
Page 881

Itaipú Dam. Hydroelectric dam spanning the PARANÁ RIVER between BRAZIL and PARAGUAY in South America. Opened in 1984 as the largest dam and one of the largest reinforced concrete structures in the world. Eighteen generators produce almost 13,000 megawatts. Providing energy for industrialized south of Brazil, the dam is administered by a Brazil-Paraguay binational state company which completed the project in 1982 at a cost of $20 billion.

João Pessoa. Capital of PARAÍBA state in BRAZIL. Located between the right bank of Sanhaú River and the Atlantic Ocean. Popular tourist city with 1990's population of just over half a million. Formerly Filipéia (under Spain), Frederikstad (under Netherlands), and Paraíba.

Juruá River. A major tributary of the AMAZON RIVER in South America, draining from the Peruvian ANDES. About 1,700 miles (2,800 km.) long, it crosses the Brazilian states of ACRE and AMAZONAS, emptying into the upper Solimões River. It has many tributaries of its own.

La Amistad International Park. International Peace Park shared between COSTA RICA and PANAMA. Along with several reserves and some Amerindian reservations, the combined landmass is about 150,000 acres (600,000 hectares) and forms the Amistad Biosphere Reserve, recognized as a World Heritage Site. The region preserves eight life zones and protects hundreds of species of plants and animals, including more than 450 species of birds, representing 60 percent of the nation's known species. One of the best places in Costa Rica to witness Amerindians in more traditional settings.

La Paz. The seat of government of BOLIVIA. Located 11,900 feet (3,630 meters) above sea level, La Paz is the highest capital in the world. The La Paz area had a 1990's population of 1.3 million people (half of whom were Native Americans), which makes it the largest city in the world at such a high eleva-

La Paz, Bolivia. (PhotoDisc)

tion. The average annual temperature is a comfortable 64 degrees Fahrenheit (18 degrees Celsius), resulting from its location near the equator.

La Plata. Outport for BUENOS AIRES on the LA PLATA RIVER ESTUARY in ARGENTINA. Buenos Aires attracts so many ships that the traffic congestion causes many of them to be rerouted to La Plata's deep-water harbor. A major industrial center for meat packing, oil refining, flour milling, and textiles. With almost 600,000 people, the well-planned city has three universities, the provincial capital, and a pleasant urban environment with many plazas and parks.

La Plata River Estuary. The place where the great URUGUAY-PARAGUAY-PARANÁ RIVER system meets the south Atlantic Ocean. BUENOS AIRES, MONTEVIDEO, and many other cities are located on the estuary's banks to take advantage of the region's outstanding navigation potential. Large amounts of silt are washed downriver from the vast continental interior basin of southern South America. Shipping channels near Buenos Aires must be continually dredged to keep them open to large ships.

Lagoa dos Patos. Largest coastal lagoon in BRAZIL, stretching along half the coast of the state of RIO GRANDE DO SUL. It is about 175 miles (280 km.) long and 40 miles (60 km.) wide. At the northwest tip of the lagoon is the Guaíba River, where the port city of PORTO ALEGRE is located. At its south end, the lagoon connects to the Atlantic Ocean and Lagoa Mirim.

Lima's Plaza de Armas. (Clyde L. Rasmussen)

Lamanai. Mayan site located near Indian Church in BELIZE. Although undergoing restoration and excavation, it is an impressive work in progress. The nearly sixty structures and ruins include a ball court, a small temple, and a late pre-Classic Mayan structure that rises more than 112 feet (34 meters) above the jungle. Was occupied until the arrival of the Spanish, as evidenced by the two ruins of Mayan churches on the site. Name is Mayan for "submerged crocodile."

Las Piedras. Suburb northwest of MONTE-VIDEO, Uruguay. Located on the floodplain of the URUGUAY RIVER, with a 1990's population of 60,000. Food and wine are major products; it is a major rail hub for the large cities along the river. The Uruguayan patriot and nationalist José Gervasio Artigas won an important battle against the Spaniards here in 1811.

Latin America. Loosely used term for countries and territories in the AMERICAS that are culturally predominantly Hispanic or Portuguese in their backgrounds. By this definition, Latin America includes BRAZIL, Mexico, and all the Spanish-speaking nations of Central and South America and the Caribbean, while excluding such English- and Dutch-speaking lands as GUYANA, SURINAME, BELIZE, Jamaica, and other English-speaking Caribbean islands. Because French—like Spanish and Portuguese—is a descendant of the Latin language, Latin America has also been seen as including such French-speaking lands as FRENCH GUIANA, Haiti, and other Caribbean islands.

León. The radical, liberal, and intellectual center of NICARAGUA, and its second-largest city. Located near the Pacific coast, 50 miles (80 km.) northwest of MANAGUA. Has many examples of fine Spanish colonial architecture but is best known for its monuments to the Sandinista political and military movement, including large wall murals.

Lima. Capital and largest city of PERU, with a 1990's population of 9 million. Founded in 1535 by the Spanish and the principal city of Spain's colonial holdings in Andean South America. Designated by the United Nations as a World Heritage Site, Lima's center has impressive architecture and numerous museums holding colonial and indigenous treasures. Lima's lush seaside suburb of Miraflores is in stark contrast to the poor shantytowns that house hundreds of thousands recent migrants to the city.

Llanos. Vast plains in northern South America. Drained by the ORINOCO RIVER and its tributaries in VENEZUELA and COLOMBIA, forming the world's fourth-largest river by volume of water. Humid, often marshy, and sparsely populated; principal land use is cattle ranching. Petroleum is produced in the eastern *llanos* of Venezuela.

Macapá. Capital of AMAPÁ state in BRAZIL. Located on western delta of AMAZON RIVER, with the equator running just south. Population in 1990's was about 200,000. Originated as a Portuguese fortress to protect the Amazon from foreign penetration; a port for shipping manganese.

Maceió. Capital of ALAGOAS state in BRAZIL. Located on the Atlantic coast on an elevated sandy area of lagoon region, with a 1990's population of over 700,000. Commercial center with light industry, offshore oil drilling, and growing tourism.

Machu Picchu. Famous lost city of the Incas, located near CUZCO in PERU. Set on

Machu Picchu Page 882

Steps and terraces at Machu Picchu. (Clyde L. Rasmussen)

a high mountain terrace on the eastern flank of the ANDES MOUNTAINS, it was abandoned in the fifteenth century before being rediscovered by U.S. explorer Hiram Bingham in 1911. Machu Picchu is a United Nations-designated World Heritage Site and a major tourist attraction in South America. Recent plans to build a cable car to the site have brought concerns that too much tourism might be detrimental to its preservation.

Manaus Pages 681, 754, 872, 883

Madeira River. The largest tributary of the AMAZON RIVER in South America. Flows southwest/northeast through Brazilian states of RONDÔNIA and AMAZONAS. About 2,000 miles (3,200 km.) long, it drains from the Bolivian ANDES and enters the Amazon below MANAUS.

Magdalena River. Largest river in COLOMBIA. Flows from its headwaters in the ANDES MOUNTAINS north 950 miles (1,540 km.) into the CARIBBEAN SEA near Barranquilla. Navigable most of the way, it is an important transportation corridor in a country that is fragmented by mountain ranges running north to south and river valleys.

Magellan, Strait of. Strait passing between the southernmost point of the mainland of South America and TIERRA DEL FUEGO. The Portuguese explorer Ferdinand Magellan discovered the passage in 1520 as an alternative to the longer route around CAPE HORN. The straits connect the Atlantic and Pacific Oceans.

Malvinas, Islas. See FALKLAND ISLANDS.

Managua. Capital of NICARAGUA. Had a 1990's population of more than 930,000 people. Natural disasters such as earthquakes have destroyed much of its architecture and heritage. A large earthquake in 1972 virtually destroyed the downtown area, little of which has

been rebuilt. Masaya Volcano National Park, near the city center, preserves and interprets the volatile nature of the living earth.

Managua, Lake. See NICARAGUA, LAKE.

Manaus. Capital of AMAZONAS state in BRAZIL. Located on the southern bank of the NEGRO RIVER just above where that river joins the Solimões River to form the AMAZON RIVER. Population in the 1990's was more than 1 million. A historic river port, especially for export of rubber; a tariff-free zone, with some industrialization and ecotourism.

Manu National Park. Largest nature reserve in PERU. Located on the Madre de Dios river near Puerto Maldonado in the southeast corner of Peru, it encompasses 4.6 million acres (1.9 million hectares). The zone of the AMAZON BASIN along the eastern flank of the ANDES MOUNTAINS is one of the world's centers of biodiversity, with the largest number of plant and animal species per square mile of any place on earth.

Manuel Antonio National Park. Most-visited park in COSTA RICA. Located on the Pacific side of Costa Rica near the town of Quepos, it has about 150,000 visitors annually. Magnificent beaches and rain forests offer hiking to view the numerous species of plant and animal life.

Mar Chiquita Lake. Largest lake in ARGENTINA. The Dulce, Primero, and Segundo Rivers flow into the lake, but there is no outlet to the sea. Like the Great Salt Lake in the United States, this salty lake is surrounded by salt flats and nearly barren land.

Mar del Plata. Fashionable seaside resort in ARGENTINA. Population of 600,000 in the 1990's. Clear blue ocean, mild temperatures, beautiful beaches and parks, and a large casino draw many summer vacationers from BUENOS AIRES. City also has a naval base, a university, and many cultural institutions.

Maracaibo. Second-largest city in VENEZUELA, with a 1990's population of 1.3 million. The center of Venezuela's oil-rich Maracaibo lowland region. With an average annual temperature of 82.5 degrees Fahrenheit (28 degrees Celsius), it is one of the warmest, most humid places in LATIN AMERICA.

Maracaibo, Lake. Brackish lake in northwestern VENEZUELA that opens into the CARIBBEAN SEA. Its area is 75 by 130 miles (121 by 209 km.). The lake and surrounding lowlands are the site of one of the earth's largest petroleum deposits (discovered in 1917) and a forest of oil derricks.

Marajó Island. The largest river delta island in the world; larger than Ireland. Situated in the mouth of the AMAZON RIVER in South America. The name also describes a type of lower Amazon indigenous ceramic.

Maranhão. State in the farthest western part of NORTHEAST region of BRAZIL. Total area of 127,242 square miles (329,557 sq. km.) with a 1990's population of more than 5 million. Capital is SÃO LUÍS. From south to north, the land gradually descends to the Atlantic coast; from west to east, it varies from equatorial rain forest to tropical savanna. Agriculture predominates, especially cultivation of *babaçú* and cattle raising; also some mining.

Mato Grosso. State in CENTER-WEST region of BRAZIL. Total area of 352,400 square miles (912,716 sq. km.) with a 1990's population of 2.25 million. Capital is CUIABÁ. Low-lying central highlands form headwaters for rivers flowing north to the AMAZON BASIN and south to PARAGUAY, with extensive wetlands in the southwest along border with BOLIVIA. Tropical agriculture and ranching; some gold and diamond mining.

Mato Grosso do Sul. State in CENTER-WEST region of BRAZIL. Total area of 140,219 square miles (363,167 sq. km.) with a 1990's population of 2 million. Capital is CAMPO GRANDE. Land gradually descends from east to west, the western half forming vast wetlands (the PANTANAL) along border with BOLIVIA and PARAGUAY. Subequatorial climate with tropical agriculture and extensive cattle raising.

Medellín. Second-largest city in COLOMBIA (population 2.6 million); capital of ANTIOQUIA province. Founded in 1616 by Spanish settlers and farmers, its growth was fueled by an early twentieth century coffee boom. The city is a dynamic commercial and industrial city, producing most of Colombia's textiles, but received international notoriety for its former drug cartel.

Mendoza. Capital of Mendoza province in ARGENTINA. Metropolitan area had close to 1 million people in the 1990's. Transportation hub on the major international route from BUENOS AIRES to SANTIAGO, Chile. Nestled at the base of the ANDES MOUNTAINS, the city is known for its natural beauty, has two universities, and is an important economic center. Alluvial soils and irrigation water from the Andes enable the fertile region to produce fruits, vegetables, and grains. As ARGENTINA's major grape-growing area, it has developed wine-making and food-processing industries. Metalworking and oil refining also are economically significant. Earthquakes and droughts are hazards.

Mesopotamia. Region of the northeast of ARGENTINA, between the PARANÁ and URUGUAY Rivers. Good soils, warm climate, and ample rainfall make this

Maracaibo Page 820

an important agricultural area for citrus, yerba maté tea, sugarcane, and vegetables. Jesuit missions dotted the area in the seventeenth century and formed the basis for productive agriculture.

Minas Gerais. State in Southeast region of Brazil. Total area of 226,707 square miles (587,171 sq. km.) with a 1990's population of 17 million. Capital is Belo Horizonte. Most mountainous state in Brazil; headwaters of São Francisco River form in the northwest. Industries include agriculture and cattle raising; mining and extensive mineral reserves, especially iron; and manufacturing. Historic site for gold and diamonds.

Missiones Province. Province in the the northeast arm of Argentina. Located between the Paraná and Uruguay Rivers. Lush, semitropical vegetation covers the area; the climate is suitable for the production of yerba maté tea, citrus, maize (corn), and other fruits and vegetables that need warm temperatures and much rain. The name of the province comes from the colonial missions founded by the Jesuits. Agricultural productivity was improved greatly in the mission stations.

Mitad del Mundo. Exact line of the equator, as determined by Charles-Marie de la Condamine of the French expedition of 1735. Located 14 miles (23 km.) north of Quito, Ecuador. One can visit the monument and straddle the equator, having one foot in the Northern Hemisphere and the other in the Southern Hemisphere. Spanish for "middle of the world."

Montecristo National Park. Cloud forest in Central America. Located at the convergence of El Salvador, Guatemala, and Honduras, several hours north of San Salvador, at an elevation of 7,900 feet (2,400 meters). Because of the altitude, it receives about 80 inches (200 centimeters) of rain a year, resulting in a wet, cloud forest environment. Flora include ferns, mushrooms, and moss-covered forest floor canopied by laurel and oak trees. Animals include the anteater, puma, toucan, and spider monkey.

Monteverde. Small community northwest of San José in the cloud forest of Costa Rica. Founded in 1951 by North America Quakers seeking a country that did not require registration for the military. Home to the Monteverde Cloud Forest Reserve, a research center for the preservation of the cloud-forest plants and animals. Name is Spanish for "green mountain."

Montevideo. Capital and primate city of Uruguay. Located on the La Plata River Estuary on trade routes between the south Atlantic Ocean and Paraná-La Plata Basin, with a population in the 1990's of about 1.3 million people—40 percent of the nation's total. The nation's political, economic, and social core.

Nahuel Huapí Lake. Lake in the Andes Mountains of South America. Located at 40°58' south latitude, longitude 71°30' west. Formed by glaciers in a deep valley, it has the typical long, narrow shape of mountain valley lakes. San Carlos de Bariloche resort on the lake is a popular vacation spot for skiers, fishermen, hikers, and those who enjoy glaciated mountain landscapes.

Napo River. Largest river in the Amazon Basin region of eastern Ecuador and part of the Amazon River drainage. In 1542 Francisco de Orellana sailed from the eastern foothills of the Andes Mountains to the mouth of the Amazon River at the Atlantic Ocean, traversing the continent of South America.

Natal. Capital of RIO GRANDE DO NORTE state in BRAZIL. Located between the right bank of the Potenji River and the Atlantic Ocean, with a 1990's population of 350,000. Important trans-Atlantic air hub to North Africa for Allies during World War II; a growing tourist city.

Nazca. Site on the southern coast of PERU known for huge geometric designs drawn on the desert that are only visible by air. The Nazca lines are thought to have been drawn between 900 B.C.E. and 600 C.E. Some animals represented are a lizard, monkey, and condor. The designs might make up a vast pre-Inca calendar.

Negro River. Descending from the ANDES MOUNTAINS in COLOMBIA, where the river is named the Guainía, it becomes the Negro River on entering BRAZIL, coursing northwest/southeast in the state of AMAZONAS. It empties into the Solimões River below MANAUS, forming the Brazilian AMAZON RIVER. It is more than 1,100 miles (almost 1,800 km.) long and has numerous major tributaries.

Negro River Reservoir. Most important hydroelectric and irrigation project in URUGUAY. Hydroelectricity helps industrialization where no fossil fuels exist, and irrigation of the central plains has converted unfenced pastures into farms that raise animals and grow grains, grapes, planted pastures, and vegetables, all important in an agricultural, pastoral economy.

Netherlands Guiana. See SURINAME.

Neuquén. Most important oasis city in northern PATAGONIA region of ARGENTINA. Population in 1990's was 100,000. The center of extensive irrigation and hydroelectric works on the Limay and Neuquén Rivers. Became important as the center of a vast fruit orchard in 1886 after the Amerindian wars ended. Industries include fruit processing, many wineries, and heavy machinery and construction materials for the nearby oil fields. National parks and beautiful Andean scenery are the backdrop for the city.

New World. Term first applied to the WESTERN HEMISPHERE by early sixteenth century geographers. "New World" differentiates the AMERICAS from the "Old World," which was seen as consisting of Europe, Africa, and Asia.

Nicaragua. Largest country in CENTRAL AMERICA, covering 50,464 square miles (130,700 sq. km.)—an area close to that of the U.S. state of Alabama. It is bordered by HONDURAS on its north, the CARIBBEAN SEA on its east, COSTA RICA on its south, and the Pacific Ocean on its west. Its climate is tropical and somewhat consistent throughout the country. Its capital is MANAGUA. Nicaragua's maximum length from north to south is about 275 miles (440 km.), and its maximum width from east to west is about 280 miles (450 km.). Its population was 3,871,000 in 1990.

Negro River Page 686

Nicaragua, Lake. Lake Nicaragua and its sister lake, Managua, are the largest natural bodies of fresh water in CENTRAL AMERICA. Located in the southern part of NICARAGUA, both drain into the CARIBBEAN SEA by way of the San Juan River. Originally an inlet of the the Pacific Ocean, the lake gradually became separated from the sea and evolved into a freshwater lake, transforming saltwater animal life-forms—including sharks—into freshwater forms. Lake Nicaragua has more than 350 islands, generally referred to as Las Isletas. The islands' inhabitants fish and engage in small-scale agriculture. Zapatera Island is a national park developed to preserve archaeological remains; the island of San Pablo has a small Spanish fort that was used to defend the area from the British in the eighteenth century. Solentiname Island, in the southern part of Lake Nicaragua, is noted for its artist colony, established by Nicaraguan poet Ernesto Cardenal.

North. Largest region of BRAZIL, comprising the states of ACRE, AMAPÁ, AMAZONAS, PARÁ, RONDÔNIA, RORAIMA, and TOCANTINS. Covers 2.3 million square miles (4 million sq. km.), with a population of over 11 million, including most of the remaining Amerindian population. Dominated by the AMAZON RIVER and its tributaries and equatorial rain forest.

Northeast Brazil. Region of BRAZIL, comprising the states of ALAGOAS, BAHIA, CEARÁ, MARANHÃO, PARAÍBA, PERNAMBUCO, PIAUÍ, RIO GRANDE DO NORTE, and SERGIPE. Covers 1 million square miles (more than 1.5 million sq. km.), with a population of more than 45 million. Region thrived in colonial times but is known for poverty, and for aridity and droughts in the upland interior. Divided into three zones: *zona da mata*, along the coast; *agreste*, between *zona da mata* and uplands; and *sertão*, in the upland interior.

Orinoco River. Largest river in VENEZUELA and the world's fourth-largest river by volume of water. Beginning at its headwaters in the GUIANA HIGHLANDS, it runs 1,615 miles (2,600 km.) eastward to the Atlantic Ocean. When Christopher Columbus first sighted the delta of the Orinoco in 1498 on his third trip to the AMERICAS, he knew that he had discovered a great continent, not just an island.

Oruro. Major mining center in BOLIVIA, also known for its colorful carnival parade. Located in the ANDES MOUN-

TAINS at an elevation of 12,150 feet (3,700 meters), with a 1990's population of 200,000. Oruro's mines produce tin, silver, and tungsten. A revolution in 1952 resulted in a government takeover of the mines and freeing of slave laborers.

Otavalo. Market town in the northern highlands of ECUADOR named for the local Amerindian peoples. The Otavalans, known for their distinctive blue-and-white dress, sell their traditional woven goods throughout Ecuador, and in the United States and Europe.

Palmas. Capital of TOCANTINS, newest state of BRAZIL. A planned city, located on the right bank of the TOCANTINS RIVER. Brazil's smallest state capital, with a 1990's population of less than 100,000. Founded in 1990 and located in center of the state. Center of an agricultural and cattle-raising area.

Pampas. The grassy plains of ARGENTINA and URUGUAY. Extending from BUENOS AIRES and MONTEVIDEO to the base of the ANDES MOUNTAINS, the plains are humid in the east with 40 inches (100 centimeters) of rainfall annually, becoming dry (7 inches/18 centimeters) at the Andes. One of the world's great food-producing areas: Cattle, maize (corn), and soybeans are grown in the wetter regions; sheep, wheat, and cotton come from the drier parts of the plains.

Panama. Central American nation that meets the South American continent at COLOMBIA—of which Panama was originally a part. Panama's only other neighbor, COSTA RICA, borders it on the west. Panama's area of 29,450 square miles (75,990 sq. km.) makes it slightly smaller than either of the U.S. states Maine and South Carolina. It had a population of about 2,808,300 in the year 2000. Panama's possession of the narrowest part of CENTRAL AMERICA made it a logical region through which to cut a canal to join the Atlantic and Pacific Oceans. With U.S. help, Panama seceded from Colombia in 1903 and signed a treaty with the United States calling for construction of a canal and U.S. sovereignty over a strip of land on either side of the structure (the Panama CANAL ZONE). Panama retook possession of the canal on December 31, 1999.

Panama Canal. Ship canal built through the Isthmus of PANAMA to provide a direct route between the Pacific and Atlantic Oceans. Constructed by the United States 1907-1914, it is a lake-and-lock type of canal consisting of sets of water locks that lift ships up to lake level, where they proceed through the canal. Stretches about 50 miles (80 km.) from PANAMA CITY on the Pacific Ocean to Colón on the Atlantic Ocean. Over twelve thousand ships go through the canal each year. The United States operated the canal until a series of treaties began turning it over to Panamanian control. On January 1, 2000, Panama assumed full control of the CANAL ZONE.

Panama Canal Zone. See CANAL ZONE.

Panama City. Capital of PANAMA. Population was 900,000 in the 1990's. Sections of the city have historical charm, but most is a modern, bustling, cosmopolitan center. Places of interest include the Interoceanic Canal Museum of Panama, the History Museum of Panama, the sixteenth century ruins of Panama Viejo, and the tropical rain forest of the Sobrerania National Park.

Pan-American Highway. System of highways extending from Alaska through South America. The northern section of the route, beginning in Fairbanks, Alaska, and continuing to the city of Dawson Creek, British Columbia is called the Alaska Highway. In Mexico and CENTRAL AMERICA, the segment known as the Inter-American Highway runs from Laredo, Texas to PANAMA CITY, Panama. Routes in the United States and Canada connect the Alaska and Inter-American highways. New highways are still being built in areas of South America as part of the system.

Pantanal. Vast wetlands in western part of Brazilian states of MATO GROSSO and MATO GROSSO DO SUL, extending into BOLIVIA and PARAGUAY, covering almost 60,000 square miles (about 150,000 sq. km.). Water level rises and falls in relation to the summer rainy season and the volume of overflow water from the PARAGUAY RIVER and its tributaries. Used as pasture land during low-water periods.

Pará. State in NORTH region of BRAZIL. Total area of 481,869 square miles (1,248,041 sq. km.), with a 1990's population of 5.5 million. Capital is BELÉM. Land forms the eastern half of AMAZON RIVER plain, with delta occupying northeast corner of state. Mouth of the river holds island of MARAJÓ, larger in size than Ireland. Equatorial climate with agriculture and ranching; mineral reserves of bauxite, iron, manganese, and gold.

Paraguay. Landlocked South American country surrounded by BOLIVIA, BRAZIL, and ARGENTINA. Its total area of 157,048 square miles (406,752 sq. km.) makes it roughly the same size as the U.S. states of California and Montana. Rivers play an important role in Paraguay's economic life, providing it with shipping access to the Atlantic Ocean and sites for hydroelectric power plants. Indeed, the very name of the country apparently derives from a local

Panama Canal Page 821

Guarani word meaning "river that gives birth to the sea." Paraguay's populace is almost entirely mestizo of Guarani Amerindian ancestry. Its population was 5,223,000 in 1998. Its capital is ASUNCIÓN.

Paraguay River. Major South American waterway that rises in southwestern BRAZIL's MATO GROSSO state and flows generally south, eventually bisecting PARAGUAY, before feeding the PARANÁ RIVER at Paraguay's southwestern tip. The river is navigable through most of its roughly 1,600-mile (2,500 km.) length.

Paraíba. State in NORTHEAST region of BRAZIL. Total area of 20,833 square miles (53,957 sq. km.) with a 1990's population of 3.35 million. Capital is JOÃO PESSOA. Arid, mountainous interior descends to tropical Atlantic coast. Cattle raising and agriculture are the main occupations; poverty has forced much of population to migrate south.

Paraíba do Sul River. Descending from mountains in SÃO PAULO, this river runs from southwest to northeast through a valley in the mountains of the northern part of the state of RIO DE JANEIRO. More than 600 miles (1,000 km.) long, it empties into the Atlantic Ocean near Campos. Because of its altitude, temperature, and soils, it became a site for coffee cultivation in BRAZIL in the nineteenth century, which eventually moved into São Paulo. The river runs through numerous industrial cities.

Paramaribo. Capital, principal port, and only large city of SURINAME. Located on the Suriname River 7 miles (12 km.) from the Atlantic Ocean, with a 1990's population of 275,000. Established by the British in 1651. Its diverse population is reflected in its churches, temples, mosques, and colorful ethnic markets.

Paraná, Argentina. River port in ARGENTINA. Located on the PARANÁ RIVER, with a 1990's population of 210,000. For ten years in the nineteenth century, when there was bitter conflict between BUENOS AIRES and the interior provinces over political control, it was Argentina's national capital. Grain, fish, cattle, and lumber are shipped from there. Cement, furniture, and ceramics are important industries.

Paraná, Brazil. State in SOUTH region of BRAZIL. Total area of 76,959 square miles (199,324 sq. km.) with a 1990's population of 9 million. Capital is CURITIBA. Its rich farmland stretches from western border with ARGENTINA (location of IGUAÇÚ FALLS) and PARAGUAY to Atlantic coastal mountains. It has subtropical agriculture; agribusinesses for coffee, sugarcane, and soybeans; and forestry and paper processing.

Paraná-La Plata River system. South American river system draining a huge basin that includes parts of BRAZIL, BOLIVIA, PARAGUAY, ARGENTINA, and URUGUAY. Waterfalls, sandbars, and great seasonal variation in water levels make the system poor for navigation. Only small river craft can navigate inland from ROSARIO, Argentina, and FRAY BENTOS, Uruguay.

Paraná Plateau. One of the world's largest lava plateaus, covering large parts of southern BRAZIL, northeast ARGENTINA, URUGUAY, and PARAGUAY. Centered at 26°0′ south latitude, longitude 53°0′ west. Dark reddish soils (*terra roxa*) result from the weathering of the diabase lava, providing excellent conditions for raising coffee, cattle, and grains.

Paraná River. Second-longest river in BRAZIL, more than 2,500 miles (c. 4,000 km.) long. Forms border between Brazil and PARAGUAY. Part of the massive Paraguay-Paraná-Plata River system. The Paraná River drains from the southwest interior of Brazil, entering the PARAGUAY RIVER, which then empties into the Plata River and the Atlantic Ocean.

Patagonia. Southern plateau region of ARGENTINA. Averages 2,000 feet (610 meters) in elevation at the ANDES MOUNTAINS and ends in a low sea cliff at the south Atlantic shore. Dry, cold winds blowing from the Andes make Patagonia a semiarid, scrub region, which constitutes the largest desert in the WESTERN HEMISPHERE. Its area of about 260,000 square miles (673,000 sq. km.) is greater than that of the entire U.S. state of Texas. People, sheep, and agriculture are confined to the flat valleys cut into the plateau by the eastward flowing streams.

Paysandú. Port on the URUGUAY RIVER and third-largest city in URUGUAY. Population in 1990's of 104,000. Has many meatpacking and meat-freezing plants. Other food processing and transportation facilities link Uruguay with ARGENTINA and interior parts of the continent.

Pernambuco. State in NORTHEAST region of BRAZIL. Total area of 39,000 square miles (101,023 sq. km.) with a 1990's population of 7.5 million. Capital is RECIFE. Arid, impoverished highland interior gradually descends to tropical Atlantic coast. A historic center of sugar cultivation; has tropical agriculture along the coast and cattle raising in arid uplands; tourism.

Peru. Country on the west coast of South America bordered by ECUADOR, COLOMBIA, BRAZIL, BOLIVIA, and CHILE. Total area is 496,224 square miles (1,280,258 sq. km.), with a 1990's population of 26.6 million, 45 percent of whom are Native Americans. Spanish and Quechua are the official languages. The center of the Inca Empire, it is unequaled in South America for its archaeological sites and colorful local culture. Peru has three distinct geographic regions. A narrow desert region runs along the Pacific coast; LIMA, the capital, is located there. The Andean highlands have long had the highest population densities and concentration of native peoples. The AMAZON BASIN region has been the focus of recent colonization efforts and oil development. Peru is LATIN AMERICA's largest exporter of fish; has substantial exports of copper and petroleum; and is the largest producer of coca leaf, from which cocaine is made.

Peru Current. Cold-water current flowing south to north along the Pacific coast of PERU. The cold waters collide with warm equatorial waters, resulting in upwelling, a nutrient-rich environment, and one of the world's richest fishing grounds. Large harvests of anchovies, sardines, and mackerel make Peru the largest exporter of fish products in LATIN AMERICA. However, periodic El Niño events disrupt the economy and weather of the region. Also known as the Humboldt Current.

El Niño
Page 694

Piauí. State in NORTHEAST region of BRAZIL. Total area of 97,017 square miles (251,274 sq. km.) with a 1990's population of 2.8 million. Capital is TERESINA. Land gradually descends from arid southern interior to narrow northern tropical coast on the Atlantic Ocean. An impoverished region, it has cattle raising in the interior, and some agriculture, particularly cultivation of *babaçu*.

Peru map
Page 883

Pico de Neblina. Situated in northwest AMAZONAS near border with VENEZUELA in a transitional zone between northeastern terminus of the ANDES MOUNTAINS and beginning of GUIANA HIGHLANDS. The highest peak in BRAZIL at nearly 10,000 feet (3,000 meters).

Pilcomayo River. Major tributary of the PARANÁ RIVER in South America. Rises in the Bolivian ANDES, forms the border between ARGENTINA and PARAGUAY, and joins the PARAGUAY RIVER at ASUNCIÓN, where the Paraná River is formed. Subject to flooding and drought, its shifting channel and sandbars are transportation hazards.

Popoyán. Beautifully preserved colonial town in the Andean highlands of southwest COLOMBIA. Its population in the 1990's was 190,000. Founded in 1537 by Sebastián de Benalcázar, it retains much of its classic architecture in the style of Andalucia, a region in southern Spain. Many important pre-Columbian ruins, including San Agustín, are nearby.

Porto Alegre. Capital of RIO GRANDE DO SUL state in BRAZIL. Population in 1990's was more than 1.25 million. Lies on north bank of Guaíba River, where it enters into a large north-south axial lagoon bordering the Atlantic Ocean. Industrial and regional services center.

Porto Velho. Capital of RONDÔNIA state in BRAZIL. Located on right bank of MADEIRA RIVER toward northern tip of state, with a 1990's population of 300,000. City originated during railway trade with BOLIVIA. A center of rubber and wood processing activities.

Potosí. A mining town in the southern highlands of BOLIVIA situated 13,350 feet (4,070 meters) above sea level. During the last half of the sixteenth century, half of the world's silver output came from Potosí mines, greatly enriching the Spanish empire. Tin and zinc are the most important minerals produced.

Puerto Madryn. City in ARGENTINA. Located on the northern coast of PATAGONIA with a 1990's population of 10,000. Founded by a group of Welsh immigrants in 1865; Welsh culture is still visible in the landscape from the architecture of the small village and irrigated farms in the Chubut River Valley. A popular cruise ship stop.

Punta Arenas. Chilean city located on the Strait of MAGELLAN near the southern tip of South America; population was 120,000 in the 1990's. To reach Punta Arenas, one must pass by boat through a fjordlike landscape that resembles the inland passage of southern Alaska. Petroleum and natural gas development is important to the region.

Punta del Este. Elegant South American seaside resort 70 miles (115 km.) east of MONTEVIDEO, Uruguay. Miles of white sand, clear ocean, and mild climate draw vacationers all year long. Luxury hotels, private villas, and picturesque residential areas make the city a haven for upscale shopping and conventioneering.

Purus River. Major tributary of the AMAZON RIVER in BRAZIL. It drains from the Peruvian ANDES and crosses the Brazilian states of ACRE and AMAZONAS. Coursing southwest-northeast, it empties into the Amazon River at MANAUS. About 1,900 miles (3,000 km.) long, it has numerous tributaries of its own.

Putumayo River. Major river in the AMAZON BASIN portion of COLOMBIA. Located in the extreme southeast of the country, it marks Colombia's border with PERU and is the main transport route in the area. Nearly one-third of Colombia's territory lies in the remote and sparsely populated Amazon Basin.

Quebracho Forests. Hardwood forests in the GRAN CHACO region of PARAGUAY. These trees have helped to make Paraguay a world leader in forest exports. The red quebracho is an excellent source of tannin, much of which is shipped to ARGENTINA and used to tan hides. Quebracho means "break ax," which reflects the tree's tough wood.

Quito. Capital city of ECUADOR. Located 14 miles (22 km.) south of the equator, at an elevation of 9,350 feet (2,850 meters). Founded in 1534 by Sebastián de Benalcázar, it is the former site of the northern capital of the Inca Empire. It has a pleasant, springlike climate and picturesque views of several snow-capped volcanoes. In 1978 the old colonial center was declared a World Heritage Site by the United Nations. Quito's 1990's population was 1.5 million and growing rapidly.

Recife. Capital of PERNAMBUCO state in BRAZIL. Its 1990's population was 1.3 million. A commercial, industrial, and regional services center and major coastal port. Ocean beaches attract growing European tourism.

Recôncavo. Area in BRAZIL, near SALVADOR around the coast of the Bay of Todos os Santos. A traditional producer of tobacco and, more recently, petroleum.

Rio Branco. Capital of ACRE state in BRAZIL. Located in far eastern section of the state on the west bank of Acre River, with a 1990's population of 200,000. Originally, the location of rubber processing enterprise and named Empresa. Named changed to that of Brazilian foreign minister who negotiated acquisition of state from BOLIVIA.

Rio de Janeiro. Capital of RIO DE JANEIRO state in BRAZIL. Brazil's second-largest city, with a 1990's population of 5.5 million; metropolitan area, more than 9 million. Was the capital of the colony of Brazil (1765-1808), kingdom of Brazil (1808-1822; the only city in the AMERI-CAS ever to be seat of European monarchy), the Brazilian Empire (1822-1889), and the Republic of Brazil (1889-1960). Of unparalleled physical beauty, the city is profiled by mountain peaks wreathed in tropical verdure, laced by beaches bordering waters of the Atlantic Ocean and Bay of GUANABARA. A major air and sea port and world tourist mecca, its economy declined after the transfer of the federal government offices to BRASÍLIA in the 1960's, the loss of shipbuilding work to other developing countries, and the movement of banking services to SÃO PAULO.

Rio de Janeiro (state). State in SOUTHEAST region of BRAZIL. Total area of 17,092 square miles (44,268 sq. km.) with a 1990's population of more than 13 million. Capital is RIO DE JANEIRO. Dominated by mountains of SERRA DO MAR from west to east, which hold numerous small plains and river valleys. Narrow coastal area; tropical climate with considerable rainfall. Declining economy of agriculture and industry. Offshore oil drilling.

Rio Grande do Norte. State in NORTHEAST region of BRAZIL. Total area of 20,528 square miles (53,168 sq. km.) with a 1990's population of 2.5 million. Capital is NATAL. Arid highland interior gradually descends to tropical coast on Atlantic Ocean. Cattle raising and agriculture, especially cotton and sisal; growing tourism.

Rio Grande do Sul. State in SOUTH region of BRAZIL. Brazil's most southern state, it borders URUGUAY and ARGENTINA. Total area of 108,951 square miles (282,183 sq. km.) with a 1990's population of 10 million. Capital is PORTO ALEGRE. Lowland hills and valleys of interior descend to Atlantic coast. Extensive cattle raising, defining dominant *gaúcho* culture; agriculture includes

Rio de Janeiro Pages 680, 809, 810, 884

911

wheat, rice, grape, and soy cultivation; some manufacturing.

Rivera. City on the URUGUAY/BRAZIL border in South America, forming an important link between the countries. "Portunol," the hybrid Portuguese/Spanish dialect spoken here, reflects an unusual cultural blend in the hinterlands of both countries. Good road and rail transportation connects Rivera with Brazil's productive RIO GRANDE DO SUL state.

Rondônia. State in southern segment of NORTH region of BRAZIL. Total area of 93,839 square miles (243,043 sq. km.) with a 1990's population of 1.25 million. Capital is RIO BRANCO. Gradually declining terrain to AMAZON BASIN. Rubber extraction and agricultural activities, especially cattle raising.

Roraima. State in NORTH region of BRAZIL. Most northern area of the country, with its highest peaks. Total area of 88,843 square miles (230,181 sq. km.); Brazil's least populated state, with a 1990's population of less than 250,000. Capital is BOA VISTA. Land descends from north to south in equatorial climate. Cattle raising is the dominant activity.

Rosario. Third-largest city in ARGENTINA. Population in the 1990's was 1.1 million people. Rail, water, and road transportation link Rosario with BUENOS AIRES and the nation's important northwest regions. A national university makes the city an educational center; it is also a major processor of food products and a manufacturing center. Steel is a regional specialty.

Salar de Uyuni. A vast salt lake in the arid southern highlands of BOLIVIA, located at 20°58′ south latitude, longitude 67°9′ west. It is approximately twice as large as the Great Salt Lake in the U.S. state of Utah.

Salta. City in ARGENTINA, founded in 1582. Population in the 1990's was 400,000. An oasis on the main route from BUENOS AIRES to the Bolivian silver mines. Mules from the Argentina plains were sent to BOLIVIA to bring out the valuable silver ores. The center of important oil and natural gas fields, and has many food-processing industries. Colonial architecture of the old city is a draw for many tourists who appreciate the city's rich colonial past.

Salto. Second-largest city in URUGUAY. Located on the URUGUAY RIVER, with a 1990's population of 108,500. Salto Falls is just north of the city. An important shipping center, and has meat-salting and meatpacking plants. Hydroelectricity generated at the falls supplies the city, requirements, and some is exported to other Uruguayan cities.

Salto Grande Lake. Lake on the URUGUAY RIVER. Formed when a dam was built at Salto Falls; full power generation was achieved in 1981. Provides recreational resources for fishing, boating, and swimming. URUGUAY has no fossil fuels, and its mostly flat terrain offers few good sites for hydroelectric development. Rapids on the Uruguay River just north of SALTO created the opportunity for Uruguay to solve its power shortages.

Salvador. Capital of BAHIA state in BRAZIL; Brazil's first colonial capital. Located on Atlantic Ocean and Bay of Todos os Santos, with a 1990's population of 2.65 million. Some industry; regional business and services center. Historic core of Afro-Brazilian culture. Historic buildings in center of city, together with ocean and bay beaches, attract extensive tourism.

San Andrés. Island province and archipelago of COLOMBIA; a popular tourist destination. Located in the CARIBBEAN

Salvador Pages 758, 885

Sea 435 miles (700 km.) northeast of Colombia and 140 miles (225 km.) east of NICARAGUA. A former British colony, San Andrés has a large population of African descent, and English is still spoken. The main island has an area of 17 square miles (44 sq. km.); the total population of the province was about 65,000 in the 1990's.

San Blas Archipelago. Caribbean string of islands extending from the Gulf of San Blas to the Colombian border. Comprises almost four hundred islands, primarily occupied by the Cuna tribe, who administer the islands as an autonomous province. They are allowed and encouraged by the Panamanian government to maintain their customs, language, dress, music, and dance. Because of this survival of Amerindian culture, the tourism sector of the island's economy is growing.

San Carlos de Bariloche. Resort city in the Andean lake region of ARGENTINA, at NAHUEL HUAPÍ LAKE. Mountains, lakes, and national parks provide year-round recreational activities, including skiing, fishing, boating, and hiking. Swiss immigrants built chalet-style hotels and villas that replicated the look of their homeland. International conferences, moviemakers, and people on holidays enjoy the alpine environment. Also known as Bariloche.

San Jorge Gulf. Largest bay in the PATAGONIA region of ARGENTINA. The gulf is an important oil-producing district; COMODORO RIVADAVIA is its most important urban center. The sea cliffs and great tidal ranges in Argentina's south makes navigation difficult. Improved land and air transportation and consequent economic development have made Comodoro Rivadavia a city of more than 100,000 people. Oil and food are shipped 1,000 miles (1,610

km.) to BUENOS AIRES and LA PLATA.

San José. Capital of COSTA RICA, since 1823. Located in the interior highlands of the country, with 1.3 million people in the 1990's. A growing, cosmopolitan area and the country's transportation and economic hub. Cultural attractions include the National Museum, the Pre-Columbian Museum of Gold, the Museum of Jade, and the city's vibrant central market district.

San Juan. Oasis at the foot of the ANDES MOUNTAINS in ARGENTINA. Irrigation has made the province of San Juan a region of intense agriculture. Wine grapes, cattle, grain, fruits, and vegetables grow prolifically. Industries in San Juan City (population 120,000 in the 1990's) are based on food processing. The region suffers numerous earthquakes.

San Nicholás. Planned industrial city in ARGENTINA. Located on the PARANÁ RIVER between BUENOS AIRES and ROSARIO, with a 1990's population of 100,000. In 1960 the government steel plant started production; this project was part of a regional development package, including oil refining, power generation, steel, and fabricated metals manufacturing, which the United Nations helped to plan and finance. Argentina has coal and iron ore, but it is cheaper to make steel out of foreign raw materials brought in to San Nicholás port.

San Rafael Mountain. The highest point in PARAGUAY, reaching 2,789 feet (850 meters). Located 47 miles (75 km.) north of ENCARNACIÓN. This eastern section of the country has the best soils, mildest climate, most dependable rainfall, and best drainage. People living there raise good crops of peanuts, tobacco, wheat, cotton, soybeans, fruits, and vegetables.

San Salvador. Capital and largest city of EL SALVADOR. Located at the foot of San Salvador volcano, with a 1990's population of 500,000. Has been the capital since 1839, but has few colonial buildings, since it has fallen victim to earthquakes, floods, and volcanic eruptions over the years. Cultural sites include the National Theater; the David Guzman National Museum, renowned for its archaeological holdings; and the Metropolitan Cathedral, where the famous archbishop Oscar Romero is buried.

San Salvador de Jujuy. City in ARGENTINA, with a 1990's population of 200,000. Founded in 1593 as a waystation between the silver mines of BOLIVIA and BUENOS AIRES, it straddles the PAN-AMERICAN HIGHWAY. With lead, zinc, iron ore, and silver mines in the vicinity, mineral production keeps the city important to the nation despite its remote location.

Santa Catarina. State in SOUTH region of BRAZIL. Total area of 37,060 square miles (95,985 sq. km.) with a 1990's population of 5 million. Capital is FLORIANÓPOLIS. Low mountain range extends along eastern half of land, waters draining east to Atlantic Ocean and west to PARANÁ RIVER. Subtropical climate with wide range of agricultural cultivation; extensive cattle ranching.

Santa Cruz. Second-largest city in BOLIVIA, with a 1990's population of 850,000. A boomtown in Bolivia's resource-rich eastern lowlands, it is a center of production of rice, soybeans, sugarcane, cattle, and timber for export.

Santa Fe. Transportation hub in ARGENTINA, connecting the nation's heartland of BUENOS AIRES Province with the northwest oases and northern humid areas. Population in the 1990's was 350,000. It serves a rich agricultural

area by processing grain, vegetable oils, and meats. Road, rail, and river traffic on the PARANÁ RIVER make it one of the nation's oldest and most important interior settlements.

Santiago. Capital and largest city in CHILE, with a 1990's population of 6 million. Situated in the fertile central valley against the magnificent backdrop of the ANDES MOUNTAINS. A modern, bustling city and the economic and cultural center of Chile, but plagued by air pollution and earthquakes.

Santiago del Estero. Oldest city in ARGENTINA; founded in 1553. Strategically located on the Dulce River, providing a watering and resting place from BOLIVIA across Argentina's semiarid plains. The city of 200,000 people (1990's population) is the center of extensive agricultural operations, such as wheat farming and cattle raising on the open range.

São Francisco River. The longest Brazilian river running entirely in the country; 1,988 miles (3,200 km.) long. Descending from the mountains of MINAS GERAIS, it runs from south to northnortheast through the states of BAHIA, PERNAMBUCO, ALAGOAS, and SERGIPE. The Paulo Afonso hydroelectric dam in Bahia (producing more than 600,000 kilowatts) is located on this river.

São Luís. Capital of MARANHÃO state in BRAZIL. Located on an Atlantic coastal bay island of same name, with a 1990's population of 800,000. Originally founded by French; a business and services center. Because of its well-preserved colonial architecture, it has been declared a World Cultural Heritage site.

São Paulo. Capital of Brazilian state of same name. Largest city in BRAZIL and South America, among five largest in the world, with a population of 10 mil-

São Paulo Pages 819, 886

914

lion; metropolitan area, almost 17 million. National industrial, commercial, banking, and services center. Stretches along hilly peaks of SERRA DO MAR. Port is located 50 miles below, in city of Santos, situated on coastal island.

São Paulo (state). State in SOUTHEAST region of BRAZIL. Total area of 95,852 square miles (248,257 sq. km.); largest state in Brazil, with a 1990's population of 35 million. Capital is SAO PAULO. Southern area that is a mountain range dropping to the Atlantic coast. Stretching north from this area are hills and plains of rich soil. Intensive cultivation of coffee, soybeans, and sugarcane, along with other agricultural products. Extensive manufacturing, including auto, computer, and aviation industries.

Sergipe. State in NORTHEAST region of BRAZIL. Smallest state in Brazil, with a total area of 8,491 square miles (21,862 sq. km.); 1990's population was 1.65 million. Capital is ARACAJU. Land descends from southwest to lowland plain in north along SÃO FRANCISCO RIVER and to eastern Atlantic coast. Tropical climate; agricultural production in lowlands, cattle raising in interior.

Serra do Mar. Mountain range that extends for more than 1,500 miles (2,500 km.) along the east coast of BRAZIL, from RIO GRANDE DO SUL to BAHIA. The mountains in the city of RIO DE JANEIRO, such as Sugar Loaf and Corcovado, are part of this range. This escarpment at times falls directly into the sea, but most of it is several to fifty miles distant from sea so that there is a coastal ribbon of land between it and the ocean. This mountain range is much older and lower than the ANDES MOUNTAINS and reveals where the eastern plate of the South American continent broke from the western plate of Africa.

At their highest, these mountains rarely exceed 7,000 feet (2,000 meters) in altitude in their midddle sections, in ESPÍRITO SANTO, and are generally half that altitude.

South. Region of BRAZIL, comprising states of PARANÁ, SANTA CATARINA, and RIO GRANDE DO SUL. Covers about 400,000 square miles (less than 600,000 sq. km.); 1990's population of more than 23 million, with many immigrants of central and southern European descent. The "breadbasket" of Brazil in terms of richness and productivity of land for rice, wheat, soybeans, vegetables, and other food staples.

Southeast. Region of BRAZIL, including states of ESPÍRITO SANTO, MINAS GERAIS, RIO DE JANEIRO, and SÃO PAULO. Covers about 650,000 square miles (900,000 sq. km.), with a 1990's population of 67 million. Because São Paulo is located there, the region is the economic powerhouse of Brazil, with the highest per capita income, contributing two-thirds of country's gross domestic product.

Sucre. The constitutional capital of BOLIVIA. Founded in 1538, Sucre is a charming colonial town of 150,000 inhabitants. Because of its well-preserved center, with adobe structures, white walls, and red-tiled roofs, Sucre was named a World Heritage Site by the United Nations in 1992.

Suriname. Country on the north coast of South America, bordered by GUYANA to the west, FRENCH GUIANA to the east, and BRAZIL to the south. Total area of 63,251 square miles (163,820 sq. km.) with a 1990's population of 430,000, mostly settled on the coast. Capital is PARAMARIBO. First permanent European settlement established in 1651 by the English. Ceded to the Dutch in 1667 (then known as Dutch Guiana) in exchange for Manhattan Island (now New York City). Gained independence in 1975. Diverse population, composed of Creoles (people of African ancestry) and descendants of laborers who were imported from India, China, and Java. Dutch is the official language, but Hindi and Javanese are widely spoken. Christianity, Hinduism, and Islam are the principal religions. Principal exports are bauxite and aluminum products; rice, shrimp, bananas, and some petroleum are also produced. (Formerly spelled "Surinam.")

Tajumulco, Volcan. Guatemalan volcano that is the highest peak in CENTRAL AMERICA, at 13,767 feet (4,196 meters).

Tapajós River. Major tributary of AMAZON RIVER in South America, that drains from MATO GROSSO and forms border between Brazilian states of AMAZONAS and PARÁ. More than 1,000 miles (1,700 km.), it flows southwest-northeast and empties into the Amazon River at the port city of Santarém.

Tarabuco. Most colorful traditional market for Amerindian weavings in BOLIVIA. The intricate designs are handmade, often taking months to complete one item, and artisans can be watched at work. Located in the southern highlands approximately 40 miles (64 km.) from SUCRE.

Tazumal Ruins. Best-known, best-preserved Mayan ruins in EL SALVADOR. Located in the town of Chalchuapa, about 47 miles (75 km.) northwest of SAN SALVADOR. First occupied about 7,000 years ago but best known for the Maya who lived there about 1,000 years ago. Archaeologists believe the site was a trade center, based on artifacts from as far away as Mexico and PANAMA. Name is Mayan for "pyramid where the victims were burned"

Tegucigalpa. Capital of HONDURAS. Had a 1990's population of 800,000. Founded as a mining center; became the national capital in 1880. Its colonial architecture includes the central park,

Tegucigalpa around the time it became the capital of Honduras. (Arkent Archive)

which is the hub of the city; the legislative plaza; the president's house; and the church of San Francisco, built during the sixteenth century. La Tigra National Park, just northeast of the city, has a well-preserved cloud forest and associated wildlife. Name means "silver hill" in the local dialect, referring to its founding by the Spanish in 1578.

Teresina. Capital of PIAUÍ state in BRAZIL; 1990's population of about 265,000. A nineteenth century planned city, it lies on right bank of Parnaíba River in the central west portion of state near border with MARANHÃO. The center of an impoverished area.

Tierra del Fuego. Archipelago at the southern extremity of South America. In shape, the main island separated from the mainland by the Strait of MAGELLAN is a triangle with its base on BEAGLE CHANNEL. The total area is 28,473 square miles (73,746 sq. km.), about two-thirds of which is part of CHILE and the rest part of ARGENTINA. Due to its latitude and proximity to Antarctica, its climate is cold. The discovery of oil at Manantiales in 1945 converted the northern part of Tierra del Fuego into Chile's only oil field. The archipelago takes its name from Tierra del Fuego Island, at its southern tip. Located at 54°0′ south latitude, longitude 70°0′ west, the island is shared by Chile and Argentina. Sheep, forestry, fishing, and oil are mainstays of the economy. USHUAIA, Argentina, on the Beagle Channel is the world's southernmost city.

Tikal. One of the most impressive Mayan sites in CENTRAL AMERICA. Located in the extreme north of GUATEMALA in the Peten, which is likened to the Mexican Yucatán. Tikal National Park contains thousands of structures and artifacts, including massive temples, such

as the Temple of the Giant Jaguar; ball courts; house sites; ceremonial platforms; palaces; reservoirs; and stelae— massive stone sculptures documenting important Mayan events. Visitors can often watch archaeologists studying the site, a long-term, continuous process.

Titicaca, Lake. Located in the ANDES MOUNTAINS region of South America on the border between PERU and BOLIVIA. At 12,500 feet (3,800 meters) above sea level, it is the world's highest large freshwater lake. The lands around the lake are populated by farmers who raise potatoes, sheep, and llamas. Reed boats once were commonly used for transportation. With no outlet to the sea, Bolivia's navy is based on Lake Titicaca.

Lake Titicaca Pages 689, 886

Tocantins. State in NORTH region of BRAZIL. Total area of 116,573 square miles (301,294 sq. km.) with a 1990's population of more than 1 million. Capital is PALMAS. From north-south axis of the central highlands, land descends to east and west in transitional equatorial climate. Cattle raising in north; agriculture in south.

Tocantins River. Major tributary of AMAZON RIVER in BRAZIL. Almost 1,500 miles (more than 2,400 km.) long, it flows south and north from GOIÁS across TOCANTINS, forming the border with MARANHÃO. Joined by the Araguaia River, it crosses PARÁ, emptying into the southeast part of the Amazon delta below BELÉM and MARAJÓ ISLAND. The Tucuruí hydroelectric dam is in Pará, below where the Araguaia and Tocantins Rivers join.

Torres del Paine National Park. South American park in the Chilean PATAGONIA, known for its spectacular scenery and wildlife. Located 90 miles (145 km.) north of Puerto Natales in the far south of CHILE. Adventurous travelers can view glaciers, towering granite pillars, and such wildlife as the condor, flamingo, emu (a relative of the ostrich), and guanaco (a relative of the llama).

Ushuaia railroad Page 821

Trujillo. Third-largest city in PERU (1990's population, 600,000) and the main settlement on its north coast. An attractive colonial city, founded in 1536 and named after Spanish conqueror Francisco Pizarro's hometown in Spain. Nearby are the ruins of the monumental Moche pyramids and the adobe Chimú ruin city of CHAN CHÁN.

Tucumán. Second-largest oasis in the arid west of ARGENTINA. Population in the 1990's was 700,000 people. Irrigation from Andean streams and warm weather gives the region unique agricultural prominence. Rice, tobacco, sugarcane, and fruit provide the raw materials for many factories. With two universities and the provincial capital, the city is important politically, culturally, and economically. A colonial city, dating from 1565; Argentine independence was declared from its municipal assembly building.

Uruguay. Country located on the southeastern coast of South America and bounded by BRAZIL and ARGENTINA. After SURINAME, Uruguay is the smallest country in South America, with an area of about 68,000 square miles (176,120 sq. km.)—very similar to the areas of Missouri and Oklahoma. Uruguay's economy is based largely on such agricultural exports as beef. Its capital is MONTEVIDEO, which has almost half of the country's population in its metropolitan area. Its population—mostly of European descent as in Argentina—was 3,216,000 in 1998.

Uruguay River. River flowing from southern BRAZIL, forming the northeast border of ARGENTINA and the western border of URUGUAY. Merges with the LA PLATA RIVER ESTUARY a little north of BUENOS AIRES. The river floodplain is some of Uruguay's best farmland, and there are important hydroelectric works along the river.

Ushuaia. Southernmost city on earth. Located in ARGENTINA. Charles Darwin visited this site on the BEAGLE CHANNEL in 1832; the glaciers, ice-sculptured mountains, and dense arctic woodlands sheltered the wildlife that helped form his evolutionary theories. The city of 15,000 people is a center for fishing, lumbering, and sheep ranching. Argentina has a navy base here.

Uspallata Pass. Easiest pass through the ANDES MOUNTAINS between MENDOZA, ARGENTINA, and SANTIAGO, Chile. The climb to 12,675 feet (3,683 meters) is direct, but heavy winter snows makes passage difficult. European settlement of Argentina was started by Spaniards from CHILE and BOLIVIA filtering through the Andean passes. A statue to Christ the Redeemer in the Uspallata Pass marks the peaceful settlement of the international boundary.

Valencia. Third-largest city in VENEZUELA, with a 1990's population of 1 million. Founded in 1555 on Lake Valencia; named after a city in southern Spain. One of Venezuela's most important commercial and industrial centers; products include agricultural products, pharmaceuticals, and automobiles. The surrounding area is known for sugarcane production.

Valparaíso. Principal port in CHILE and the location of the Chilean parliament, which was moved there in the 1980's as part of a movement to decentralize government functions. Located 75 miles (120 km.) northwest of SANTIAGO, with a 1990's population of 284,000. It was an important trading city and a British Naval center until the PANAMA CANAL opened in 1914.

Venezuela. Country on the north coast of South America, bordered by Colombia, Brazil, and GUYANA. Total area of 352,143 square miles (912,050 sq. km.), with a 1990's population of 23.7 million, 83 percent living in cities. Capital is CARACAS. Venezuela has a diverse physical geography. ANDES MOUNTAINS in the west rise to 16,000 feet (5,000 meters). Vast plains of the LLANOS and ORINOCO RIVER dissect the country. The largely undeveloped GUIANA HIGHLANDS and AMAZON territory encompass the east and south. The first colony to revolt against Spanish rule, Venezuela achieved independence in 1830 under Simon Bolivar. Venezuela is one of LATIN AMERICA's richest countries, based on the oil wealth of the Lake MARACAIBO area, but has suffered from corruption. Second-largest oil producer in Latin America. Iron ore, steel, and aluminum are also important exports. The name "Venezuela" means "Little Venice," so named because explorers observed Amerindians living in houses on stilts on Lake Maracaibo.

Viña del Mar. One of South America's premier seaside resorts, located in central CHILE near SANTIAGO. The site of an internationally recognized musical festival, a casino, and Chile's presidential summer palace. The population in the 1990's was 330,700

Vitória. Capital of ESPÍRITO SANTO state in BRAZIL. Located on an Atlantic coastal island of same name; 1990's population of 300,000. Noted for its fish cuisine; growing tourism. Port of Tubarão is a major mineral exporter.

Volcan Tajumulco. See TAJUMULCO, VOLCAN.

Western Hemisphere. Portion of the earth that contains North and South America; generally demarcated as within longitude 20° west and 160° east. Historically known as the NEW WORLD.

Xingú River. Major tributary of AMAZON RIVER in BRAZIL. It flows south and north from MATO GROSSO across PARÁ for almost 1,400 miles (about 2,200 km.). It enters the Amazon where the river's delta begins to form. Upper reaches of river house Xingú National Park, a major indigenous homeland.

Xunantunich. Most impressive archaeological park in BELIZE. near the Guatemalan border. Was a large ceremonial center controlling the area from the present-day BELIZE-GUATEMALA border to the CARIBBEAN SEA. Archaeologists believe the site was abandoned about 1,000 years ago when a major earthquake devastated the area. El Castillo, the largest and tallest structure there, rises about 130 feet (40 meters) above the tropical forest. Name is Mayan for "stone maiden."

Ypacaraí Lake. Popular vacation spot in PARAGUAY. Located about 18 miles (29 km.) east of ASUNCIÓN, at the edge of the PARANÁ PLATEAU. Part of Paraguay's best farmland. Early German immigrants helped make this region prosperous through intensive cultivation of grains and fruits, and the raising of meat animals. San Bernardino is the resort city on the lake.

Ypoa Lake. Lake in PARAGUAY. Located 40 miles (65 km.) south of ASUNCIÓN. Occupies a lowland at the southern edge of the PARANÁ PLATEAU; its borders merge into extensive swamps. Four hundred species of birds make homes in the swamp; large mammals found here include jaguar, wild boar, deer, and capybara (water hog).

Yungas. A frontier and colonization zone in BOLIVIA. Located north of LA PAZ in the foothills of the AMAZON BASIN, the Yungas provide a welcome retreat from the high altitude of the capital. The area produces citrus, bananas, coffee, and coca—sometimes for use as a traditional herb, and sometimes converted into cocaine.

Douglas Heffington; James R. Keese; Dana P. McDermott; Judith C. Mimbs; Edward A. Riedinger; Robert J. Tata

INDEX TO VOLUME 3

See volume 8 for a comprehensive index to all eight volumes in set.

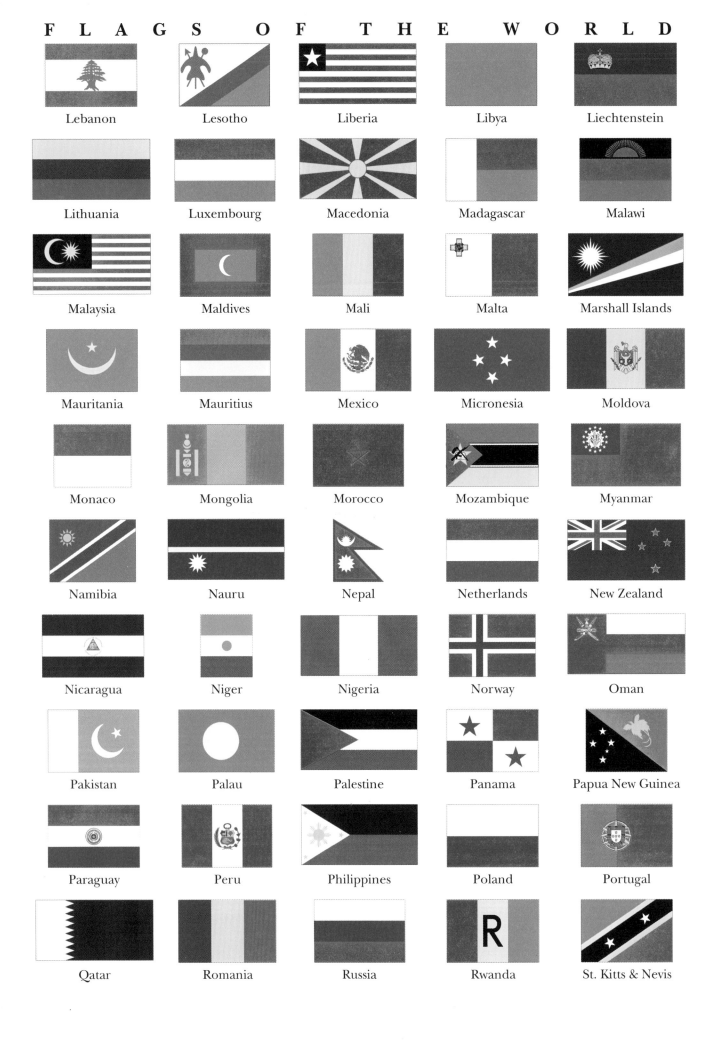

FLAGS OF THE WORLD

Lebanon

Lesotho

Liberia

Libya

Liechtenstein

Lithuania

Luxembourg

Macedonia

Madagascar

Malawi

Malaysia

Maldives

Mali

Malta

Marshall Islands

Mauritania

Mauritius

Mexico

Micronesia

Moldova

Monaco

Mongolia

Morocco

Mozambique

Myanmar

Namibia

Nauru

Nepal

Netherlands

New Zealand

Nicaragua

Niger

Nigeria

Norway

Oman

Pakistan

Palau

Palestine

Panama

Papua New Guinea

Paraguay

Peru

Philippines

Poland

Portugal

Qatar

Romania

Russia

Rwanda

St. Kitts & Nevis